THE
PRIMATE
MALARIAS

G. ROBERT COATNEY, Ph. D., D. Sc. in Public Health (hon.), Sc.D. (hon.) Formerly: Chief, Laboratory Parasite Chemotherapy, National Institute of Allergy and Infectious Diseases, NIH, Bethesda, Md.; Professor of Pharmacology, Louisiana State University Medical School. Presently: Visiting Professor of Community Health Practice, Howard University Medical School; Visiting Lecturer in Tropical Public Health, Harvard University School of Public Health; Visiting Professor of Pharmacology, Tulane University School of Medicine; Member, Expert Panel on Malaria, World Health Organization; Member, Commission on Malaria, Armed Forces Epidemiological Board, Department of Defense; Consultant on Malaria, Center for Disease Control, Atlanta, Ga.

WILLIAM E. COLLINS, Ph.D. Research Biologist, Section on Primate Malaria, Laboratory Parasitic Diseases, NIH, Chamblee, Ga.

McWILSON WARREN, Ph.D. Scientist Director, Center for Disease Control, Central America Malaria Research Station, San Salvador, El Salvador, C.A.

PETER G. CONTACOS, Ph.D., M.D. Head, Section on Primate Malaria, Laboratory of Parasitic Diseases, NIH, Chamblee, Ga.; Member, Expert Panel on Malaria, World Health Organization; Associate Member, Commission on Malaria, Armed Forces Epidemiological Board, Department of Defense.

U.S. DEPARTMENT OF HEALTH, EDUCATION, AND WELFARE
National Institutes of Health
National Institute of Allergy and Infectious Diseases
Bethesda, Maryland 20014

1971

Library of Congress Number 71–610655

For sale by the Superintendent of Documents
U.S. Government Printing Office
Washington, D.C. 20402
Price $7
Stock Number 1744–0005

Dedicated to

DR. DON EDGAR EYLES
4 September 1915 to 4 October 1963

and

to the inmates at the United States Penitentiary, Atlanta, Georgia, who volunteered to accept infection with human and simian malarias.

Preface

This book is about the malaria parasites of Primates. It deals with the parasite as seen in the vertebrate host and in the mosquito with comments on each of these hosts as their life habits or geographical location may contribute to the biology of the plasmodium. The knowledge that primates have malaria is not new, but the fact that lower primates, especially the monkeys and apes, harbor malarias infective to man, and, which produce disease in him, is a relatively new concept and one of special significance in the light of worldwide programs of malaria eradication and control.

Because of the dramatic suddenness with which this concept burst upon the world community of malariologists, we have included a detailed account of the initial happenings and their ramifications during the next ten years.

The first section deals with the evolution of the Haemosporidia, historical review, ecology of the hosts, and life-cycle including relapse. In subsequent sections each species is dealt with separately, beginning with its discovery and taxonomy, the cycle in the peripheral blood, the sporogonic cycle, the cycle in the tissues, the course of the infection, host specificity, and immunity and antigenic relationships. Pathology, chemotherapy, and the clinical aspects of the disease process are considered outside the scope of this work except as they may have a direct bearing on the specific malaria under discussion.

In dealing with individual species, it is recognized that, at present, the key to their identification rests with the cycle in the blood. It is not unlikely, however, that in the hands of the zoologist, knowledge of the sporogonic cycle will contribute greatly to species identification. In support of this concept, we have included comparison studies, done under controlled conditions, which, in some situations confirm, and in others pose some doubt, as to taxonomic identities and species relationships. The cycle in the tissue, except in a broad sense, can contribute little in this regard because these stages fail to show different, distinct, and constant morphological characteristics which permit species identification. Blood smear preparations must be used in the routine identification of species in man and lower animals but the specialist may find it advantageous to turn to the cycle in the mosquito or, to examine the serologic relationships for absolute identification in closely related species.

The course of the infection in the normal vertebrate host is described and illustrated, followed by its manifestations in other hosts, man or lower primates, or vice versa, if data are available.

The portion dealing with host specificity treats that item in both the vertebrate and invertebrate hosts in order to cast light on distribution and host specificity. Likewise, the discussion of immunity and antigenic relationships is treated in the light of speciation.

The synonomy of the malaria species is discussed in the introductory portion of a given chapter but for the human malarias it is given in tabular form, too, directly preceding the text. In presenting the presently accepted zoological name of the vertebrate host, we have relied on the Handbook of Living Primates by Napier and Napier, 1967. In cases where the synonymy seemed clouded, we accepted the name given in the Checklist of Palearctic and Indian Mammals by Ellerman and Morrison-Scott, 1951. For the correct synonymy of the mosquitoes we accepted A Synoptic Catalog of the Mosquitoes of the World by Stone, Knight, and Starcke, 1959.

The literature on human malaria and some of the simian malarias, too, is so vast that we elected to base this work on selected references considered to be the most interesting and relevant through 1969; in a few instances, because of the importance of the work, we have included work published in 1970. Most references have been seen by one of us and where that was not possible, the listed reference is followed by (NS) = not seen.

The colored plates are an important part of this work and in planning for them we decided on certain requirements which would have to be met in order for a plate to be included: (1) the material for the plate must be our own, (2) the smear preparations would be stained by one of us and under exactly the same conditions as to stain, time, and pH, and (3) all of the illustrations would be done by a single artist working under the direct supervision of either McWW or GRC.

Our greatest difficulty was in fulfilling the first requirement. It took us something over two years to obtain an infection of *Plasmodium reichenowi* and one of us (McWW) made a special trip to Borneo in order to get material for the *P. pitheci* plate. We were never able to obtain an animal infected with *P. rodhaini* or parasitized blood for infecting our own animal; as a consequence, there is no plate depicting this parasite. We had to relax our requirements in the case of the malarias of lemurs. The material for that plate is copied from the work of the original describers.

This work was started in early 1966 by the senior author and Dr. McWilson Warren while colleagues in the Laboratory of Parasite Chemotherapy at the National Institutes of Health in Bethesda, Maryland, and continued, with interruptions, during the three years the senior author was Professor of Pharmacology at the Louisiana State University Medical School, New Orleans, Louisiana and finished, with the collaboration of Drs. William E. Collins and Peter G. Contacos, at the Center for Disease Control, Atlanta, Georgia.

ATLANTA, GA.   G.R.C.
December, 1970   W.E.C.
                                                      McW.W.
                                                      P.G.C.

Acknowledgements

Specific acknowledgement is made for support, facilities, and special services received from the National Institute of Allergy and Infectious Diseases, National Institutes of Health; the Department of Pharmacology, Louisiana State University Medical School, New Orleans, La.; and the Center for Disease Control, Health Services and Mental Health Administration, Atlanta, Ga.

We wish to thank the Director of the Bureau of Prisons, Department of Justice, and his staff and the inmate volunteers for allowing us to carry on transmission studies at the U.S. Penitentiary, Atlanta, Ga. We are indebted for numerous contributions from Dr. G. M. Jeffery, who was Chief, Laboratory of Parasite Chemotherapy, NIAID, NIH, during 1966-1969. We also extend thanks to the Institute for Medical Research, Kuala Lumpur, West Malaysia, the South Carolina State Hospital, Columbia, South Carolina, and to the Delta Regional Primate Research Center, Covington, Louisiana for their interest and cooperation in many of the studies reported here.

Particular acknowledgement is made of important contributions to this monograph by Mrs. Gertrude Nicholson, Medical Illustrator, NIH, who painted the colored plates; by Mr. J. C. Skinner, Biologist, who prepared the charts and graphs; by Mrs. Nancy Herbon, formerly of the Louisiana State University staff, for valuable aid and, especially, for her diligence in locating many hard-to-find references; and to Mr. Clinton S. Smith, Biologist, for the unique photographs of the sporogonic and EE stages.

Contents

CONTENTS (Continued)

SECTION 1
GENERAL

1

Evolution of the Primate Malarias

THE evolution of the Haemosporidia has occupied the attention of many investigators and detailed discussions of the subject have been presented by Baker (1965), Ball (1943, 1960), Bray (1957, 1963), Bruce-Chwatt (1965), Christophers (1934), Garnham (1955, 1963, 1966), Manwell (1955), and others. The subject is extremely complex since not only must the evolution of the protozoan be accounted for but the concomitant evolutionary development of both the vertebrate and invertebrate hosts as well. Conclusive proof has not been presented to substantiate a particular evolutionary scheme for these parasites and their hosts and it seems unlikely that incontrovertible evidence to support any particular theory will be forthcoming. However, the subject does provide exciting grist for the evolutionary biologist to the extent that now it is more than an academic exercise. There are some very practical considerations to the evolutionary trends in the primate malarias and these will be discussed in more detail later.

Most workers agree that the malaria parasites descended from a coccidian ancestor. However, there are two schools of thought as to whether this ancestor was parasitic in an insect host or in the intestine of a vertebrate. The strongest evidence for the theory of an insect origin of the malaria parasites has been put forth by Huff (1938, 1945) and concentrates on two fundamental observations: 1) The parasites are found in a very diverse group of vertebrates (reptiles, birds, and mammals) but the invertebrate hosts are always dipterans. Development patterns in the insect are similar in all the species of malaria parasites and the invertebrate hosts form a much

closer group than do the vertebrate hosts of the same parasites. 2) The Haemosporidia are relatively apathogenic for the insect in contrast to the situation in many of the vertebrate infections. Traditionally, high levels of pathogenicity in a host-parasite system are considered to be indicative of a recent association. There is undoubtedly an increased potential for survival in any parasite that creates as little discomfort as possible for its host and obviously there is no real lasting advantage to a parasite which destroys its host. Ultimately, this logic can be extended and symbiosis becomes the goal of all parasites. If this tenant is accepted, it is reasonable to assume that less pathogenic associations are older than those in which the whole gamut of the host's resistance mechanisms are forced into play. It is thus reasoned, by many workers, that the malaria parasite has been in association with the insect for a longer period than it has with the vertebrate host and, therefore, the coccidian ancestor of the Haemosporidia was originally an insect parasite.

The first of these two arguments is plausible and difficult to refute. Christophers (1934) suggested that the association between dipterans and plasmodia was established because of the tree dwelling habits of mosquitoes, birds, rats, and monkeys. This argument does not appear to be very strong and is based on the assumption that since the initial vertebrate infections were possibly in reptiles, these animals were tree dwellers also. Such an explanation does not help to understand the failure of the protozoans to develop in fleas, ticks, lice, and mites since certainly these ectoparasites intimately share an environment with their hosts which probably antedated the dipterans in the development of a blood-sucking activity. Thus Christopher's argument is an interesting one but seems much less convincing than the evidence presented by Huff to support the probable insect origin of the coccidian ancestor of the contemporary members of the genus *Plasmodium*. (The same idea was put forth by Fantham (1936) but without elaboration).

It is interesting to note how a different emphasis can influence the interpretation of the same information. Huff considers the dipteran hosts of malaria parasites to be closely related when compared to the vertebrate hosts of the same parasites. At the same time, Bruce-Chwatt (1965) refers to the same group of insects as "diverse". Thus the same information has been used to support the insect origin of the malaria parasites (Huff) and the antithesis of this point of view (Bruce-Chwatt).

The second body of evidence is, in our view, somewhat less convincing. The absolute associations between pathogenicity and the age of a particular host-parasite system is possibly *too simple*. One cannot argue with the biological success of symbiosis over parasitism. However, we have to agree with Ball (1960) in that although long host-parasite associations frequently result in lowered pathogenicity there is no reason to assume that this is always the case. In addition, it should not be assumed that a new host-parasite association will be pathogenic. If we accept the proposition that the developmental sequence was from free living forms, to commensals, to parasites, then apathogenicity actually preceded pathogenicity.

Support of a coccidian parasite of the vertebrate intestine as the ancestor of the Plasmodiidae comes primarily from Manwell (1955), Bray (1957, 1963), Baker (1965), Bruce-Chwatt (1965), and Garnham (1966). Manwell (1955) notes that malaria parasites occur in birds and reptiles which probably preceded the blood sucking diptera in their evolution. Baker emphasizes the tendency of coccidians of the vertebrate intestine to become tissue parasites as further evidence to support the intestinal coccidian as the most likely ancestor of the malaria parasites. Garnham (1966) points out the difficulty in

visualizing the existence of the plasmodia as dipteran parasites without intervention of a vertebrate if the life cycle in these insects was similar to that seen in contemporary species of *Plasmodium*. Bray presents a well constructed discussion of this subject in which he points out that the developmental stages of malaria parasites found in the vertebrate host seem to be reversed if the parasite ancestor had been an insect coccidian. In other words schizogony and gametogony should be in the mosquito host and sporogony in the vertebrate host.

The first of these arguments is interesting but the parasite could well have evolved after the blood sucking dipterans were on the scene. The second argument is important in that it reveals the potential of the coccidian intestinal parasites to invade tissues, but such a potential did not have to be realized.

The last two arguments of Bray and Garnham are possibly the most convincing in defense of a vertebrate coccidian as the ancestor of the malaria parasites in that they seem to offer the greatest challenge when one is searching for alternative explanations.

It is our conclusion that the immediate ancestor of the plasmodia is still not clear. However, the greatest weight of available evidence seems to support the position that a tissue invading parasite of the vertebrate intestine, in a reptile, found its way into the blood of the animal and eventually into a blood-sucking dipteran. The peculiar association of mammalian malarias and culicines probably reflects an early development of rather circumscribed feeding habits on the part of the mosquitoes. The perplexing absence of involvement in the life cycles of these parasites by other blood sucking arthropods, namely fleas, ticks, mites, and/or lice remains one of the most difficult aspects of this problem to understand if the parasites did arise in the vertebrate and therefore were presumably provided with many opportunities to adapt to some, if not all, of this latter group of the ectoparasites.

The long period between the initial efforts of the primitive tissue invading coccidian to adapt to the blood stream of a vertebrate and the digestive tract of a blood sucking dipteran, and the development of our contemporary genera and species of the malaria-like parasite remains obscure. Undoubtedly there were many failures as new vertebrate and invertebrate hosts were tried. However, these efforts were successful to a large degree since the genus *Plasmodium* alone is now found in all major groups of terrestrial vertebrates and is represented by a large number of distinct species. As the malaria parasites evolved, they maintained certain basic features of morphology (particularly pigment production in the erythrocytic stages), life cycle (all presumably have schizogonic development in both fixed tissue cells and circulating blood cells of the vertebrate host) and host range (all undergo a sexual period of development with the subsequent production of sporozoites in the alimentary tract and haemocoele of a dipteran). To discuss the evolution of all the species of *Plasmodium* is beyond the scope of this work; so, we will direct our attention to a more detailed examination of those forms found in primates.

The differentiation of the primate malarias is relatively recent and the trends that produced the currently known aspects of speciation and distribution are, in our opinion, part of a dynamic process which is still not completed. Many theories have been advanced in an effort to correlate the distribution of contemporary primate plasmodia with various known aspects of their vertebrate hosts; i.e., physiology, distribution, and ecology. The evolutionary relationships of most parasites must necessarily be speculative since direct knowledge is confined to very recent history. This is particularly true of the malaria parasites since they were discovered less than 100 years ago. Prior to this century, we have only vague historical references to clinical entities which we struggle to attribute to currently known disease agents. Therefore, an understanding of the evolution and interrelationships of the contemporary species of primate plasmodia and associated aspects of host and geographic distribution will depend, for the most part, on our knowledge of primate evolution.

Different approaches to the evolution of primates vary in detail but there are some concepts on which there is considerable agreement. There seems little doubt that there was a lemuroid-tarsieroid ancestor for all of the contemporary primate species and that the evolutionary changes resulting in today's simians and anthropoids began in the middle or late Eocene some 35–40 million years ago. In addition, there is little conflict over the idea that the ancestor of the New World monkeys was isolated from the main Old World line at a very pivotal point when a variety of new morphological and physiological features were being tested for their ability to survive. Thus, the non-human primates of the Western Hemisphere are monkey-like, reflecting a close ancestral relationship to the African and Asian forms. However, differences between the two great groups are in many ways quite marked, revealing an extensive period of isolated development.

The Old World primate stock undoubtedly produced not only the common monkeys of Asia and Africa but all of the anthropoids as well. There is a considerable amount of controversy concerning the precise line through which man eventually evolved. Three major theories on the branching points between pongids and hominids were reviewed by Mayr (1963). Briefly, these three theories are: 1) that the hominid line branched from the common stem before the living anthropoids split into three different lines; 2) that the hominid line branched off after the gibbon line but before the pongids split into lines that eventually gave rise to *Pan* and *Pongo;* and 3) that the hominid line branched off from the line of the African apes at a comparatively recent date and long after the pongid line had split into an Asiatic (*Pongo*) and an African (*Pan* and *Homo*) branch. Fossil records supporting either of these theories are limited but hemoglobin and serum protein data make the third alternative more likely. Supportive evidence for the closeness of the hominid and African lines of evolution has been reviewed and expanded by Dunn (1966), with particular reference to their parasites.

Efforts to orient the evolution of the malaria parasite to the general trends of primate evolution have been successful only to a limited extent. It would be convenient to pick up the story with a primitive hepatocystis-plasmodium-like ancestor in one of the lemuroid progenitors of contemporary primates and follow the development of both the parasite and the primates through successive evolutionary stages. Unfortunately, such an approach runs into difficulties when the current distribution of the primates and their plasmodia is considered. There are true plasmodia in the lemurs of Madagascar but the biological isolation of this island presents many problems in evolutionary origins. Also, considerable difficulty is found in accounting for the distribution of malaria parasites among the living species of monkeys. The proliferation of species in Asia presents a probable picture of long association of a host-parasite system and indicates a considerable amount of success on the part of the parasite. If we confine our examination of parasite-primate evolution to southern Asia, then we encounter relatively little difficulty in arriving at a sequence of events which lead directly to current associations of monkeys, apes, and man and their respective malarias.

We can readily postulate a probable aperiodic hepatocystis-like parasite in a cercopithecoid ancestor of the Old World monkeys. After an ecological separation of Asian and African monkey groups, the parasite in the Asian monkeys began to undergo a series of changes which gradually produced malaria parasites with biological and morphological characteristics with which we are familiar today. It is probable that a quartan branch from this main line gave rise to contemporary tertian and quartan species in various primates as well as the successful but geographically limited quotidian experiment, *P. knowlesi*. Meanwhile, *Hepatocystis* resulted from a more conservative and less innovative series of changes from the primitive tissue coccidian than was involved in the evolution of the plasmodia. The stimuli responsible for the development of the malaria parasites were either not associated with African primates or, malaria-like parasites developed but were not initially successful. Thus, in Asia a reasonable hypothesis concerning the simultaneous development of primates and their malaria parasites can be proposed. However, since there are both primates and primate malarias in Africa and in the Western Hemisphere, any

hypothesis concerning the origins must encompass these forms, too.

In Africa, the human and ape malaria parasites are remarkably similar and at least two species, *P. malariae* and *P. schwetzi*, may be shared. This situation fits well with the hypothesis that the hominid line was a comparatively recent offshoot from the African ape line if we assume that the malaria parasites were evolving at the same time and through the same lines as the primates. However, only one species of plasmodia (*P. gonderi*) has been identified in African monkeys although *Hepatocystis* is quite common in these animals. It is difficult to understand the evolutionary sequence that would yield six species of *Plasmodium* representing three basic types in the apes and man in Africa and in the process see the development of only one species of one type in monkeys in the same area. It is possible that ancestors of living African monkeys had malaria parasites at one time which have been lost subsequently. However, these factors seem to indicate that the malaria parasites in apes and man in this area were introduced relatively recently rather than the end product of a long evolutionary process involving both the host animals and their parasites.

Problems are also encountered in the Western Hemisphere when the primates and their malaria parasites are considered. The evolutionary line of the New World primates was isolated from the Old World line quite early. There are no hepatocystis-like parasites in New World monkeys. The success of the primates in the Western Hemisphere is well demonstrated by the large variety of genera and species of these animals found in Central and South America. The Haemosporidia have not been as prolific; there are only two species described from the many potential host animals. *Plasmodium simium* seems to be limited in both host and geographic distribution being found only in howler (*Alouatta* sp.) and woolly-spider (*Brachyteles arachnoides*) monkeys in the forests of southern Brazil (Deane *et al*, 1969). *Plasmodium brasilianum* has a much wider range, but there are large areas, with suitable host animals, where it is not found, and, where natural infections in the same genera of monkeys, vary considerably even over relatively short parts of its range. These factors would seem to indicate that these host-parasite associations are much more recent than the 35 million years since the apparent isolation of the primitive ancestral primates of the New World by continental drift. Finally, the two species of plasmodia from this area are virtual duplicates of the human *P. vivax* and human and chimpanzee *P. malariae*, a phenomenon that severely challenges even the most extravagant views of convergent evolution. It is almost as though these parasites arose full grown like the mythological appearance of Athena from Zeus' head.

The evolution of the Haemosporidia has been reviewed by Baker (1965), Bruce-Chwatt (1965), and Garnham (1966) where efforts were made to correlate the evolution of the primates and their malaria parasites. Some of the problems associated with such an effort have been pointed out in the preceding paragraphs. We believe that the most uncomplicated and, therefore, possibly, the most likely explanation for the peculiar features of host and geographic distribution, as well as species proliferation of the primate malarias, has not been given a full hearing. Our suggestion is, that the nidus of the primate plasmodia universe lies somewhere in the jungles of Southeast or South Central Asia and that there, there has been a simultaneous development of non-human primates and their malaria parasites. Possibly during the early Pleistocene, some one to two million years ago, there appeared the first of many incursions into this reasonably stable millieu by a new and more highly evolved primate, from the west and north, in the form of an ancient hominid ancestor. This invader, the product of a long evolutionary sequence in Central Africa, was already demonstrating that peripatetic feature so characteristic of his descendants. The invader was still a hunter and forest dweller and, therefore, shared the forest environment, including anopheline mosquitoes, with the more primitive native primates of the area and their malaria parasites; the latter, probably already possessed characteristics of morphology and periodicity similar to those we recognize today. The situation was thus ideal for the introduction of the parasites into this *new* primate. Such a potential still exists, when man and non-human primates intimately share the same jungle environment.

The peripatetic nature of the *restless primate* increased and over the next 500,000 to one million years introduced, probably on numerous occasions, his malaria parasites into the apes and monkeys and his fellow hominids of West and Central Africa. It was in this African environment that the biological experimentation on the part of the parasites which eventually produced *Plasmodium schwetzi*, *P. ovale*, and the *P. falciparum-P. reichenowi* complex took place. It seems probable that the ancestors of *P. malariae* and possibly even *P. vivax* came out of Southeast Asia pretty much as we know them now. The older quartan parasite found an environment in which it could readily develop and thus the quartan malaria species of man and the African apes are considered generally to be conspecific.

The situation was less sympathetic for the tertian parasites. The indigenous negroid hominids in Africa were even then probably not very receptive to this latter group and adaptations were necessary. From the vivax-like stem developed a morphologically similar species, *P. ovale*, that was capable of surviving in the indigenous hominds. At the same time, a similar type of adaptation was taking place in the anthropoid cousins of the hominids in the area with the development of an additional species from the same stem, *P. schwetzi*. Coatney (1967) proposed that *P. schwetzi* was in all likelihood a chimpanzee equivalent of *P. ovale*. Such a relationship would not be surprising in the light of the hypothesis being presented here. However, it would be difficult, if not impossible, to say whether *P. ovale* and *P. schwetzi* arose simultaneously from the introduced *P. vivax* stem, or, whether the development was sequential in man and then the chimpanzees, or, the reverse. Probably the most interesting and most recent manifestation of attempts by the tertian parasite stem to adapt to African primates is seen in the development of the *P. falciparum-P. reichenowi* complex. Three features of *P. falciparum* seem to set it apart. First, the presence of crescent-shaped gametocytes; second, the tendency toward deep circulation schizogony; and third, the apparent absence of a mechanism, either relapse or long term recrudescence, by which the parasite can more safely assure its survival. It is interesting that each of these characteristics can be seen to a greater or lesser extent in parasites of non-human primates in Asia. The potential of the Haemosporidia for producing crescent-shaped gametocytes has been well demonstrated by the bird parasites. In the primates, *P. coatneyi* and *P. fragile* are most closely related to *P. falciparum-P. reichenowi*. In the latter parasites, there is a definite tendency toward the production of oval gametocytes, especially in the younger stages (Fig. 27, Plate XLII). Deep circulation schizogony is present in *P. coatneyi* and *P. fragile* of Asian monkeys. The possession of a true relapse mechanism appears to be limited among the primate malarias. This phenomenon has been seen in *P. vivax*, *P. cynomolgi*, *P. ovale*, *P. fieldi*, and *P. simiovale*, all of which are tertian parasites in stippled cells. Relapse is not known to occur in *P. fragile* or in *P. coatneyi*, and is apparently absent in all the quartan species, including *P. malariae*. Thus *P. falciparum* and *P. reichenowi* are not far removed from the mainstem of evolution in the primate malarias when we consider that there are other similar developments from the tertian ancestor among Asian non-human primates.

The dynamics of this relationship between the malaria parasites and the primates probably remained fluid for thousands of years. As the migratory habits of the hominid increased he carried his parasites to all areas of Asia, Africa, and Europe and, if anopheline mosquitoes were present, a focus of infection was established. Eventually, in the 16th century, man introduced his malaria parasites into the last remaining fertile area for their development. With the arrival of the southern European conquerors and their West African slaves into the Carribean area, the last large malaria-free primate population, in an appropriate environment, had been drawn into a process that had begun millions of years previously in the monkeys of Southeast and/or South Central Asia. This latest experiment is, of course, still underway in the jungles of Central and South America. At the present time, the parasites have had unqualified success in human populations of the area, both indigenous and recently introduced. The situation in the non-human primates has been less successful but at least two of the human forms seem to have established themselves in the monkeys, in certain areas, of Central and South America. The older and, apparently, the more stable quartan *P. malariae* has become well adapted as *P. brasilianum* to a variety of monkeys in many parts of Central and South America. The tertian parasites have adapted less readily in the New World monkeys with only limited success as *P. simium* in the howler and wooly-spider monkeys of Brazil. The *P. falciparum* line has not, in so far as is presently known, found a suitable host among the non-human primates of the Western Hemisphere.

The hypothesis that primate malarias arrived in the New World with Europeans and their West African slaves in the 16th century is not new. Recent authors who have defended this point of view have included Boyd (1949), Jarcho (1964), and Dunn (1965). However, there is a considerable body of literature that supports the existence of human and other primate malarias in pre-Columbian America. Bruce-Chwatt (1965) has presented an extremely interesting and well written article on this subject in which he summarizes the three kinds of evidence which are used to support the extreme antiquity of malaria in America; i.e., linguistic, botanical, and historical.

The linguistic evidence seems to be primarily oriented around the appearance in the Indian dialects, from both Mexico and Peru, of words which were roughly translated to mean chills and fever. The earliest translations were made by Spanish soldiers and priests who were familiar with chills and fever (probably from malaria) and, therefore, their interpretation of Indian words referring to general classes of illness may not have been without bias. In addition, "chills and fever" is not a syndrome unique to malaria.

The botanical evidence is probably even more fraught with uncertainty than the linguistic evidence. The romanticism that has developed around the discovery of the effectiveness of an extract of cinchona bark against malaria has left us with a number of intriguing stories but little concrete evidence (see Haggis, 1941). Considerable importance is given to the belief that the use of cinchona was widespread among the New World Indians for the treatment of fevers. Since cinchona extract is known to be a febrifuge there is no reason to assume that the fever being treated was malaria. Undoubtedly there were many febrile agents in the area. Finally, there is a growing body of evidence as reviewed by Jarcho (1964) that cinchona was not widely used in Indian medicine.

The historical evidence is, in our opinion, not only controversial as Bruce-Chwatt points out but, also, unconvincing. There is no doubt that the early Spanish explorers in the Caribbean and along the Atlantic coasts of Central and Northern South America suffered terribly from outbreaks of disease. However, the evidence for these early problems being due to malaria is vague in the extreme. The earliest slaves probably arrived in Cuba in the first decade of the 16th century. They undoubtedly brought malaria with them, but the Europeans themselves were also subject to malaria and undoubtedly assisted in establishing the parasites in the New World. Bruce-Chawtt (1965) notes that since the number of slaves was initially small, it is doubtful if large scale epidemics could have started with such a small source of parasites. There are two factors to be emphasized here; first, the evidence that the early disease outbreaks in the Spanish colonies were due to malaria is, to say the least, tenuous. Second, in the settlement areas, the Indians, as non-immunes, constituted an immediately available and readily infectable population. There is no doubt that human malaria became well established early in the Spanish conquest of Central and South America. Actually, this is not surprising considering the hardiness of the parasite and the fact that it was introduced into an area with a surfeit of both vertebrate and invertebrate hosts and an environment for transmission that has proved to be most efficient.

Possibly the most convincing evidence for the post-Columbian introduction of malaria into the New World is the difficulty in finding any other means by which it could have arrived. (We assume that there is no question that primate malarias were *introduced* into the New World. The alternative would be that these parasites evolved in the Western Hemisphere and became established only recently in the Old World primates; a proposal for which we believed there is little, if any, support.) The advocators for the existence of malaria in pre-Columbian America usually postulate that the parasites were introduced with man. Most anthropologists agree that man arrived in America via a land bridge from northeastern Asia between 15,000 and 25,000 (possibly as much as 40,000) years ago. More recent movements of small numbers of people from islands in the Central and Eastern Pacific to South America would also seem possible since the epic voyage of the Kon-Tiki. Finally, there is now no doubt that the Vikings reached the shores of North America 500 years before Columbus. Thus, there were at least three opportunities for man to have introduced malaria into the Western Hemisphere prior to the advent of the Conquistadores, with their malarious slaves, into the tropical area of the Caribbean.

What are the chances that any or all of the migrants were infected with malaria when they arrived? The land bridge from Asia connected two areas which have been, during historical times at least, incompatible with the transmission of malaria, and the evidence available indicates that the climate at the time of the migrations was at least as severe as today (Hopkins, 1959). Additionally, there is no evidence that there was any malaria-like illness among North American Indians prior to historical times.

Assuming that *Homo sapiens* did cross the Pacific to reach the shores of South America, it is probable that such a movement was made in stages using the islands of the Central and Eastern part of this area. These islands have been, and are now, free of anophelines and hence malaria in historical times, a biological condition that did not occur suddenly and therefore probably reaches back some distance into prehistory.

Finally, during the time the Vikings were journeying to Iceland, Greenland, and North America, their home area was free of malaria. Therefore, it would seem difficult, if not impossible, for malaria to have accompanied any of the pre-Columbian human invasions into the Western Hemisphere.

There are, undoubtedly, many flaws in the hypothesis we have presented. However, it does account for most of the known aspects of the biology of the primate malarias especially with reference to morphology, host, and geographic distribution. The intimate relationships between the plasmodia of man and non-human primates is possibly as recent as one million years, and there were probably fairly consistent interchanges throughout the long history of man's development. Obviously, such an exchange was related not only to the biology of the parasites in question but to the specific ecological niches which were occupied by man and other primates. As man evolved from a hunter and forest dweller into a planter and builder of houses, he became more and more separated from the vectors of non-human primate plasmodia and the biology of the now more or less separate groups of parasites began to diverge. The trend toward the separation of the malaria parasites of man and non-human primates has probably been progressing for thousands of years. However, the potential for exchange remains. This was demonstrated by the arrival of malarious Europeans and Africans in the New World early in the 16th Century and, through initmate sharing of anophelines with native primates, malaria was introduced to them. Such exchanges still occur, as shown by two recent reports of natural infections in man with malaria parasites of monkeys. Chin, *et al* (1965) documented a human infection with *P. knowlesi* from West Malaysia and in the same year Deane *et al* reported a human infection with the vivax-like *P. simium* which was believed to have been contracted in a forest area outside São Paulo. In each of these situations, man had introduced himself into the forest environment where transmission of malaria among the non-human primates was constant.

When such exchanges of parasites occur today and man is on the receiving end, we have a zoonosis. The situation with regard to the monkey parasites of the New World can be described as an anthroponosis or a reverse zoonosis if the point of view is particularly anthropocentric. Thus, the study of the evolutionary history of the primate malarias becomes something more than an academic exercise, since such information may provide an insight into future trends in the relationships among these parasites and help to assess the zoonotic potential in human malaria. At the present time, the potential role of the simian and anthropoid malarias in human infections is still primarily a matter of speculation.

The genus *Plasmodium* has been very successful in monkeys, apes, and man in Asia since it infects naturally every genus of contemporary higher primate in the area. All of the primate malarias have their origin in Asia except *P. falciparum* and *P. ovale* which, according to the hypothesis presented here, probably originated in Africa. The tertian species are found in a variety of host animals which may be a reflection of the much less specific vector requirements in these parasites than in the quartan species, thereby providing more opportunities for their introduction into new hosts. *Plasmodium knowlesi* is the only quotidian malaria of primates. It has particular vector relationships which, combined with the lethal impact on monkeys other than the natural host, have served to keep it confined to the jungles of Malaysia, the Philippines, and, possibly, some islands in Indonesia.

In Africa, there has been a great reduction over that seen in Asia not only in the number of species present but in the host and geographic range in which they have been successful. It is proposed that all of these species developed from malariae-vivax stock introduced from Asia by a hominid ancestor. In Africa, the tertian parasites have had considerable success, while *P. malariae* is the only quartan species found and the quotidian stem was too fragile to survive in this new and apparently hostile environment.

In American primates, the trend toward a reduction in species is more pronounced. The success of the human forms in indigenous primates in the New World is limited to only two species. It may be, that in the near future, *P. brasilianum* and *P. simium* will be made conspecific with *P. malariae* and *P. vivax*, respectively. Such a situation presents the problem of how extensive a period of isolation in a new host animal, associated with what level of physiologic and/or morphologic changes, is required for a new species of parasite to be recognized. We support the position that the human *P. vivax* and *P. malariae* are the immediate and recent ancestors of *P. simium* and *P. brasilianum*, but believe that these latter parasites are nevertheless valid species, at least for the present, in spite of the close morphologic similarities between the monkey and human forms. Therefore, it would seem that the only really startling innovation in the development of the primate plasmodia outside of Asia has been the rise of the falciparum-like parasites of Africa. The remainder of the species in both Africa and the New World are closely related to the stock Asian forms.

The evaluation of the role of simian and anthropoid malaria in human disease would not be complete without a word on possible *new* simian malarias. Recent successes in cultivating human malaria parasites in owl monkeys from South America and splenectomized gibbons from Asia have served to remind us again that *Homo sapiens* was a possible source of the simian and anthropoid parasites of Africa and the New World and, that the evolutionary processes that brought about this development are dynamic and contemporary. New species of simian malaria may still be adapting in the jungles of Africa or South America.

The current status of our knowledge makes it difficult, if not impossible, to relate the evolution of primate malarias to the earlier offshoots of the same ancestral line in reptiles, birds, rodents, bats, and a few ungulates. Rodent and bat plasmodia are found only in Africa. Two of the three ungulate species are African and one is Asian. No non-primate mammalian malarias are found in the New World. The most puzzling aspect of the primate plasmodia is the presence of two species in lemurs on the island of Madagascar. These are malaria parasites in a true but primitive African primate. Probably this enigma reflects the long period of biological isolation of Madagascar from the mainstreams of either Asian or African animal evolution. *Plasmodium girardi* and *P. lemuris* are poorly understood parasites which may be examples of convergent evolution arising from the same hepatocytis-like ancestor as the other plasmodia of which *P. foleyi* (also from the lemur and considered by Garnham (1966) to be more probably *Hepatocystis* than *Plasmodium*) is the more direct, contemporary descendant.

Undoubtedly, there are alternative explanations for the evolutionary processes which gave rise to the current distribution of the primates and their malaria parasites. The hypothesis proposed here seems logical in the light of our present knowledge, suggesting that the origin of at least the primate malarias was in Asia and that man in his wanderings has been responsible for the introduction of these parasites into African and New World primates. For thousands of years man and non-human primates occupied the same environment with what was probably a fairly free interchange of malaria parasites. However, man's development as an agricultural animal tended to separate him ecologically from his simian and anthropoid relatives and at the same time from their malarial parasites. This trend has continued until it is obvious that today the relationships between the human and non-human primate malarias are very tenuous and, in the overall aspects of human health, of limited importance. However, it is probable that occasional cases of human malaria of simian origin will be detected in deep jungle areas of Asia, Africa, and South America once malaria eradication has advanced to a point where such cases can be individually evaluated.

REFERENCES

BAKER, J. R., 1965. The evolution of parasitic protozoa (pages 1–27). In: Third Symposium of the British Society for Parasitology, Blackwell Scientific Publications, Oxford.

BALL, G. H., 1943. Parasitism and evolution. Am. Nat. 77 : 345–364.

BALL, G. H., 1960. Some considerations regarding the sporozoa. J. Protozool. 7 : 1–6.

BOYD, M. F., 1949. Malariology, 2 Vol. W. B. Saunders, Philadelphia, Pa.

BRAY, R. S., 1957. Studies on the exo-erythrocytic cycle in the genus *Plasmodium*. London School of Hyg. & Trop. Med. Memoir No 12. pp. 192.

BRAY, R. S., 1963. The exo-erythrocytic phase of malaria parasites. Int. Rev. Trop. Med. 2 : 41–75.

REFERENCES—Continued

BRUCE-CHWATT, L. J., 1965. Paleogenesis and paleo-epidemiology of primate malaria. Bull. Wld. Hlth. Org. *32* : 363–387.

CHIN, W., CONTACOS, P. G., COATNEY, G. R., and KIMBALL, H. R., 1965. Naturally acquired quotidian type malaria in man transferable to monkeys. Science *149* : 865.

CHRISTOPHERS, R., 1934. Malaria from a zoological point of view. Proc. Royal Soc. Med. *27* : 991–1000.

COATNEY, G. R., 1967. Simian malarias in man: facts, implications, and predictions. Am. J. Trop. Med. & Hyg. *17* : 147–155.

DEANE, L. M., DEANE, M. P., and NETO, J. F., 1965. Studies on transmission of simian malaria and on a natural infection of man with *Plasmodium simium* in Brazil. Bull. Wld. Hlth. Org. *35* : 805–808.

DEANE, L. M., FERREIRA NETO, J. A., OKUMURA M., and FERREIRA, M. O., 1969. Malaria parasites of Brazilian monkeys. Rev. Inst. Med. Trop. São Paulo *11* : 71–86.

DUNN, F. L., 1965. On the antiquity of malaria in the western hemisphere. Human Biology *37* : 385–393.

DUNN, F. L., 1966. Patterns of parasitism in primates: phylogenetic and ecological interpretations with particular reference to the Hominoidea. Folia Primatol. *4* : 329–345.

FANTHAM, H. B., 1936. The evolution of parasitism among the protozoa. Scientia. Milano *49* : 316–324.

GARNHAM, P. C. C., 1955. The comparative pathogenicity of protozoa in their vertebrate and invertebrate hosts. Symposium No. 5 of Soc. Gen. Microbiol.: 191–206.

GARNHAM, P. C. C., 1963. Distribution of simian malaria parasites in various hosts. J. Parasit. *49* : 905–911.

GARNHAM, P. C. C., 1966. Malaria parasites and other haemosporidia. Blackwell Scientific Publications, Oxford. pp. 1114.

HAGGIS, A. W., 1941. Fundamental errors in the early history of cinchona. Bull. Hist. Med. *10* : 417–459; 568–592.

HOPKINS, M., 1959. Cenzoic history of the Bering land bridge. Science *129* : 1519–1528.

HUFF, C. G., 1938. Studies on the evolution of some disease producing organisms. Quart. Rev. Biol. *13* : 196–206.

HUFF, C. G., 1945. A consideration of the problems of evolution of malarial parasites. Rev. Inst. Salub. enferm. trop., Mex. *6* : 253–258.

JARCHO, S., 1964. Some observations on disease in prehistoric North America. Bull. Hist. Med. *38* : 1–18.

MANWELL, R. D., 1955. Some evolutionary possibilities in the history of malaria parasites. Ind. J. Malariol. *9* : 247–253.

MAYR, E., 1963. Animal species in evolution. Harvard University Press, Cambridge, Mass.

2

Historical Review

THE malaria parasite is a well organized, highly adapted end-product of thousands of years of biological evolution which would mark it as successful, regardless of the criteria. Species of the genus *Plasmodium* are currently found in every group of strictly terrestrial vertebrates and adaptive capacities have been particularly well demonstrated in birds and primates where the level of speciation is high. When one considers the complexity of the life cycle, including the necessity for adjustment to two decidedly different host environments, the precise combination of temperature and humidity required, plus vector and vertebrate host habits necessary to assure continued transmission of the parasite, its survival in nature alone, is amazing. Recent history has confirmed the hardiness of these parasites. Man's concentrated attacks on the parasites and their vectors have met with only limited success and a great deal of frustration. Even areas freed of human malaria remain in a precarious position because the parasites keep up an unrelenting pressure on their borders, maintaining a constant threat of re-invasion with the production of epidemics such as occurred in Ceylon in 1968.

The chronicle of human malaria begins in pre-history and continues for thousands of years through a tortuous path of sickness and death. The full antiquity of the man-malaria parasite association remains obscure, but Hippocrates, "The Father of Medicine" and the first malariologist, described the various malaria fevers of man 400 years before the birth of Christ. Progress in understanding the disease was slow, but about 30 A.D., Celsus described two types of tertian fevers; 150 years later, Galen recognized the appearance of these fevers with the summer season and a jaundice in infected people. For approximately the next 1500 years, man did little about malaria but suffer and die from it. Then, in the middle of the 17th century, the bitter extract from the bark of a New World tree was found to have remarkable powers against these intermittent fevers so common in the Mediterranean area. The romance surrounding the discovery of quinine has served to obscure the real story, and today, there are a number of versions from which to choose. It now seems doubtful that the Countess of Chinchon was ever treated for malaria with Peruvian bark, but her name was used as the genus name for the Cinchona tree, by way of a spelling error, by Linnaeus. Cinchona bark first appeared in European medical literature in Heyden's *Discours et Aris sur les flus de ventre Doloureux* published in Antwerp in 1643. The efficacy of the extract was known by that time and it is probable that it had been used in Lima and possibly Spain, earlier. Its value was soon recognized and thus began a long period of intrigue and frustration associated with efforts to secure sufficient quantities of the extract to treat the increasing number of malaria infections in the world.

The 18th century saw three advances which can, in the light of our present knowledge, be recognized as important. Lancisi noted the presence of black pigment in human brains and spleens, but did not associate these changes with malaria, and in 1717 suggested a relationship between marsh insects and the occurrence of malaria. In 1775, Torti recognized that quinine was not therapeutic for all fevers, thus effectively separating the malarias from human febrile illnesses of other etiologies.

It can be seen that the status of knowledge of malaria at the beginning of the 19th century was at a very low level. Meanwhile, the problem was becoming more acute due to European explorations and settlements in the tropics of Asia. In addition, the malarias introduced into the New World in the 16th and 17th centuries had found fertile ground, and, by the early 1800's, severely challenged man's ability to survive in parts of the American tropics and subtropics.

The 19th century proved to be a momentous one in the field of malaria. Initially, information continued to be fragmented and unco-ordinated. In 1820, two French chemists, Pelletier and Caventou, isolated the active anti-malaria component from quinine powder. Boyle (1831) while working in Africa gave credence to the swamp theory of malarial etiology. The probable relationship between malaria and swamps was so firmly established that it had given the two most frequently used names to the disease *mal'aria*, later shortened to one word *malaria*, and *paludisme*. The black pigment, first noted by Lancisi, was specifically associated with malaria by Schutz (1848) when he observed it in the internal organs of patients who had died of malaria. Meckel in 1847, without recognizing its true importance, probably saw malaria parasites for the first time when he described black pigment in protoplasmic masses in the blood of a patient with fever; it was not until 1879, however, that Afanasiev proposed that these bodies might be the agents of the disease.

The scene was now set for the dramatic events which crowded into the last 20 years of the 19th century. In 1880, Laveran, working in North Africa, described exflagellation of the *Plasmodium falciparum* male gametocyte in the blood of a malarious patient. The reception of Laveran's discovery was less than enthusiastic. Most of the scientific world was convinced of the bacterial etiology of malaria. Meanwhile, according to Garnham (1966), Danilewsky (1884) was able to observe parasites of malaria in the blood of wild birds, and, in the same year, Laveran's influential countryman, Pasteur, became convinced of the soundness of the former's observations. The true nature of the organisms seen by Laveran

was finally made clear by MacCallum in 1897 who, while in Canada, observed fertilization in bird malaria and later, at the Johns Hopkins Hospital in Baltimore, in *P. falciparum* in man. In 1891, Romanowsky developed a stain which allowed for differential identification of blood parasites, including malaria.

The animal nature of the malaria parasite had fairly wide acceptance by the last decade of the 19th century. It is during this period that some of the most dramatic and far-reaching work in the field of malaria was to take place. The possible association of insects and the transmission of malaria had been discussed in various parts of the world for a long time. As early as 1848, Nott published a paper in the U.S.A. which contrasted yellow fever and remittent fever and proposed that mosquito involvement was the best explanation for the occurrence and distribution of both kinds of fever. In 1856, Burton noted that some African tribes believed that mosquitoes were responsible for certain fevers. The development of filarial larvae in mosquitoes was demonstrated by Manson in 1883, and in 1893, Smith and Kilborne reported the transmission of Texas cattle fever by ticks.

Information on the probable association of insects and certain disease syndromes had no doubt begun to accumulate on both sides of the Atlantic before Ronald Ross's epoch making work on mosquitoes and malaria in India; communications were poor, however, and there was little opportunity to correlate the various observations arising from such divergent points as Russia (Danilewsky) and the U.S.A. (Nott). Patrick Manson, who encouraged, stimulated, and advised Ross, was committed to the idea that insects were involved in disease transmission.

Ross's early results, reported by Manson in 1896, included the observation of exflagellation by *P. falciparum* gametocytes in the stomach of a mosquito. Manson (loc. cit.) therefore concluded that the mosquito's stomach provided an appropriate medium for the development of the malaria parasite outside the vertebrate host. In the same year, according to Russell (1955), Theobald Smith came to the conclusion that mosquitoes were vectors of malaria. The following year, Ross reported the presence of pigmented bodies in spotted winged mosquitoes after the insects had fed on patients with malaria. At that point, Ross was forced to interrupt his investigations on human malaria, but was soon (1898) able to observe the sporogonic cycle of a bird malaria (*P. relictum*) in the mosquito, and, to transmit the parasite to healthy sparrows.

It is at this time that the famous, acrimonious and long-lived conflict began between the British and Italian malariologists over priority in the transmission of malaria by mosquitoes. Bignami, in 1898, successfully infected a volunteer with *P. falciparum* by the bites of mosquitoes collected from a malarious area. There is no serious challenge to the validity of either Ross's or Bignami's work. The acrimony arose over who was the first to demonstrate the role of the mosquito in malaria. It would seem that Bignami's was the first report but both Ross and Manson insist that the ideas for the Italian investigations came from unpublished reports of Ross's work. Confirmation of the mosquito role in the transmission of malaria came in 1900 when Manson arranged for three people from the London School of Tropical Medicine to spend the summer near Ostia in the Roman Campagna. Their days were spent in various excursions in the vicinity, but each night was passed in a screened hut. The three did not come down with the disease, although transmission of malaria continued at its usual high rate in the surrounding area. Final proof came when mosquitoes previously fed on a malaria patient in Rome were allowed to bite healthy volunteers in London. The London participants in these experiments, including Manson's son, came down with typical vivax malaria two weeks after exposure. The complete cycle of *P. falciparum* was observed by Grassi, Bignami, and Bastianelli in 1899 and in the same year, Bastianelli and Bignami accomplished the same feat with *P. vivax*. The Italian studies on the sporogonic cycle of malaria were summarized in what was to become a classical monograph by Grassi in 1900.

Meanwhile, the same group of Italian workers had been busy with other facets of the rapidly developing fund of knowledge about malaria. Credit for the genus name *Plasmodium*

goes to Marchiafava and Celli (1885) and the initial differential descriptions of *P. vivax* and *P. malariae* were made by Grassi and Feletti in 1890. However, the situation was not as clear-cut as would be indicated by this short statement. Chaos was the order of the day in the taxonomy of the malaria parasites for many years. Numerous generic names were proposed, including *Haemamoeba, Oscillaria, Laverania,* and *Haemomonas*. Confusion continued well into the 20th century over whether all of the parasites belonged to one species or to several. In the confusion, it is difficult to know exactly which parasite was under observation by some of the early authors. There is little doubt that Laveran saw and described parasites of what was to become *P. malariae* in 1881, and that he first used the species name "malariae." It is also clear that Laveran first saw the gametocytes of *P. falciparum*, but he firmly believed that all of the parasites belonged to one species. In 1890, Grassi and Feletti described and illustrated two parasites that were to become *P. vivax* and *P. malariae*. Seven years later, Welch (1897) proposed the name *Haematozoon falciparum* for the parasite with the crescent-shaped gametocytes which Laveran had seen some 17 years earlier. The end result of this taxonomic chaos is now well known. The genus name *Plasmodium* of Marchiafava and Celli was maintained for all species. The species name of the parasite described by Grassi and Feletti as *Haemamoeba vivax* was eventually accepted to designate the benign tertian parasite of man, *Plasmodium vivax*. Welch's specific name gained wide acceptance for the malignant tertian parasite and *Plasmodium falciparum* became a permanent part of the malaria literature. With *P. malariae*, the situation is even more confused. In 1890, Grassi and Feletti gave *malariae* as the specific name for the quartan parasite and on the basis of priority, that name and date is valid.

The 20th century part of the malaria story began in what might be termed organized confusion. The last two decades of the 19th century had produced more information than could readily be assimilated, but a firm basis for the epidemiologic investigations, which were to dominate work in the early part of the 20th century, had been established. Three different human parasites were recognized (though not universally accepted) both clinically and morphologically, and the role of the anopheline mosquito in the transmission of the parasite had been established.

The stage was now set for the development of new concepts of control based on biological aspects of mosquito transmission and the erection of some type of barrier between man and the insect vector of the disease. In 1900, Gorgas began his momentous work on the control of malaria and yellow fever in Havana and following his success there, he transferred his activities, in 1907, to the Panama Canal Zone where he achieved equal, if not greater, results in reducing the incidence of two deadly diseases—malaria and yellow fever. There is little doubt that Gorgas, LePrince, and Carter must, in a large measure, be given credit for the ultimate completion of the Panama Canal. During the same period, Watson began his classical work of draining the salt marshes, which made parts of the west coast of Malaya habitable. During the next two decades evolved the well known concepts of ditching and draining which achieved such notable results in malaria control in the southern United States and in Italy. In 1939, the Malaria Service of Northeast Brazil was organized to combat the populations of *Anopheles gambiae* which had been introduced from Africa. This effort at species eradication was enormously successful and the mosquito is still absent from the area. The control of malaria took a giant step forward in the late 1930's and early 1940's with the development of residual insecticides and synthetic antimalarials. However, the history of these developments is outside the scope of this work.

The capacity of a malaria fever to frequently improve the condition of people suffering from general paralysis of the insane by Wagner-Jauregg (1922) may be one of the most important discoveries in the history of malaria in that it allowed for the systematic study of the disease under controlled conditions. It was in such mental hospitals as those in Milledgeville, Georgia and Columbia, South Carolina in the U.S.A.; Horton Hospital in England; and in Bucharest and Socola, Roumania that studies on induced malarias revealed much of

our information on pathology, biology, drug responses, and relapse mechanisms. It would be difficult to overestimate the contribution that thousands of patients, in many such institutions, have made to our understanding of malaria.

There is no doubt that the evolution of concepts of control and eradication have been the predominant feature story of malaria during the 20th century. However, significant strides have been made in its biology, parasitology, and therapy as well. One of the most important new developments was the discovery of the exoerythrocytic stages of the primate malarias. This story is reviewed in detail in Chapter 6. Actually, Grassi suggested as early as 1900 the possibility that the sporozoite did not develop directly into blood parasites. However, it was not until 1948 that Shortt and Garnham finally demonstrated the pre-erythrocytic stages of a primate malaria.

No discussion of the history of man's conflict with malaria would be complete without consideration of the plasmodia of other animals. The genus is extremely widespread in reptiles, birds, and mammals, and, in the light of this monograph, a brief review of the development of our knowledge of the malarias of non-human primates is in order. The evolution of an understanding of the plasmodia of non-human primates parallels, in many ways, and complements, the story of human malaria. The first plasmodium-like parasite (*P. kochi*) described from non-human primates was not a true malaria but a member of the genus *Hepatocystis* which was subsequently reported from a number of species of African monkeys (Kossel, 1899; Laveran, 1899). Most of the early observations on the blood protozoa of non-human primates were made on animals imported into Europe from Africa, Asia, and America. Laveran (1905) saw the parasite, later described by Halberstaedter and Prowazek (1907) as *Plasmodium pitheci*, in the blood of Javan orangutans housed in Berlin. In the same year, Halberstaedter and Prowazek examined blood of *Macaca irus* and *M. nemestrina* imported from Indonesia and Borneo and found another malaria parasite which they described as *P. inui*. In the same year, while Halberstaedter and Prowazek were working in

Berlin, Mayer, working with Asian monkeys at the Hamburg Institute, described a parasite from the blood of a *Macaca irus*, from Java, which he named *P. cynomolgi*. The following year, a cacajao (*Brachyurus calvus*) from Brazil was encountered in a circus in Hamburg and Gonder and von Berenberg-Gossler found a parasite in its blood which they named *P. brasilianum*. In 1932 and 1933, Sinton and Mulligan reviewed the confused situation with regard to the malaria parasites of monkeys, and, in a well reasoned two part paper, managed to bring some order out of the chaos. The African parasites fell into two obvious categories—one without schizogony in the blood which remained as *Plasmodium* (later to become *Hepatocystis*) *kochi*. The second parasite did have multiplication in the peripheral blood and the authors considered it to be more closely related to the *P. inui* of Asia; they therefore established *P. inui* var. *gonderi*. The Asian parasites also received careful attention. A parasite described but not named by Knowles and Das Gupta (1932) from a *M. irus* (=*fascicularis*) from Singapore was considered by Sinton and Mulligan (loc. cit.) and was given specific rank as *P. knowlesi*, on the basis of morphological characters and on the presence of a 24- rather than a 48-hour schizogonic cycle. The parasite of Mayer, *P. cynomolgi*, was believed to be a separate species also, but the investigators (Sinton and Mulligan, loc. cit.) considered the information available at that time to be too meager; they therefore established *P. inui* var. *cynomolgi*.

So well had Sinton and Mulligan done their work that the only change made later in their taxonomic arrangements was elevation of the two "varieties" of *P. inui* to specific rank. Rodhain and van den Berghe (1936) found the African parasite to be tertian in periodicity rather than quartan, as in *P. inui*, and gave *P. gonderi* specific rank. Mulligan (1935) established *P. cynomolgi* as a species separate from *P. inui* on the basis of morphology and its tertian periodicity.

The work of Sinton and Mulligan (loc. cit.) became the base on which the future taxonomy of the monkey malarias was to be developed. Workers in Malaya and India in the 1960's faced a much less complicated problem, and

with reasonable confidence, described five new species of malaria in monkeys from these areas.

The malarias of apes created a major problem in taxonomy. Much of the confusion arose because, for some time, their parasites were considered to be the same as their three morphological counterparts in man. *Plasmodium reichenowi* was given specific rank in 1922 by Sluiter, Swellengrebel, and Ihle. In 1939, Brumpt gave the *P. vivax* and *P. malariae* counterparts the specific names of *P. schwetzi* and *P. rodhaini*, respectively. Previous efforts had failed to establish these parasites in man, but Rodhain (1940) working with *P. malariae* transferred it, by blood inoculation, to the chimpanzee, and, in 1948, by the same route, transferred *P. rodhaini* from the chimpanzee to man. As a result of this work, some investigators have synonymized *P. rodhaini* with *P. malariae*. It is of interest in this connection that, as early as 1920, Mesnil and Roubaud had transferred *P. vivax* to the chimpanzee by blood inoculation but had not attached any significance to it. Recently, Contacos *et al* (1970) infected human volunteers with *P. schwetzi*, via mosquito bites, and pointed out the close similarity between the blood forms of *P. schwetzi* and of *P. ovale*. Coatney (1968) suggested that *P. schwetzi* might actually be *P. ovale*. The true relationship of these ape- and man-forms is still to be determined.

The taxonomic status of the malaria parasites of Asian apes is much less confused. Only one species, *P. pitheci*, has been found in orang-utans. The situation with the gibbons is interesting in that taxonomic difficulties do not arise with the four distinct species known from these animals, but the systematic position of the apes themselves is so confused that it is sometimes difficult to clearly establish the type host for a given parasite.

The parallel histories of the malarias of human and non-human primates first became mixed when it was believed that the malaria parasites of the great apes of Africa were identical with those of man. Then in 1932 Knowles and Das Gupta reported the infection of a human volunteer, by the inoculation of blood stages of a parasite from the Malaysian monkey, *M. irus*. This parasite was later described as *P. knowlesi* by Sinton and Mulligan

(1932). In 1934, Ionesco-Mihaiesti *et al* successfully infected mental patients with a parasite which they believed to be *P. inui* but which was later identified as *P. knowlesi* (Garnham, 1966). Earlier, Clark and Dunn (1931) failed to infect man with the blood stages of *P. brasilianum* of the New World. The relationship between human and non-human primate malarias remained primarily of academic interest even though Mesnil and Roubaud (1920) had produced infection in the chimpanzee with *P. vivax* and Rodhain (1948) was able to induce infection in man with the *P. malariae*-like parasite of chimpanzees. All of these infections were blood induced and seemed to be of little natural significance. Then, in 1960, Eyles *et al* reported a natural infection of man with *P. cynomolgi*. True, it had occurred in the laboratory, but the transmission was accomplished by a mosquito. The fact that simian malaria was a true zoonosis was finally established by Chin *et al* (1965) with the report of a human infection with *P. knowlesi* acquired in the jungles of peninsular Malaysia. More recently, various workers have been successful in infecting owl monkeys (*Aotus trivirgatus*) with human malarias (Young *et al*, 1966; Porter and Young, 1966; Geiman and Meagher, 1967; Geiman and Siddiqui, 1969).

With the primate malarias, malariologists were provided with a tool for the controlled study of various aspects of malaria including drug responses, relapse mechanisms, immunity, transmission studies, and pathogenesis. At the same time, unfortunately, Eyles's discovery (loc. cit.) raised the unwelcome specter of an animal reservoir for malarias infective to man. This situation underwent intensive study in Southeast Asia from 1961 to 1965 and the results form the substance of this monograph. The investigators concluded that the simian malarias of Asia might produce an occasional infection in man, but were not considered to be a serious public health problem. It was recognized, however, that such cases might threaten the eradication of malaria in the tropics where natural infections occur in monkeys and apes.

The 1970's find man's struggle against the malaria parasite still unfinished. The dream of eradication is no longer considered attainable within the foreseeable future in parts of Central America, South America, Africa, and Asia. The XXIInd World Health Assembly, meeting in Boston in 1969, called for a re-evaluation of the concept of eradication with a reversion to classical approaches to control where necessary. Giant strides have been made against the disease, especially through the eradication programs, but we have probably reached the limit imposed by the techniques available and the last quarter of this century may need to be as innovative as was the first quarter, if we are to make real progress against the age-old scourge—malaria.

REFERENCES

AFANASIEV, V. I., 1879. On the pathology of malarial infection. Protocol of Meeting of Russian Physicians in St. Petersburg, December 27th, No. 10, 380. (NS).

BASTIANELLI, G. and BIGNAMI, A., 1899. Sullo sviluppo die parassiti della terzana nell'*Anopheles claviger*. Atti. d. Soc. per gli studi d. malaria *1* : 28–49.

BIGNAMI, A., 1898. Como si prendono le febbri malariche. Richerche speriment. Bull. della R. Accad. med. di Roma, 15 Nov. 1898. (NS).

BOYLE, J., 1831. A practical medico-historical account of the western coast of Africa. Highley, S. London; Oliver and Boyd, Edinburgh. (NS).

BRUMPT, E., 1939. Les parasites du paludisme des chimpanzés. C. R. Soc. Biol. *130* : 837–840.

BURTON, R. F., 1856. First footsteps in East Africa. Longmans, London.

CELSUS, ALUS CORNELIUS, 30 A.D. (According to L. J. Warshaw, 1949 in Malaria—The biography of a killer.

Rinehart & Co., Inc., New York & Toronto. pp. 348).

CHIN, W., CONTACOS, P. G., COATNEY, G. R., and KIMBALL, H. R., 1965. A naturally acquired quotidian-type malaria in man transferable to monkeys. Science *149* : 865.

CLARK, H. C. and DUNN, L. H., 1931. Experimental efforts to transfer monkey malaria to man. Am. J. Trop. Med. *11* : 1–7.

COATNEY, G. R., 1968. Simian malarias in man: facts, implications, and predictions. Am. J. Trop. Med. & Hyg. *17* : 147–155.

CONTACOS, P. G., COATNEY, G. R., ORIHEL, T. C., COLLINS, W. E., CHIN, W. and JETER, M. H., 1970. Transmission of *Plasmodium schwetzi* from the chimpanzee to man by mosquito bite. Am. J. Trop. Med. & Hyg. *19* : 190–195.

EYLES, D. E., COATNEY, G. R., and GETZ, M. E., 1960. Vivax-type malaria parsite of macaques transmissible to man. Science *132* : 1812–1813.

REFERENCES—Continued

GALEN, 180 A.D. (According to L. J. Warshaw, 1949 in Malaria—The biography of a killer. Rinehart & Co., Inc., New York & Toronto. pp. 348).

GARNHAM, P. C. C., 1966. Malaria parasites and other haemosporidia. Blackwell Scientific Publications, Oxford. pp. 1114.

GEIMAN, Q. M. and MEAGHER, M. J., 1967. Susceptibility of a New World monkey to *Plasmodium falciparum* from man. Nature *215* : 437–439.

GEIMAN, Q. M. and SIDDIQUI, W. A., 1969. Susceptibility of a New World monkey to *Plasmodium malariae* from man. Am. J. Trop. Med. & Hyg. *18* : 251–254.

GONDER, R. and VON BERENBERG-GOSSLER, H., 1908. Untersuchungen über Malariaplasmodien der Affen. Malaria Lpz. *1* : 47–56.

GRASSI, B., 1900. Studi di un zoologo sulla malaria. Rome. (NS).

GRASSI, B., BIGNAMI, A., and BASTIANELLI, G., 1899. Ulteriori ricerche sul ciclo parassiti malarici umani nel corpo del zanzarone. Atti. Reale accad. dei Lincei, Ser. 5; *8* : 21–28. (NS).

GRASSI, B. and FELETTI, R., 1890. Parassiti malarici negli uccelli. Nota preliminarie. Bull. Mens. Accad. Gioenia Sc. Nat. Catania, n.s. *13* : 3–6.

HALBERSTÄDTER, L. and VON PROWAZEK, S., 1907. Untersuchungen über die Malariaparasiten der Affen. Arb. K. Gesundh. -Amte (Berl.) *26* : 37–43.

HIPPOCRATES. Epidemics I. 24, 25. From Jones, W. H. S. 1923–1931. Hippocrates with an English translation, Loeb Classical Library, New York. G. P. Putnam's Sons, Vols. I, II, and IV. (NS).

IONESCO-MIHAIESTI, C., ZOTTA, G., RADACOVICI, E., and BADENSKI, G., 1934. Transmission expérimentale à l'homme du paludisme propre des singes. C. R. Soc. Biol. *115* : 1311–1313.

KNOWLES, R. and DAS GUPTA, B. M., 1932. A study of monkey-malaria, and its experimental transmission to man. Ind. Med. Gaz. *67* : 301–320.

KOSSEL, H., 1899. Über einen malariaähnlichen Blutparasiten bei Affen. Zschr. Hyg. Infekt. krankh. *32* : 25–32. (NS).

LANCISI, 1717. De noxiss paludum effluviis, eorumque remediis. Romae, Salvioni. (NS).

LAVERAN, A., 1880. Nouveau parasite du sang. Bull. Acad. Med. 2nd ser. *9* : 1235–1236. (NS).

LAVERAN, A., 1881. Nature parasitaire des accidentes de l'impaludisme. Description d'un nouveau parasite trouvé dans le sang des malades atteints de fièvre pallustre. Paris, Baillière et Fils. pp. 104.

LAVERAN, A., 1899. Les hématozoaires endoglobulaires (Haemocytozoa). Cinquantenaire Soc. Biol. pp. 124–133.

LAVERAN, A., 1905. Haemacytozoa. Essai de classification. Bull. Inst. Pasteur (Paris). *3* : 809–817.

LINNAEUS, C., 1749. Materia Medica *1* : 24. (According to A. W. Haggis in Bull. Hist. Med. *10* : 417–592, 1941).

MANSON, P., 1883. The *Filaria sanguinis humanis* and certain new forms of parasitic disease in India, China and warm countries. London. H. K. Lewis.

MANSON, P., 1896. The life history of the malaria germ outside the human body. Lancet 695–698, 751–755, and 831–833. (NS).

MANSON, P., 1900. Experimental proof of the mosquito-malaria theory. Brit. Med. Jour. *2* : 949–951. (NS).

MARCHIAFAVA, E. and CELLI, A., 1885. Nuove ricerche sulla infezione malarica. Arch. per le sc. med. Torino *9* : 311–340.

MAYER, M., 1907. Über malaria beim Affen. Med. Klin. *3* : 579–580.

MACCALLUM, W. G., 1897. On the flagellated forms of the malarial parasite. Lancet *2* : 1240–1241.

MECKEL, H., 1847. Über schwarzes Pigment in der Milz und dem Blute einer Geisteskranken. Allgem. Zschr. Psychiatrie u. psychisch-gerichtliche Med. *4* : 198–226. (NS).

MESNIL, F. and ROUBAUD, E., 1920. Essais d'inoculation du paludisme au chimpanzé. Ann. Inst. Pasteur, Paris *34* : 466–480.

MULLIGAN, H. W., 1935. Descriptions of two species of monkey *Plasmodium* isolated from *Silenus irus*. Archiv. Protistenk. *84* : 285–314.

NOTT, I. C., 1848. Yellow fever contrasted with billious fever. Reasons for believing it a disease *sui generis*. Its mode of propogation, etc. New Orleans Med. & Surg. Jour. *4* : 563–601. (NS).

PELLETIER, P. J. and CAVENTOU, J. B., 1820. Recherches chimiques sur les quinquinas. Ann. de chimie et de physique *15* : 289–318, 337–365. (NS).

PORTER, J. A., JR. and YOUNG, M. D., 1966. Susceptibility of Panamanian primates to *Plasmodium vivax*. Mil. Med. *131* : 952–958.

RODHAIN, J., 1940. Les plasmodiums des anthropoides de l'Afrique centrale et leur relations avec les plasmodiums humains. Réceptivité de l'homme au *Plasmodium malariae* (*Plasmodium rodhaini* Brumpt) du chimpanzé. C. R. Soc. Biol. *133* : 276–277.

RODHAIN, J., 1948. Susceptibility of the chimpanzee to *P. malariae* of human origin. Am. J. Trop. Med. *28* : 629–631.

RODHAIN, J. and VAN DEN BERGHE, L., 1936. Contribution a l'etude des plasmodiums des singes Africains. Ann. Soc. Belge de Méd. Trop. *16* : 521–531.

ROMANOWSKY, D. L., 1891. Zur frage der Parasitologie und Therapie der Malaria. St. Petersb. Med. Wschr. *16* : 297–307. (NS).

ROSS, R., 1897. On some peculiar pigmented cells found in two mosquitoes fed on malarial blood. Brit. Med. Jour. *2* : 1786–1788. (NS).

ROSS, R., 1898. Report on the cultivation of Proteosoma, Labbé, in grey mosquitoes. Government Press, Calcutta (dates 21st May 1898). Also in Ind. Med. Gaz., November and December, 1898. (NS).

RUSSELL, P. F., 1955. Man's mastery of malaria. Oxford University Press, London. pp. 308.

SCHUTZ, P., 1848. Chronic disorder of the spleen. Dissection of body, presence of black pigment in the blood and other organs. Peculiar dyscrasia of the blood. Milit. med. J. Part 51, sect. II, 13–33. (NS).

SHORTT, H. E. and GARNHAM, P. C. C., 1948. Pre-ery-

REFERENCES—Continued

throcytic stage in mammalian malaria parasites. Nature *161* : 126.

SINTON, J. A. and MULLIGAN, H. W., 1932–1933. A critical review of the literature relating to the identification of the malarial parasites recorded from monkeys of the families Cercopithecidae and Colobidae. Rec. Malar. Surv. India. *3* : 357–380; 381–444.

SLUITER, C. P., SWELLENGREBEL, N. H., and IHLE, J. E., 1922. De dierlijke parasiten van den mensch en van onze huisdieren, 3rd ed. Scheltema & Holkema, Amsterdam.

SMITH, T. and KILBORNE, F. L., 1893. Investigation with the nature, causation and prevention of southern cattle fever. Rep. Bureau Animal Indust., U.S. Dept. Agri. for years 1891 and 1892. (NS).

TORTI, F., 1775. La terapia speciale delle febbri perniciose. Translated by Giulio Liga of the 1775 edition. Roma, Casa Luigi Possi. (NS).

WAGNER-JAUREGG, J., 1922. Treatment of general paresis by inoculation of malaria. J. Nervous & Mental Dis. *55* : 369–375. (NS).

WATSON, M., 1921. The prevention of malaria in the Federated Malay States. E. P. Dutton & Co., New York.

WELCH, W. H., 1897. Malaria: definitions, synonyms, history and parasitology; in Loomis and Thompson's Syst. Pract. Med. *1* : 17–76. (NS).

YOUNG, M. D., PORTER, J. A., JR., and JOHNSON, C. M., 1966. *Plasmodium vivax* transmitted from man to monkey to man. Science *153* : 1006–1007.

(NS) = Not seen.

3

Ecology of the Hosts in Relation to the Transmission of Malaria

BECAUSE the ecology of human malaria has been discussed by many authors, we will focus our main attention on the transmission biology of the malarias of non-human primates; man and his malarias will be included, but only in those situations where the two groups of primates and their parasites become part of the same transmission system.

The level of speciation in the plasmodia of non-human primates is high; 17 species have been described from Asia, 3 from Africa (not including 2 from Madagascan lemurs), and 2 from the New World. The fundamental ecology of the malarias of apes and monkeys is similar to that of the human species. Susceptible mosquitoes must live for a sufficient period of time to allow for completion of sporogony and they must have a predilection for returning to the same group of vertebrates for a second blood meal. In addition, it is essential that the parasite be able to maintain an infection in the vertebrate host long enough for the vector to become infected. Some degree of chronicity is required, too, since either the rapid destruction of the parasite by the vertebrate host or the rapid destruction of the vertebrate host by the parasite would be detrimental, if not fatal, to the maintenance of the transmission system. Our approach to the discussion of the ecology of the malarias of apes and monkeys has for convenience and continuity been organized on a geographical basis.

ASIA

Parts of Southeast Asia are the only areas for which reasonably complete information is available, and proven natural vectors of non-human primate malaria have been identified only from West Malaysia (Wharton and Eyles, 1961; Wharton et al, 1962; Eyles et al, 1963; and Cheong et al, 1965). In 1960, the U.S. Public Health Service (NIH,LPC) established a cooperative project with the Institute for Medical Research in Kuala Lumpur, Malaysia, to investigate the potential for the natural transmission of malaria parasites of monkeys to man. The baseline information on the ecology of malaria in the area was essentially complete because the personnel of the Institute for Medical Research had maintained a high degree of interest in the bionomics of anophelines of the Malay Peninsula for many years.

The NIH-IMR team approached the problem on an ecological basis, studying separately, but by the use of essentially the same techniques, the several distinct types of environments found on the Malay Peninsula which supported monkeys and their malarias (Fig. 1). The basic techniques used in these studies were described in detail by Wharton et al (1963). Briefly, they consisted of monkey-baited net traps erected on platforms in the forest canopy and run in conjunction with human-baited net traps, of similar design, on the ground nearby. Mosquito collections were

19

believed to transmit human malaria in areas where simian malaria was found, also. Studies to investigate the possibility that a single species might be responsible for the transmission of both simian and human malaria, in the same environment, were undertaken in a forest area of Cambodia where the local authorities had experienced serious difficulties in trying to prevent transmission of human malaria by using chloroquinized salt and/or residual insecticides. *Anopheles balabacensis balabacensis* was believed to be important in the transmission of human malaria in the area. These investigations revealed that in that area of Cambodia, *A. b. balabacensis* is predominatly a forest mosquito, attracted to monkeys in the canopy and to man on the ground. Sporozoites from 13 wild caught mosquitoes were inoculated into malaria-free rhesus monkeys, but no infections were produced. Some of the naturally infected mosquitoes were collected in deep forest areas believed to be considerably beyond flight range from the human habitations. The authors concluded that the sporozoites were non-human species (possibly, gibbon parasites) not infective to rhesus monkeys (Eyles *et al*, 1964).

The confirmation of *A. b. balabacensis* as a vector of monkey malaria came as a result of epidemiologic investigations in Northwest Malaysia. In this area, *A. b. balabacensis* was considered to be a vector of human malaria. The study area was a monsoon forest where malaria transmission was believed to be highly seasonal. Rainy and dry seasons occupied approximately equal parts of the year. Sporozoites from naturally infected mosquitoes, trapped in the forest, produced *P. cynomolgi* and *P. inui* infections in malaria-free rhesus monkeys (Cheong *et al*, 1965).

Mangrove Forests. Early in the studies, it was realized that some of the largest monkey populations lived in the extensive mangrove forests along the coast. Actually, it was in this habitat that *M. fascicularis* acquired one of its many local sobriquets, i.e., the crab-eating macaque. Samples of blood from members of a typical troop at Rantau Panjang, near Klang, on the west coast of Malaysia, revealed that these animals did indeed harbor malaria infections. Investigations to determine the vec-

tor of the monkey malaria were immediately successful. An *A. hackeri*, collected at the base of a nipah palm during a daytime-resting catch, was found to have sporozoite positive salivary glands. The sporozoites, produced a *P. knowlesi* infection following inoculation into a malaria-free rhesus monkey (Wharton and Eyles, 1961). Further elaboration of this discovery proved frustrating. Sentinel monkeys, placed in cages near the mosquito daytime resting sites and breeding areas, failed to become infected. Night-time trapping with both human- and monkey-bait were singularly unsuccessful. *Anopheles hackeri* continued to be plentiful and monkeys were seen whenever the area was visited. Captured *M. fascicularis* were always infected and 29 percent of the leaf-eating langur monkeys (*Presbytis* sp.) carried malaria parasites, too (Wharton *et al*, 1964). Transmission continued to occur because infected mosquitoes were still found at the resting sites. Still, no *A. hackeri* came to any type of primate bait.

At this juncture, a thorough review of the investigative site and its surroundings was made. The mosquito breeding sites were in cavities in the base of nipah palms left after the fronds had been cut for thatch, a major source of income for the people in the area. The land on which these trees were grown had been reclaimed from a tidal area by the use of a series of low bunds, or dams. Tidal changes are not great along the Straits of Malacca, so these dams did not have to be very high. The area, where the mosquitoes were breeding and resting, had been under cultivation for some 20 years. Rubber trees, and some fruit trees, had been planted among the nipah palms, providing an area of deep shade and high humidity where the rainwater would remain in catchments for long periods.

Monkeys could be seen feeding and moving about in this cultivated area during the day but toward the evening they moved to the tidal mangrove forest, a distance of some 500 yards, for the night. Platforms were constructed in the mangrove trees on the tidal side of the bund and equipped with monkey-baited net traps; *A. hackeri* were caught the first night. An extensive search failed to locate mosquito breeding sites other than those previously described, i.e., the bases of the nipah palms, several hundred yards from the trapping area. This enigma was finally clarified when marked mosquitoes (*A. hackeri*), released near the breeding and resting sites, moved purposefully, within a few hours, to monkey-baited net traps in the tidal mangrove.

Ultimately, *A. hackeri* was proven to be a natural vector of *P. coatneyi*, *P. cynomolgi*, *P. inui*, and *P. fieldi* as well as *P. knowlesi* (Warren and Wharton, 1963). These species of plasmodia all produce chronic long-lasting infections in the local monkeys and the density of *A. hackeri* did not apparently vary greatly from one time of the year to another. This mosquito is a member of the "jungle breeding" *A. leucosphyrus* group of mosquitoes. Its normal habitat is in the primary hill forests where it breeds in hollow logs and fallen bamboo. The man-made environment near Rantan Panjang had provided a suitable breeding site for the mosquito and there were plenty of monkeys to satisfy their predilection for simian blood. However, a certain amount of adaptation was necessary, for the mosquitoes had to fly a considerable distance, from their fresh-water breeding site, in order to feed on the sleeping monkeys. The adaptation was successful because 5 species of malaria were identified from the area and, as previously noted, 100 percent of the *M. fascicularis* examined from the area were found infected.

Finding this "transmission laboratory" in a man-made environment demonstrated several pertinent points about the ecology of simian malaria in Malaysia. The primate-*A. leucosphyrus* group association is old and apparently highly evolved. It emerges when the two prime elements are combined even in a highly artificial situation. Not only do members of this species complex transmit a variety of simian malarias, but *A. balabacensis balabacensis* is virtually a universal vector. In short, this monkey malaria-mosquito system is flexible as demonstrated by its ability to function in a variety of habitats under numerous environmental stresses.

The most recent studies on the ecology of simian malaria in Southeast Asia were also conducted in West Malaysia. This project was specifically designed to investigate the epide-

miology of the first reported natural infection of man with a simian malaria (Chin *et al*, 1965). The infection with *P. knowlesi* had apparently been contracted in a jungle area of Central Malaysia. In 1970, Warren *et al* reported the results of studies in the jungle, where the human *P. knowlesi* infection was probably acquired, and in nearby villages. Human-baited net traps were operated in a village near the forest and on the forest floor. Monkey-baited net traps were maintained on a series of platforms constructed in the forest canopy. Total mosquito collections were augmented by bare-leg catches. Two familiar members of the *A. leucosphyrus* group, *A. leucosphyrus* and *A. b. introlatus*, were caught in both human- and monkey-baited jungle traps, but neither species was found to invade the village. *Anopheles maculatus* was collected in both village and jungle traps but in such small numbers that it did not seem seriously involved in the transmission of monkey malaria to man.

The forested hill on which these studies were conducted was surrounded by swamp forests and some *A. letifer* were collected from the monkey-baited canopy traps reviving the old enigma of the relationship between this mosquito and the transmission of monkey malaria in nature.

The investigators concluded, that the *A. leucosphyrus* group of mosquitoes were essentially primate feeders. Since most of the species are forest dwellers and breeders, they maintain a high level of endemic malaria among the non-human primates and are quite prepared to transmit the same parasites to man if he enters the jungle under appropriate circumstances. It seemed highly likely that this was the manner in which the natural human infection with *P. knowlesi* was acquired. Since the *A. leucosphyrus* group mosquitoes do not leave the forest, in this particular area, at least, there is little or no opportunity for the routine introduction of simian malarias into nearby human populations. However, the chances of man becoming involved with these simian malarias is much greater in areas where the *A. leucosphyrus* group of mosquitoes is represented by *A. b. balabacensis* which maintains the jungle breeding activities of the group but also readily invades villages to feed on man.

Little is known about the epidemiology of simian malaria in the remainder of Asia, but the experience in Malaysia indicates that the presence of *A. leucosphyrus* group mosquitoes is essential. The map, Figure 2, shows the approximate distribution of this species complex in Southeast and Southcentral Asia. Generally, the known distribution of monkey malarias in Asia closely follows the distribution of these mosquitoes. Particular note should be made of the discontinuous distribution in India. Initially, it was thought that the Indian rhesus monkey was free of malaria. It was soon discovered, however, that those trapped in Assam and eastern parts of East Pakistan were sometimes infected and, therefore, unsuitable for malaria research as non-infected animals. In contrast, thousands of *M. mulatta* from central, northern, and western India have been examined, and no infections have been found. We believe, the explanation for this phenome-

non lies in the distribution of *A. leucosphyrus* mosquitoes (see map, Fig. 2). They are conspicuously absent from central, northern, and western India, but present in Assam and parts of East Pakistan. The representative of this species complex in southern India and Ceylon, where simian malaria is quite common, is *A. elegans* which we predict will be identified as a natural vector of simian malaria in that area.

Other ecological and epidemiological factors obviously enter into the distribution of the simian malarias in Southeast and Southcentral Asia. For example, *P. knowlesi* is highly pathogenic to *M. mulatta*, following a rapid and almost invariably fatal course. Therefore, without severe modifications on one or both sides, this parasite and the monkey could not survive in the same area. There are probably other malaria parasites which develop readily in a limited range of hosts. There are, for example, strains of malaria in Malaysian leaf monkeys (*Presbytis* sp.) which grow only with

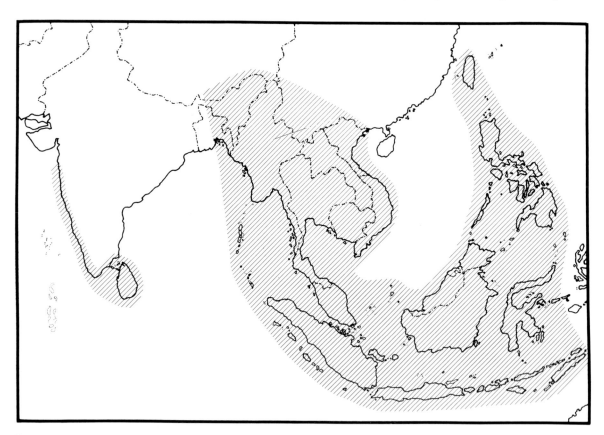

FIGURE 2.—Approximate distribution of *Anopheles leucosphyrus* group mosquitoes in Southeast and Southcentral Asia (modified from Colless, 1956).

difficulty in *M. mulatta* (Eyles *et al*, 1962). However, these factors do not seem to contribute to the distribution of the parasite at the same level as the limitations imposed by the vector characteristics. The correlation between malaria parasite distribution and the distribution of the *A. leucosphyrus* group mosquitoes is apparently due to feeding preferences and biting habits of the vectors rather than the susceptibility of the mosquito to the parasite. Experimentally, the simian malarias from Southeast Asia can be transmitted by a large number of mosquito species (Warren and Wharton, 1963; Warren *et al*, 1963; Collins *et al*, 1965, 1966, 1967, 1967a, 1968, 1968a; Collins, 1969). In addition, it seems probable that in local situations, highly specific relationships may have evolved, and mosquitoes, other than members of the *A. leucosphyrus* group, may be involved. *Anopheles letifer*, in fresh water swamp forests in Malaysia, is a prime candidate for such a role. However, it is our opinion that the relationships between simian malaria and the *A. leucosphyrus* group mosquitoes is so intimate that future extensions in the geographic distribution of the simian malarias in Southeast and Southcentral Asia will be associated with established populations of one or more members of this mosquito species complex.

AFRICA

Information currently available on the epidemiology of non-human primate malaria in Africa is limited. Three species of *Plasmodium* have been described from the great apes of Africa, one of which may be shared with man (*P. rodhaini*). The other 2 species, *P. reichenowi* and *P. schwetzi* are closely related to the human *P. falciparum* and *P. vivax—P. ovale* stocks. Only one true malaria parasite has been reported from African monkeys, *P. gonderi*, although the related genus, *Hepatocystis*, is common in these animals.

We are not aware of any studies that have been specifically directed toward identifying the natural vectors of the ape and monkey malarias in Africa. Gillies and De Meillon (1968) in their comprehensive work on the anophelines south of the Sahara do not record any species naturally attracted to non-human primates. Garnham (1951) used monkeys as bait in his studies on the natural history of simian hepatocystis in Uganda. Platform and ground traps were used. Two *A. coustani* and 8 *A. implexus* were caught; the author did not record whether these came from ground or from platform traps. The paucity of information available on the natural attraction of African non-human primates for anophelines is surprising considering the interest of many workers in the possibility that man and chimpanzees shared their malaria parasites, and that the apes might well serve as reservoirs for human malaria. Eventually, one species, *P. malariae*, was said to exist naturally in both man and the chimpanzee. Still, there was no concerted effort to determine which mosquitoes were responsible for maintaining the infections in the apes, nor if such vectors were prone to feed on man as well.

There is scant information on the experimental susceptibility of a variety of anophelines to malaria parasites of African apes and monkeys. However, most of the work was carried out in Europe and the United States; the species of mosquitoes involved were not African. Bray (1957) fed *A. gambiae* on chimpanzees infected with *P. reichenowi* and reported gut infections; the salivary glands did not become positive. The same investigator (Bray, 1958) succeeded in transmitting *P. schwetzi* with *A. gambiae*, but no sporozoites were seen in the inoculum. He concluded, that this mosquito would be a poor natural vector since the sporozoites survived only a short time in the salivary glands. *Anopheles gambiae* were also shown to be refractory to at least one strain of *P. malariae* isolated from the chimpanzee (Bray, 1960).

There is no information available on possible vectors of *P. gonderi*. There are a great number of species of anophelines in Africa that are strictly forest breeders and biters but information on host preferences is too incomplete at present to allow for speculation on their possible role in the transmission of non-human primate malaria.

Likewise, there is no information available on either natural or experimental vectors of the two malaria parasites described from Madagascan lemurs (*P. girardi* and *P. lemuris*).

AMERICA

Information on the epidemiology of non-human primate malaria in the monkeys of South and Central America is more complete than for Africa. Deane and his colleagues in São Paulo have been studying the distribution and epidemiology of the simian malarias in Brazil for a number of years. The results of ground and platform mosquito catches, using monkey-bait, implicate the bromeliad breeding *A. cruzi* as the mosquito responsible for the holoenzootic status of *P. simium* in Horto Florestal da Cantareira near São Paulo. Similar results were obtained in other study areas in southeastern Brazil (Santa Catarina and Espiritu Santo) (Deane *et al*, 1969).

The situation becomes more complex in Amazonas where a greater variety of mosquitoes invade the canopy to feed on monkeys. At Porto Maria, where only one monkey was found to be parasite positive, a variety of anophelines were found feeding in or near the canopy; *A. mediopunctatus* being particularly numerous. The investigators felt that these mosquitoes were probably not important in the transmission of monkey malaria since the same species was found in other areas where infections in monkeys were nil. We would suggest that such areas should be monitored regularly, because the simian malarias of South and Central America are still in the process of extending their host and geographic range. The argument, that a given species of anopheline is probably not involved in malaria transmission, because it is abundant in an area where no vertebrate infections occur, may be debatable since it is likely that all Western Hemisphere anophelines existed for thousands of years in the absence of malaria.

Two species in the subfamily Anophelinae, *Anopheles neivai* and *Chagasia bonneae*, were found to be attracted to monkeys consistently in the forest canopy near Manaus, and Deane *et al*. (loc. cit.) felt that these species were probably responsible for the transmission of *P. brasilianum* in that area.

There is less information available on the vectors of *P. brasilianum* in other parts of South and Central America. Galindo *et al* (1950), working in Panama, trapped mosquitoes, with human bait, on the ground and on platforms, at various levels, in the forest canopy. A variety of anophelines were caught, but no single species was present in large numbers. They found *A. neivai* in the forest canopy, in an area near Panama City; a species Deane *et al*. (loc. cit.) considered a probable vector of *P. brasilianum* in the Manaus area. Undoubtedly, new information on the epidemiology of simian malaria in Central America will be available soon, for this subject is now under investigation by Young and his colleagues at the Gorgas Memorial Laboratory in Panama.

There is not enough information available to allow for speculation on the influence of epidemiological factors on the distribution and prevalence of simian malarias in the Western Hemisphere. *Plasmodium brasilianum* has adapted well to a variety of genera and species of monkeys from southeastern Brazil to the jungles of Panama and, possibly, even further north. During the same period, *P. simium* has remained confined to an area of southern and eastern Brazil. However, we are of the opinion that there are many anophelines in the jungles of South America capable of transmitting *P. simium*, and the limits in its present distribution are due to a lack of movement, after a recent introduction into an exotic environment, rather than to failure in many areas due to an unreceptive transmission system. Under such circumstances, it is possible that in areas where the sub-human primates are now negative for malaria, future investigations will reveal infections in the same primates. Therefore, we believe that the host(s), geographic distribution, and aspects of vector limitations of the simian malarias in South and Central America will remain confusing, unstable, and subject to change until the parasites have tested all environmental niches in the available vertebrate and invertebrate hosts.

It would be convenient, if investigators of simian malaria ecology in Africa and South America were able to find a correlating factor as specific as the *A. leucosphyrus* group of mosquitoes seems to be in Asia. However, as pointed out earlier, the relationship between the simian malarias of Southeast and Southcentral Asia and the *A. leucosphyrus* group of mosquitoes is probably a very old and highly evolved one. It is our belief, that the primate plasmodia have been living in Africa for a shorter period than in Asia and are only recent arrivals in the New World. Therefore, it would seem that the chances of finding a single species complex of mosquitoes, south of the Sahara, responsible for the transmission of non-human primate malarias, is unlikely and the opportunity for such a specific relationship to have developed in Central and South America is dim indeed.

REFERENCES

BRAY, R. S. 1957. Studies on malaria in chimpanzees. III. Gametogony of *Plasmodium reichenowi*. Ann. Soc. Belge de Méd. Trop. 37 : 169–174.

BRAY, R. S., 1958. Studies on malaria in chimpanzees. V. The sporogonous cycle and mosquito transmission of *Plasmodium vivax schwetzi*. J. Parasit. 44 : 46–51.

BRAY, R. S., 1960. Studies on malaria in chimpanzees. VIII. The experimental transmission and pre-erythrocytic phase of *Plasmodium malariae*, with a note on the host-range of the parasite. Am. J. Trop. Med. & Hyg. 9 : 455–465.

CHEONG, W. H., WARREN, McW, OMAR, A. H., and MAHADEVAN, S., 1965. *Anopheles balabacensis balabacensis* identified as vector of simian malaria in Malaysia. Science 150 : 1314–1315.

CHIN, W., CONTACOS, P. G., COATNEY, G. R., and KIMBALL, H. R. 1965. A naturally acquired quotidian-type malaria in man transferable to monkeys. Science 149 : 865.

COLLINS, W. E., JONES, F. E., and DOBROVOLNY, C. G., 1965. Transmission of the RO strain of *Plasmodium cynomolgi* by *A. stephensi*, *A. quadrimaculatus* and *A. labranchiae atroparvus*. Mosq. News 25 : 389–392.

COLLINS, W. E., CONTACOS, P. G., GUINN, E. G., and HELD, J. R., 1966. Studies on the transmission of simian malarias. I. Transmission of two strains of *Plasmodium inui* by *Anopheles maculatus* and *A. stephensi*. J. Parasit. 52 : 664–668.

COLLINS, W. E., CONTACOS, P. G., and GUINN, E. G., 1967. Studies on the transmission of simian malarias. II. Transmission of the H strain of *Plasmodium knowlesi* by *Anopheles balabacensis balabacensis*. J. Parasit. 53 : 841–844.

COLLINS, W. E., CONTACOS, P. G., GUINN, E. G., and HELD, J. R., 1967a. Studies on the transmission of simian malaria. III. Infection and transmission of *Plasmodium coatneyi* with *Anopheles freeborni* and *A. balabacensis balabacensis* mosquitoes. J. Parasit. 53 : 1130–1134.

COLLINS, W. E., CONTACOS, P. G., GUINN, E. G., and HELD, J. R., 1968. Transmission of *Plasmodium fieldi* by *Anopheles maculatus*, *A. stephensi* and *A. balabacensis balabacensis*. J. Parasit. 54 : 376.

COLLINS, W. E., CONTACOS, P. G., GUINN, E. G., and HELD, J. R., 1968a. Some observations on the transmission of *Plasmodium inui*. J. Parasit. 54 : 846–847.

COLLINS, W. E., 1969. Some observations on the transmission of simian malaria. Proc. 56th Ann. Meeting New Jersey Mosq. Exterm. Assoc. pp. 152–158.

COLLESS, D. H., 1956. The *Anopheles leucosphyrus* group. Trans. Roy. Ent. Soc. London 108 : 37–116.

DEANE, L. M., FERREIRA NETO, J. A., OKUMURA, M., and FERREIRA, M. O., 1969. Malaria parasites of Brazilian monkeys. Rev. Inst. Med. Trop. São Paulo 11 : 71–86.

EYLES, D. E., LAING, A. B. G., WARREN, McW., and SANDOSHAM, A. A., 1962. Malaria parasites of Malayan leaf monkeys of the genus *Presbytis*. Med. J. Malaya 17 : 85–86.

EYLES, D. E., WARREN, McW., GUINN, E., WHARTON, R. H., and RAMACHANDRAN, C. P., 1963. Identification of *Anopheles balabacensis introlatus* as a vector of monkey malaria in Malaya. Bull. Wld. Hlth. Org. 28 : 134–135.

EYLES, D. E., FONG, Y. L., DUNN, F. L., GUINN, E., WARREN, McW., and SANDOSHAM, A. A., 1964. *Plasmodium youngi* n. sp., a malaria parasite of the Malayan gibbon, *Hylobates lar lar*. Am. J. Trop. Med. Hyg. 13 : 248–255.

GALINDO, P., TRAPIDO, H., and CARPENTER, S. J., 1950. Observations on diurnal forest mosquitoes in relation to sylvan yellow fever in Panama. Am. J. Trop. Med. 30 : 533–574.

GARNHAM, P. C. C., 1951. An attempt to find the vector of *Hepatocytis* (= *Plasmodium*) *kochi* (Levaditi and Schoen). Exp. Parasit. 1 : 94–107.

GARNHAM, P. C. C., 1959. A new subspecies of *Plasmodium cynomolgi*. Riv. di Parassit. 20 : 273–278.

GILLIES, M. T. and DE MEILLON, B., 1968. The anophelinae of Africa south of the Sahara (Ethiopian zoogeographical region). South African Inst. Med. Res., Johannesburg. Pub. 54, pp. 343.

HODGKIN, E. P., 1956. The transmission of malaria in Malaya. Stud. Inst. Med. Res. Fed. Malaya. No. 27, pp. 98.

WARREN, McW. and WHARTON, R. H., 1963. The vectors of simian malaria: Identity, biology, and geographical distribution. J. Parasit. 49 : 892–904.

WARREN, McW., EYLES, D. E., WHARTON, R. H., and OW YANG, C. K., 1963. The susceptibility of Malayan anophelines to *Plasmodium cynomolgi bastianellii*. Ind. J. Malariol. 17 : 81–101.

WARREN, McW., CHEONG, W. H., FREDERICKS, H. K., and COATNEY, G. R., 1970. Cycles of jungle malaria in West Malaysia. Am. J. Trop. Med. Hyg. 19 : 383–393.

WHARTON, R. H. and EYLES, D. E., 1961. *Anopheles hackeri*, a vector of *Plasmodium knowlesi* in Malaya. Science 134 : 279–280.

WHARTON, R. H., EYLES, D. E., WARREN, McW., and

REFERENCES—Continued

MOORHOUSE, D. E., 1962. *Anopheles leucosphyrus* identified as a vector of monkey malaria in Malaya. Science *137* : 758.

WHARTON, R. H., EYLES, D. E., and WARREN, McW., 1963. The development of methods for trapping the vectors of monkey malaria. Ann. Trop. Med. Parasit. *57* : 32–46.

WHARTON, R. H., EYLES, D. E., WARREN, McW., and CHEONG, W. H., 1964. Studies to determine the vectors of monkey malaria in Malaya. Ann. Trop. Med. Parasit. *58* : 56–77.

4

Life Cycle and the Phenomenon of Relapse

A. LIFE CYCLE

IN *the Primate Host.* The cycle of malaria in the primate host is initiated by the inoculation of sporozoites by the female mosquito when she punctures the skin to obtain blood (Fig. 3). Instead of setting-up a cycle in the blood, as maintained by Schaudinn in 1902, and not disproved until 46 years later by Shortt and Garnham (1948), the sporozoites soon leave the blood stream and enter the parenchyma cells of the liver, initiating the cycle of exoerythrocytic (EE) schizogony. As the parasite grows, it assumes different shapes (round, oval, or lobulate). It may contain vacuoles, and from several to many flocculi. Normally, the EE body develops within a single parenchyma cell of the liver, displacing its nucleus. The nuclei of the parasite multiply by division, eventually increasing in number up to as many as 40,000 per EE body; pigment is absent. When the schizont is mature, in 5 to 15 days, depending on the species, the merozoites are released into the blood where they invade the host's erythrocytes, and thereby initiate the schizogonic cycle in the blood.

The merozoites of some species display a marked predilection to invade reticulocytes, others prefer mature red cells and some are non-selective. The young asexual parasite, or trophozoite, appears ring-shaped, the "stone" being the nucleus. As the trophozoite grows, it may assume various shapes, amoeboid as in *Plasmodium vivax*, compact as in *P. inui*, or it

may be decidedly vacuolated, as in *P. hylobati*. The growing trophozoite feeds on the hemoglobin of the host red cell by phagotrophy. However, the hemoglobin is incompletely metabolized by the parasite and what remains, principally hematin, is malaria pigment. The shape and color of these pigment particles vary from one species of malaria to another and, consequently, often serve as an aid in species diagnosis. Just prior to nuclear division, the vacuole disappears and the cytoplasm appears more compact. The parasite nucleus now undergoes a series of mitotic divisions which ultimately produces a mature schizont. The nuclei surrounded by a small amount of cytoplasm are now termed merozoites. The number of merozoites in a schizont varies according to the species of *Plasmodium* although there is considerable variation even within a given species. *Plasmodium eylesi* produces 20 to 34 merozoites, the average is 25, whereas *P. malariae* may produce 4 to 12 merozoites with an average number of 8. When the schizont is mature, the merozoites are released into the blood and, unless destroyed by the host's immune mechanism, invade other erythrocytes which initiates another asexual cycle.

The length of time required for completion of the erythrocytic cycle ranges from approximately 24 hours (quotidian peridocity) to approximately 72 hours (quartan periodicity). Only one species of primate malaria, *P. knowlesi*, has a 24-hour cycle. Most of the pri-

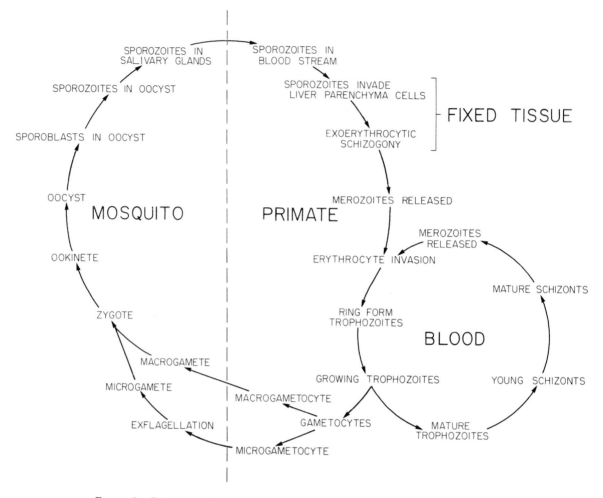

SPOROZOITES IN
SALIVARY GLANDS

SPOROZOITES IN OOCYST

SPOROBLASTS IN OOCYST

OOCYST

MOSQUITO

OOKINETE

ZYGOTE

MACROGAMETE

MICROGAMETE

EXFLAGELLATION

SPOROZOITES IN
BLOOD STREAM

SPOROZOITES INVADE
LIVER PARENCHYMA CELLS

EXOERYTHROCYTIC
SCHIZOGONY

FIXED TISSUE

MEROZOITES RELEASED

PRIMATE

MEROZOITES
RELEASED

ERYTHROCYTE INVASION

MATURE SCHIZONTS

RING FORM
TROPHOZOITES

BLOOD

GROWING TROPHOZOITES

YOUNG SCHIZONTS

MACROGAMETOCYTE

GAMETOCYTES

MATURE
TROPHOZOITES

MICROGAMETOCYTE

FIGURE 3.—Diagrammatic presentation of the life cycle of the primate malaria parasite.

mate malarias have a 48-hour asexual cycle (tertian periodicity). The exact interval varies; for example, different strains of *P. vivax* require from 41.5 to 45.8 hours (Young, 1944), whereas *P. ovale* requires 49 hours (Jeffery *et al*, 1954). The primate malarias known to have a 72-hour cycle are *P. malariae*, *P. brasilianum*, and the various strains of *P. inui*. The parasites in subsequent chapters will be referred to as having developmental cycles of 24, 48, and 72 hours.

During the growth of the parasite, the host erythrocyte often exhibits secondary changes; the most prominent are enlargement (as with *P. vivax* and *P. cynomolgi*) and the presence of stippling. The latter is made visible by staining the air-dried blood film with Romanowsky stains. These important diagnostic features will

be readily seen in the illustrations of the different species. After one or more generations of erythrocytic schizogony, some parasites develop into gametocytes. It is impossible in the very early stages of development to differentiate the young gametocytes from the developing trophozoites. However, as the gametocytes approach maturity, they are easily distinguished from the mature trophozoites (see individual chapters for specific differences). The exact origin of these forms is unknown. They must arise as a product of schizogony, but whether certain schizonts are predestined to produce asexual parasites and others sexual forms is one of several mysteries in the life-cycle of malaria. Their tendency to be produced in waves would suggest that the host's immune response may be associated with gametocyte production. However, certain strains have become gametocyteless, such as the Santee Cooper strain of *P. falciparum* (Jeffery, 1951), which suggests that the host may have little, if any, influence on the initiation of gametocyte production. Two forms are produced: micro- and macro-gametocytes, commonly referred to as male and female gametocytes. In general, the latter predominate. In some cases, notably *P. falciparum*, gametocytes will continue to circulate in the peripheral blood long after their initial production. However, their infectivity appears to be short-lived and there is some evidence to suggest that their infectivity may be associated with a certain period of the day (Hawking *et al*, 1968).

In the Mosquito. The cycle in the peripheral blood exists only, in terms of species survival, for the production of sexual forms, the gametocytes. The gametocytes of the primate malarias can only complete their destiny in an anopleline mosquito.

The female anopheline seeks a primate host because she is hungry, a fact clarified by the late Dr. Robert W. Burgess in the early 1940's. Her hunger is satisfied by biting and in the process she takes blood containing gametocytes and other blood-stages of the parasite into her digestive tract. In the mid-gut, or mesenteron, the mature gametocytes shed their red cell envelopes and transform into gametes, which we now know to be the mature sexual forms. Laveran (1880) and many other workers had seen the 'strange' forms in the blood, but it was a 3rd year American medical student, William George MacCallum, who discovered their sexual nature. MacCallum (1897), during his summer vacation in Canada, studied the malaria parasites in crow blood and deduced that the non-segmenting forms were male and female parasites. Upon his return to Johns Hopkins Medical School in the fall, he confirmed his suspicions while studying blood from a woman infected with *P. falciparum*. He watched the process of exflagellation whereby the male (micro-) gametocyte throws out thread-like processes which lash about and soon separate from the parent body. He observed one of these thread-like bodies, saw it penetrate and thus fertilize the rounded-up female (macro-) gamete. The microgametes are produced by a process termed exflagellation. Soon after ingestion, the nucleus of the microgametocyte divides, giving rise to 8 nuclei. These migrate to the periphery and enter long cytoplasmic processes which project from the surface of the parasite. The microgametes lash about vigorously and soon separate from the parent body. The microgamete enters the macrogamete to form the zygote. Shortly thereafter, the oökinete is formed. This vermiculate body moves actively and forces its way into an epithelial cell of the host's mid-gut. A cyst wall is formed and this stage, the oocyst, now commences its growth lying between the basement membrane of the gut wall and the cells, and projecting into the haemocoele of the mosquito. Oocysts are only found on the mid-gut and are usually more concentrated toward the posterior end. Meiotic division occurs within the young oocyst, usually commencing about 48 hours after the blood meal (Bano, 1959). Succeeding mitotic divisions produce nuclei with the particular haploid number of chromosomes for that species. As the oocyst grows (sometimes reaching a diameter of 100 μ), the number of nuclei increases; vacuoles appear as the cytoplasm divides into sporoblasts. From these arise the sporozoites. Oocysts in which the sporoblasts and developing sporozoites are visible under light microscopy will be referred to, in subsequent chapters, as differentiated. Each sporozoite contains a single nucleus and the number of sporozoites produced per oocyst has been estimated as about 10,000 (Pringle, 1965). Upon maturity, the time depending on the temperature and humidity conditions, the oocyst ruptures and the sporozoites are released into the haemocoele of the mosquito. The sporozoites migrate to all parts of the body but some enter the acinal cells of the salivary glands. When the infected mosquito begins to feed, the sporozoites enter the salivary duct and are thereby introduced into the blood stream of the primate host, initiating the infection in a new environment.

B. RELAPSE

The phenomenon of relapse has intrigued malariologists for decades. As early as 1893,

Golgi suggested that parasites of human malaria may develop in endothelial cells not affected by antimalarial drugs and that the protected parasites could be the source of relapses.

In 1897, almost at the time that Ronald Ross was completing his basic studies on the transmission of malaria, Thayer published a series of lectures with several references to relapse in vivax malaria. In his speculations to explain latency, which must obtain preceding a relapse, he postulated that there must be an undiscovered form of the parasite. He wrote "the organism may remain perhaps within the cell body of certain phagocytes for long periods of time, only to be set free again as a result of some insult, the nature of which is not as yet appreciable to us." More than 70 years later, we still do not know the exact nature of these phenomena, but it is generally accepted that: 1) fixed-tissue forms of the true relapsing malarias (i.e., *Plasmodium vivax, P. ovale, P. cynomolgi, P. fieldi,* and *P. simiovale*) release young forms periodically which parasitize the erythrocytes and thereby initiate the relapse (Fig. 4) and 2) along with the above type of reactivation of the infection is the one arising from renewed activity, after a period of quiescence, in the conventional red cell cycle. This renewed activity, which we call a recrudescence, is due, possibly, to the development of new antigenic variants of the parasite as was shown by Brown *et al* (1968) for *P. knowlesi,* Voller and Rossan (1969) for *P. cynomolgi,* and by ourselves for *P. brasilianum.*

The first experimental evidence of rhythm in relapse activity came in 1900 when Sir Patrick Manson allowed infected mosquitoes to bite his son, P. Thurburn Manson, then a young medical student. The younger Manson came down with vivax malaria and the infection was treated with quinine. Following treatment, he continued in good health until 9 months later when he had a typical relapse which he himself reported in detail in 1901. Another volunteer, in the same time period, was Major C. F. Fearnside who had a relapse experience similar to that of young Manson which he reported in 1903. In retrospect, these early reports set a pattern which was later recognized as a common phenomenon in many strains of *P. vivax.*

After Schaudinn's description of the direct invasion of a red blood cell by the sporozoite of *P. vivax* (1902), attention was concentrated, almost entirely, on this stage of the parasite. However, as information accumulated, especially the data derived from the study of induced malaria in the treatment of general paresis, it became apparent that all human malarias did not have the same relapse potential, and that there was a difference in the response to therapy in blood-induced and sporozoite-induced infections (Yorke, 1925;

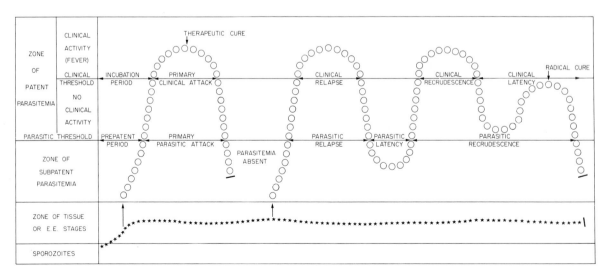

FIGURE 4.—Diagrammatic presentation of the parasitologic and clinical cycle in the vertebrate host of those malarias which have a true relapse mechanism.

Yorke and Macfie, 1924). In 1931, James suggested that sporozoites, after being injected by the mosquito, are carried to the internal organs where they enter reticulo-endothelial cells and go through a cycle of development with the eventual production of merozoites which parasitize red blood cells. This proposal was based primarily on the fact that therapeutic regimens known to be effective against malaria could not cure an infection when administered during the incubation period. It was reasoned, that if sporozoites entered directly into the red blood cells and became trophozoites and schizonts, they would have been destroyed by the drugs and no active infection could have resulted. Meanwhile, research in the avian malarias had been developing rapidly, and in 1935, Huff and Bloom clearly demonstrated exoerythrocytic stages to be a fundamental part of the life cycle of *P. elongatum*.

As data about fixed tissue parasites from birds accumulated, mainly the work of James and Tate (1937) and the brilliantly executed studies of Huff and his co-workers (1943 to 1948), it became abundantly clear that such a cycle must also occur in primate malarias. In 1946, Sapero, in his Craig Lecture (Sapero, 1947) presented presumptive evidence for the link between fixed tissue stages and relapse in such lucid language that their actual demonstration seemed an easy task.

In 1945, Fairley *et al* had shown that sporozoites, following their introduction, disappeared from the circulating blood during the first hour and no evidence of infection was to be found until 6 days later in falciparum infections and 8 days later in vivax infections, when blood transfusions from the infected individuals produced infection in the recipients.

The evidence in support of the existence of preerythrocytic stages in primate malarias was now so strong that it seemed only a matter of time until they were demonstrated. Coatney and Cooper (1948) summarized the information available on drugs with apparent action against preerythrocytic stages of avian and primate malarias. These investigators reported that 8-aminoquinolines and certain biguanides were active against the presumed exoerythrocytic forms of human and simian malarias, the presence of which had been deduced from in-

direct evidence. The direct evidence came in the same year, with the description by Shortt and Garnham (1948) and Shortt, Garnham, and Malamos (1948) of the exoerythrocytic stages of *P. cynomolgi* in the liver of an experimentally infected rhesus monkey. Soon, similar preerythrocytic forms were demonstrated in the livers of human volunteers infected with *P. vivax* (Shortt *et al*, 1948) and *P. falciparum* (Shortt *et al*, 1949; Jeffery *et al*, 1952).

With the demonstration of the exoerythrocytic stages of avian and primate malarias, a whole new developmental phase of the parasites could be examined. Various proposals were advanced to explain the phenomenon of relapse in malaria. The hiding place of the parasite, during long periods when the patients were clinically and parasitologically negative, had been debated for many years. The discovery of the exoerythrocytic stages of primate malarias seemed to have revealed their hiding place. With the report of an EE schizont in the liver of a monkey 3½ months after sporozoite inoculation (Shortt and Garnham, 1948), most workers in the field came to believe that a direct relationship existed between these fixed tissue stages and true relapses.

The relationship of relapse of primate malarias to an exoerythrocytic stage of the parasite was not new. Various workers, involved in experimental therapy of malaria, had predicted that an exoerythrocytic stage of the parasite was responsible for long term relapses in *P. vivax*. The absence of a persistent tissue phase in *P. falciparum* was also proposed (Shannon and Earle, 1945; Fairley *et al*, 1947) prior to the actual demonstration of EE schizonts of *P. cynomolgi* by Shortt and Garnham (loc. cit.). The persistent tissue phase as the source of the parasites in typical *P. vivax* relapses was firmly supported by Shannon and Earle (1945) and Fairley *et al* (1947), and at least tentatively, by Huff (1947). The evidence to support this hypothesis was primarily based on the extensive work on EE stages in avian malarias by a variety of workers in the 30's and 40's and the striking differences in response to therapy in blood-induced and sporozoite-induced infections with *P. vivax*. Coatney and Cooper (1948a), based on data from studies with the St. Elizabeth strain of *P. vivax*, not only supported the EE stage theory as the mechanism of relapse, but proposed a concept of latency which we will reintroduce later in this discussion.

It is clear that a large number of workers in the field of malaria were convinced, not only of the existence of EE stages in primate malarias, but of their association with relapses. Therefore, the results of the remarkable series of experiments by Shortt and his group which conclusively demonstrated the EE schizonts of *P. cynomolgi*, *P. vivax*, and *P. falciparum* were generally sympathetically received. When the work of Coatney and Cooper (1948a), showing that massive blood transfusions during latency, following treatment of the initial attack, failed to produce infections in recipients, although the donors' infections relapsed later, was combined with the demonstration of an EE schizont of *P. cynomolgi* 3½ months after sporozoite inoculation, most workers considered the relapse story to be complete (Shortt and Garnham, 1948a). The specific mechanism proposed was that merozoites from mature EE schizonts enter red blood cells, producing the familiar clinical and parasitological features of malaria. Other merozoites, possibly from the same schizont, enter normal liver cells and continue the cycle of exoerythrocytic schizogony. This latter process would continue indefinitely, and, when the active immunity of the host was, for any reason, reduced, some of the merozoites would invade the red blood cells to produce a relapse. This concept of Shortt and Garnham (loc. cit.) was widely but not universally accepted as the most likely explanation for the production of relapses in certain species of both human and simian malaria.

It has been noted that acceptance of the exoerythrocytic stage of malaria as the source of relapses was not universal. Huff (1948) and Huff and Coulston (1948) were convinced of the existence of the exoerythrocytic stages in primate malarias, but Huff (1950) expressed serious reservations concerning the parasitic nature of the bodies described by Shortt. Fairley (1949) did not entirely agree with the continuing exoerythrocytic cycle, as described by Shortt and Garnham, either. In 1950, Corradetti expressed categoric disagreement with the idea that relapses in mammalian ma-

laria were in any way related to the exoerythrocytic stages of the parasite. This investigator insisted that "not a single fact" went against the initial opinion of Bignami (1910) that relapses were related to the persistence of endoerythrocytic parasites.

It is appropriate, at this point, to discuss these two theories concerning the origin of relapses in malaria inasmuch as the controversy has remained essentially unchanged since the early 50's. Corradetti accepts the existence of EE stages of primate malarias, but still (1966), believes that relapses are due entirely to the persistence of erythrocytic stages of the parasite; Corradetti's position has not changed appreciably since 1950 (Corradetti and Verolini, 1950). Bray (1967) produced an excellent review of his position on the relationships between EE stages and relapse mechanisms in which he considered the individual points in Corradetti's thesis. Bray's arguments generally reflect the contemporary opinion of most malariologists. There are several aspects of this controversy which warrant a more detailed consideration.

Corradetti (1965) presented a number of well reasoned points and his strongest argument rests with the fact that blood-induced infections, of quite long duration, have been observed with *P. cynomolgi*, *P. malariae*, and *P. falciparum*. It is also agreed, that the blood may be negative for malaria parasites by routine microscopic examination for periods of varying duration during any of these extended infections. Actually, work from our laboratory indicates that even stronger support for his thesis would be found with blood-induced infections of *P. inui* which are known to persist in monkeys for years. This we consider to be a well reasoned argument and could well support Corradetti's case if it were taken no further. However, all of the evidence must be considered. It is true that blood-induced infections with *P. cynomolgi* persist for long periods, but such infections can be quickly and totally eradicated with schizonticidal drugs, such as chloroquine or quinine. Sporozoite-induced infections, with the same parasite, can be cleared of parasites in the peripheral circulation with the same drugs, but the infection returns with a frequency which is dependent upon the strain of parasite used. This evidence is, of course, not new. Differences in the response of sporozoite- and blood-induced infections of *P. vivax* to schizonticidal drugs have been recognized for many years (Yorke and Macfie, 1924). Corradetti (1966) did not include data from chemotherapeutic studies of *P. vivax* and *P. cynomolgi* in his discussion of relapse mechanisms.

The extreme duration of infections with *P. malariae* naturally occupies an important position in any discussion of relapse mechanisms in malaria. There are reports of persistence of infection for 30 to 40 years and recrudescences are generally expected through a period of from 5 to 8 years. Ciuca *et al* (1964) followed the course of a blood-induced infection and found erythrocytic parasites 525 days after inoculation. The same workers reported that schizonticides were radically curative in sporozoite-induced *P. malariae* infections, and, they concluded, that this parasite possessed no secondary exoerythrocytic stages. Corradetti called attention to this finding, a point which was well taken since radical cures with schizonticidal drugs had been interpreted by others to be associated either with blood-induced infections or with sporozoite-induced infections of malarias not possessing a relapse potential. More recent data from our laboratory suggest that *P. malariae* has no true relapse mechanism. Furthermore, schizonticidal drugs have been found to produce radical cures of sporozoite-induced *P. inui* infections, the quartan parasite of Asian monkeys.

One of the strongest pieces of evidence to support the exoerythrocytic source of malaria parasites in relapse situations is the total absence of these parasites from the peripheral blood during negative intervals. These negative intervals may occur naturally or may be induced by the use of schizonticidal drugs. The absence of parasites during these periods was established by the inoculation of massive amounts of whole blood from infected to malaria-free volunteers without producing infections (Cooper *et al*, 1949). Cooper *et al* (1947) demonstrated the susceptibility of volunteers during the long negative interval in St. Elizabeth strain *P. vivax* infections by successfully superimposing a blood-induced infec-

tion, with the homologous strain parasite, in the same person. This experiment clearly indicated that the absence of parasites from the peripheral circulation was real and not a suppression to very low levels by immunologic activities. We consider these experiments to be conclusive, but Corradetti (1966) felt that it would be necessary to transfer *every* red blood cell without producing an infection, before one could know that no parasites were present. In the same paper, it is noted that Corradetti and Verolini (1950) subinoculated blood during negative periods from monkeys with blood-induced *P. cynomolgi* infections with negative results. We have carefully reviewed this reference and cannot find the account of a subinoculation, with negative results, of whole fresh blood from an infected, but negative donor, that at a later time demonstrated a patent parasitemia. Even a single result of this nature would be interesting; if any parasite could consistently produce this response, it would be quite important.

The final evidence in support of the direct involvement of exoerythrocytic stages in malarial relapses which has been challenged is the demonstration of the parasites themselves. Corradetti was skeptical because of the low number of late EE schizonts that have been seen. Actually, as Bray (1967) pointed out, the number of liver stages seen 30 days or more after sporozoite inoculation is considerably greater than that noted by Corradetti. However, the questions posed by the latter investigator concerning: 1) how such stages are known to be secondary and not the result of some form of latency and 2) why 'nests' of parasites are not found in the area where an earlier schizont matured, have not been answered satisfactorily.

The accumulation of evidence relating long term relapses to a persistent tissue stage of the parasite seems to us to be absolutely conclusive. There remain a number of gaps in our knowledge and a number of areas in which generally accepted concepts do not provide all of the answers. We consider the theory of a continuing cycle of exoerythrocytic schizogony to be an inadequate explanation from two points of view. It seems inescapable that the mechanism responsible for the long term relapse in the St. Elizabeth strain of *P. vivax* is also involved in the delayed patency phenomenon seen with other strains of *P. vivax* (Tiburskaya, 1964). The delayed primary attacks of *P. ovale* reported by Chin and Contacos (1966) and Trager and Most (1963) were apparently due to the use of suppressive drugs at the time of infection. There seems to be no doubt that each of these infected individuals was susceptible during the long period between infection and the primary clinical attack. Therefore, there is no immediately available explanation why an earlier erythrocytic multiplication would not have occurred if parasites were continually being released into the blood from maturing liver schizonts. The same question can be asked concerning the delayed patency phenomenon in certain strains of *P. vivax* (Tiburskaya, loc. cit.). This weakness in the Shortt and Garnham (1948b) theory of continuing exoerythrocytic schizogony was considered much earlier by Fairley (1949) and by Coatney *et al* (1950).

The second area in which the cyclic maturation of fixed tissue schizonts might be challenged is in the relationship between declining immune levels and the eventual reappearance of parasitological and clinical relapse. The original concept, as introduced by Shortt and Garnham (1948a), was that merozoites continually entering the blood from maturing tissue schizonts would be destroyed by the immune mechanisms of the host. Eventually, when the level of immune activity was sufficiently low, the parasites would be able to multiply and thereby produce a relapse. Cooper *et al* (1947) were able to superinfect volunteers with sporozoite-induced infections of the St. Elizabeth strain of *P. vivax* by inoculating whole blood infected with the homologous strain during the long interval between primary attack and initial relapse. It is therefore clear, that the subject was susceptible to blood-stage parasites from an extraneous source —why not, then, from tissue schizonts? It is difficult to understand how the immune response in sporozoite-induced infections would ever drop to the level postulated by Shortt and Garnham (1948b) with the constant antigenic stimulus that would be present with merozoites entering the blood continually from exoery-

throcytic schizonts. It is generally believed that the immune mechanisms of the malaria-infected vertebrate do not reach the liver stages but are only effective against the erythrocytic stages of the parasite. If exoerythrocytic schizogony were a continuing process, it would follow that, once established, the infection would be terminated only by the death of the host.

Garnham (1967) has reviewed this subject and agrees that the process of continuous secondary exoerythrocytic schizogony has not been established. In this publication, he reintroduced the concept of latency or a dormant stage of the parasite as a possible explanation for the relapses seen in certain species of primate malaria and noted that "if such an idea could be proved, then many puzzling features of relapses and latency would be explained." Shute (1946) pointed out that sporozoites could survive in the salivary glands of mosquitoes for considerable periods of time and suggested that they might also be able to do the same thing in the human host. It is interesting that Corradetti (1966) suggested that the late tissue forms described by Bray (1957) might have been derived directly from sporozoites whose development had been delayed by some "unfavorable condition." However, the same author apparently never entertained the possibility that the same delayed development could be responsible for relapses.

There is recent experimental evidence to support the concept of a latent stage as an essential part of the mechanism of relapse in malaria. Warren *et al* (1970) have found that *P. cynomolgi* sporozoites from mosquitoes exposed to X-irradiation immediately prior to dissection and inoculated into malaria-free monkeys produced infections which appeared to be normal, although profound damage was observed in EE schizonts from the same animals. However, monkeys infected with irradiated sporozoites demonstrated fewer relapses than seen in the controls which had received comparable numbers of sporozoites. The authors concluded, that their findings were the result of a random destruction of sporozoites with the concomitant elimination of specific, predetermined relapses.

Experiments, more specifically designed to

demonstrate this point, were carried out by Warren *et al* (manuscript) in which a series of monkeys were inoculated with varying numbers of sporozoites of *P. cynomolgi*. Prepatent periods were only slightly delayed in animals which received low numbers of sporozoites. Infections followed the expected course in all animals and no differences were noted until after treatment with chloroquine. Once relapses began to occur, there was a clear-cut reduction in their number directly related to the number of sporozoites received. These authors concluded that the results strongly challenged the concept of a continuing cycle of histiotrophic merozoites in the liver being responsible for relapses in malaria, since, by this theory, the number of relapses should not be influenced by the number of sporozoites in the original infecting inoculum; one sporozoite should be capable of initiating the complete sequence. In Figure 5 we have presented the hypothetical course of infection for malarias with different potentials for relapse and/or recrudescence.

The survival value of a long term relapse mechanism to a malaria parasite is undoubtedly great and contributes significantly to its ability to be transmitted to new non-immune hosts. We believe that the need for making gametocytes available in the peripheral blood of appropriate hosts is of such biological urgency that two mechanisms for such an activity have evolved and have been maintained by the primate plasmodia.

We would surmise that a dormant or latent tissue phase of the parasite was the first to evolve and was probably brought forward from an ancient coccidian ancestor. Sufficient information is not available at the present time to establish the exact developmental stage of the parasite which becomes dormant, but one must certainly suspect that either the sporozoite or an intermediary stage, between the sporozoite and the exoerythrocytic schizont, possesses the capacity to settle down and remain quiescent for long periods of time. The extent of this period would seem to be dependent upon the species and even the strain of parasite in question.

It is clearly evident that there are many lacunae in our knowledge of the relapse mechanism. Eventually these gaps will be filled in but until then, the complete picture of the relapse phenomenon is denied to us.

REFERENCES

BANO, L., 1959. A cytological study of the early oocysts of seven species of *Plasmodium* and the occurrence of postzygotic meiosis. Parasitology 49 : 559–585.

BIGNAMI, A., 1910. Sulla patogenesi delle recidive nelle febbri malariche. Atti. Soc. Studi. 11 : 731–746.

BRAY, R. S., 1957. Studies on the exo-erythrocytic cycle in the genus *Plasmodium*. London School of Hyg. and Trop. Med., Memoir No. 12. H. K. Lewis & Co. Ltd., London pp. 192.

BRAY, R. S., 1967. The origin of relapses in human and simian malaria infections. J. Fac. Med. Baghdad 9 : 1–6.

BROWN, I. N., BROWN, K. N., and HILLS, L. A., 1968. Immunity of malaria: The antibody response to antigenic variations by *Plasmodium knowlesi*. Immunology 14 : 127–138.

CHIN, W. and CONTACOS, P. G., 1966. A recently isolated West African strain of *Plasmodium ovale*. Am. J. Trop. Med. & Hyg. 15 : 1–2.

CIUCA, M., LUPASCO, G., NEGULICI, E., and CONSTANTINESCO, P., 1964. Recherches sur la transmission expérimentale de *P. malariae* à l'homme. Arch. Roum. Path. Exp. Microbiol. 23 : 763–776.

COATNEY, G. R. and COOPER, W. C., 1948. Symposium on exoerythrocytic forms of malarial parasites. III. The chemotherapy of malaria in relation to our knowledge of exoerythrocytic forms. J. Parasit. 34 : 275–289.

COATNEY, G. R. and COOPER, W. C., 1948a. Recrudescence and relapse in vivax malaria. 4th Int. Cong. Trop.

Med. & Malaria 1 : 629–639.

COATNEY, G. R., COOPER, W. C., RUHE, D. S., YOUNG, M. D., and BURGESS, R. W., 1950. Studies in human malaria. XVIII. The life pattern of sporozoite-induced St. Elizabeth strain vivax malaria. Am. J. Hyg. 51 : 200–215.

COOPER, W. C., COATNEY, G. R., and RUHE, D. S., 1947. Studies in human malaria. V. Homologous strain superinfection during latency in subjects with sporozoite-induced vivax malaria (St. Elizabeth strain). Am. J. Hyg. 46 : 141–148.

COOPER, W. C., RUHE, D. S., and COATNEY, G. R., 1949. Studies in human malaria. XVI. Results of massive subinoculation during latency from patients infected with St. Elizabeth strain vivax malaria. Am. J. Hyg. 50 : 189–193.

CORRADETTI, A., 1950. (See Corradetti and Verolini, 1950.)

CORRADETTI, A., 1966. The origin of relapses in human and simian malaria infections. WHO/Mal/66.565. [Revision of 1965 paper in Med. Parasit. (Moska) 34 : 673 (NS).]

CORRADETTI, A. and VEROLINI, F., 1950. Studies on relapses in blood-induced infections from *Plasmodium malariae* and *Plasmodium cynomolgi*. J. Nat. Mal. Soc. 9 : 327–331.

FAIRLEY, N. H. et al, 1945. Chemotherapeutic suppression and prophylaxis in malaria. Trans. Roy. Soc. Trop. Med.

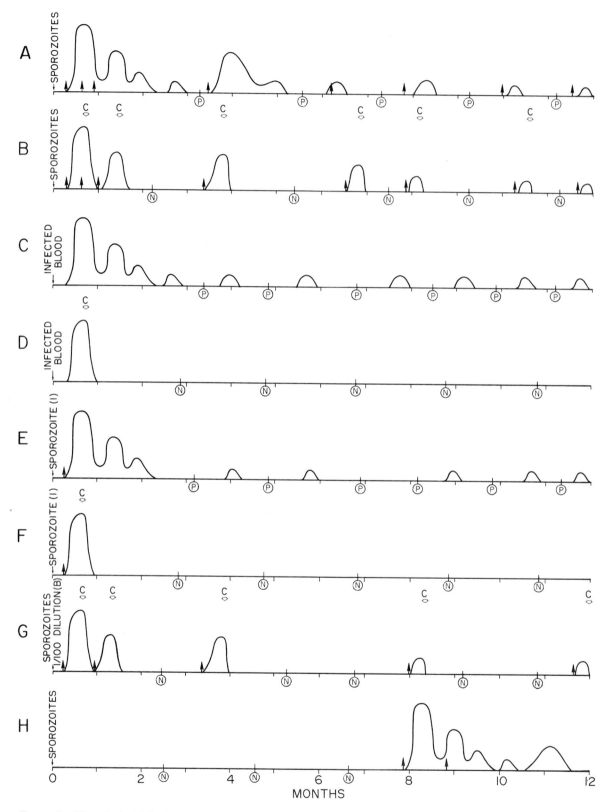

FIGURE 5.—Hypothetical infections of malaria with different relapse potentials. Infections A–G. Relapse and recrudescence potential of hypothetical infections with *Plasmodium cynomolgi.*

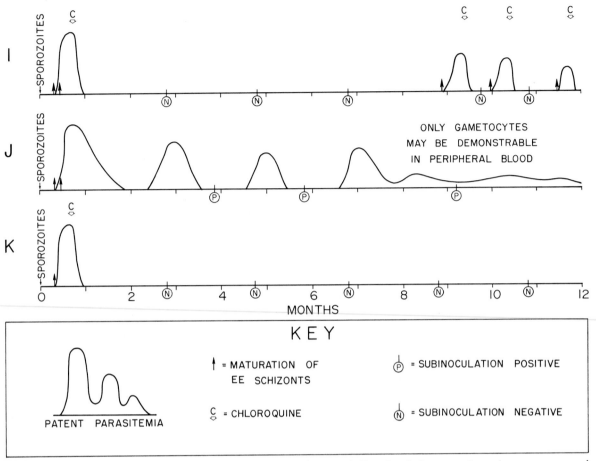

INFECTION A.—Sporozoite-induced infection with *P. cynomolgi* (M strain). Parasitemia is present for at least one year and subinoculation during this period results in infection.

INFECTION B.—Sporozoite-induced infection as in Infection A. Following the initial attack and each subsequent relapse, chloroquinine was used to eliminate the parasitemia. Subinoculations after treatment failed to produce infection.

INFECTION C.—Infection induced by inoculation of parasitized blood. Parasitemia is present for at least one year and subinoculation during this period results in infection.

INFECTION D.—Infection induced by inoculation of parasitized blood as in Infection C. Treatment of the initial infection with chloroquine results in radical cure.

INFECTION E.—Infection induced by the inoculation of a single sporozoite. Parasitemia is present for at least one year and subinoculation during this period results in infection.

INFECTION F.—Infection induced by the inoculation of a single sporozoite. Treatment with chloroquine results in radical cure.

INFECTION G.—Infection induced by the inoculation of 1/100th of the number of sporozoites used in Infection B. The number of relapses is randomly reduced.

INFECTION H.—Infection resulting from sporozoites from a strain of *P. vivax* with extended prepatent period.

INFECTION I.—Type of infection produced by sporozoites of *P. vivax* (St. Elizabeth strain). Initial parasitemia treated with chloroquine.

INFECTION J.—Sporozoite-induced infection with a non-relapsing malaria, *P. falciparum*. Parasitemia is present for at least one year but during the last few months, only gametocytes may be demonstrable.

INFECTION K.—Sporozoite-induced infection with a non-relapsing malaria, *P. falciparum*. Treatment with chloroquine results in radical cure.

REFERENCES—Continued

& Hyg. *38* : 311–365.

FAIRLEY, N. H., *et al* 1947. Sidelights on malaria in man obtained by subinoculation experiments. Trans. Roy. Soc. Trop. Med. & Hyg. *40* : 621–676.

FAIRLEY, N. H., 1949. Malaria with special reference to certain experimental, clinical, and chemotherapeutic investigations. Brit. Med. Jour. *2* : 825–831.

FEARNSIDE, C. F., 1903. Experimental inoculation of malaria with a relapse after eight months. Ind. Med. Gaz. *38* : 10.

GARNHAM, P. C. C., 1967. Relapses and latency in malaria. Protozoology *2* : 55–64. Festschr. in honor of H. E. Shortt on the occasion of his 80th birthday 1967. Suppl. to J. Helmin. Dec. 1967.

GOLGI, C., 1893. Sulle febbri malariche estivo-autumnali di Roma. Gass. Med. di Pavia *2* : 481–493, 505–520, 529–544, 553–559.

HAWKING, F., WORMS, M. J., and GAMMAGE, K., 1968. 24- and 48-hour cycles of malaria parasites in the blood; their purpose, production and control. Trans. Roy. Soc. Trop. Med. & Hyg. *62* : 731–760.

HUFF, C. G., 1947. Life cycle of malarial parasites. Ann. Rev. Microbiol. *1* : 43–60.

HUFF, C. G., 1948. Exoerythrocytic stages of malarial parasites. Am. J. Trop. Med. *28* : 527–531.

HUFF, C. G., 1950. Pre-erythrocytic stages of simian and human malarial parasites. (Letter to the Editor, Trop. Med. News). *7* : 22–23.

HUFF, C. G. and BLOOM, W., 1935. A malaria parasite infecting all blood and blood-forming cells of birds. J. Infect. Dis. *57* : 315–336.

HUFF, C. G., COULSTON, F., and CANTRELL, W., 1943. Malarial cryptozoites. Science *97* : 286.

HUFF, C. G. and COULSTON, F., 1944. The development of *Plasmodium gallinaceum* from sporozoite to erythrocytic trophozoite. J. Infect. Dis. *75* : 231–249.

HUFF, C. G., COULSTON, F., LAIRD, R. L., and PORTER, R. J., 1947. Pre-erythrocytic development of *Plasmodium lophurae* in various hosts. J. Infect. Dis. *81* : 7–13.

HUFF, C. G. and COULSTON, F., 1948. Symposium on exoerythrocytic forms of malaria parasites. II. A search for pre-erythrocytic stages of *P. vivax* and of *P. cynomolgi*. J. Parasit. *34* : 264–274.

JAMES, S. P., 1931. The use of plasmoquine in the prevention of malaria infections. Proc. Roy. Acad. Amsterdam *34* : 1424–1425.

JAMES, S. P. and TATE, P., 1937. New knowledge of the life-cycle of malaria parasites. Nature *139* : 545–549.

JEFFERY, G. M., 1951. Observations on a gametocyteless strain of *Plasmodium falciparum*. J. Nat. Mal. Soc. *10* : 337–344.

JEFFERY, G. M., WOLCOTT, G. B., YOUNG, M.D., and WILLIAMS, D. JR., 1952. Exo-erythrocytic stages of *Plasmodium falciparum*. Am. J. Trop. Med. & Hyg. *1* : 917–926.

JEFFERY, G. M., YOUNG, M. D., and WILCOX, A., 1954. The Donaldson strain of malaria. 1. History and characteristics of the infection in man. Am. J. Trop. Med. & Hyg. *3* : 628–637.

LAVERAN, A., 1880. Un nouveau parasite trouvé le sang des malades atteints de fièvre origine parasitaire des accidents de l'impaludisme. Bull. et Mémoires Soc. Méd. Hôpitaux de Paris. (2 ser.) *17* : 158–164.

MACCALLUM, W. G., 1897. On the flagellated form of the malarial parasite. Lancet *2* : 1240.

MANSON, P. T., 1901. Experimental malaria: Recurrence after nine months. Brit. Med. Jour. *2* : 77.

PRINGLE, G., 1965. A count of the sporozoites in an oocyst of *Plasmodium falciparum*. Trans. Roy. Soc. Trop. Med. & Hyg. *59* : 289–290.

SAPERO, J. J., 1947. New concepts in the treatment of relapsing malaria. The Charles Franklin Craig Lecture, 1946. Am. J. Trop. Med. *27* : 271–283.

SCHAUDINN, F., 1902. Studien über Krankheitserregende Protozoen. II. *Plasmodium vivax* Grassi u. Feletti der erreger der Tertian Fiebers beim Menschen. Arb. K. Gesundh. -Amte (Berl.) *19* : 169–250. (NS).

SHANNON, J. A. and EARLE, D. P., 1945. Recent advances in the treatment of malaria. Bull. N.Y. Acad. Sci. *21* : 467–481.

SHORTT, H. E. and GARNHAM, P. C. C., 1948. Pre-erythrocytic stage in mammalian malaria parasites. Nature *161* : 126.

SHORTT, H. E. and GARNHAM, P. C. C., 1948a. Demonstration of a persisting exo-erythrocytic cycle in *Plasmodium cynomolgi* and its bearing on the production of relapses. Brit. Med. Jour. *1* : 1225–1228.

SHORTT, H. E., GARNHAM, P. C. C., and MALAMOS, B., 1948. The pre-erythrocytic stage of mammalian malaria. Brit. Med. Jour. *1* : 192–194.

SHORTT, H. E., GARNHAM, P. C. C., COVELL, G., and SHUTE, P. G., 1948. The pre-erythrocytic stage of human malaria, *Plasmodium vivax*. Brit. Med. Jour. *1* : 547.

SHORTT, H. E., FAIRLEY, N. H., COVELL, G., SHUTE, P. G., and GARNHAM, P. C. C., 1949. The pre-erythrocytic stage of *Plasmodium falciparum*. A preliminary note. Brit. Med. Jour. *2* : 1006–1008.

SHUTE, P. G., 1946. Latency and long-term relapses in benign tertian malaria. Trans. Roy. Soc. Trop. Med. & Hyg. *40* : 189–200.

THAYER, W. S., 1897. Lectures on malarial fevers. D. Appleton & Co., New York. pp. 326.

TIBURSKAYA, N. A., 1964. Classification of *P. vivax* strains into groups by type of incubation. Med. Parazit., Moscow *33* : 204–216.

TRAGER, W. and MOST, H., 1963. A long-delayed primary attack of ovale malaria. Am. J. Trop. Med. & Hyg. *12* : 837–839.

VOLLER, A. and ROSSAN, R. N., 1969. Immunological studies with simian malaria. I. Antigenic variants of *Plasmodium cynomolgi bastianellii*. Trans. Roy. Soc. Trop. Med. & Hyg. *63* : 46–56.

WARREN, McW., POWERS, K., GARNHAM, P. C. C., and SHIROISHI, T., 1970. The influence of X-irradiation and dilution of sporozoites on relapse patterns of infections with *Plasmodium cynomolgi*. (in press)

YORKE, W., 1925. Further observations on malaria made during treatment of general paralysis. Trans. Roy. Soc. Trop. Med. & Hyg. *19* : 108–122.

YORKE, W. and MACFIE, J. W. S., 1924. Observations on malaria made during treatment of general paralysis. Trans. Roy. Soc. Trop. Med. & Hyg. *18* : 13–33.

YOUNG, M. D., 1944. Studies on the periodicity of induced *Plasmodium vivax*. J. Nat. Mal. Soc. *3* : 237–247.

(NS) = Not seen.

SECTION 2

Vivax-Type Parasites

5

Plasmodium vivax (Grassi and Feletti, 1890)

SYNONYMS: *Haemamoeba malariae* Feletti and Grassi, 1890, *partim; Haemamoeba vivax* Grassi and Feletti, 1890; *Plasmodium malariae tertianae* Celli and Sanfelice, 1891; *Plasmodium malariae tertianae* Kruse, 1892; *Haemamoeba laverani* var. *tertiana* Labbé, 1894 (?); *Haemosporidium tertianae* Lewkowicz, 1897; *Haemamoeba malariae tertianae* Laveran, 1901; *Plasmodium camarense* Ziemann, 1915.

The first person to see and describe the true malaria parasite of man was the French army surgeon, Louis Alphonse Laveran. There is little doubt that during his investigations of 1880 and 1881 he saw the human tertian parasite in the blood of patients at Contantine, Algeria. He made no attempt to attach names other than calling the organisms *Oscillaria malariae* referring, undoubtedly, to the fine hair-like projections he saw develop from a pigmented spherical body in fresh blood from a patient with malaria.

The parasite of tertian malaria was well recognized by Golgi (1886, 1889). In the first paper, he mentioned that a tertian parasite must have a developmental cycle different from quartan. He then proceeded to describe the course of the disease during four tertian attacks (giving Prof. Reva credit for allowing him to use his patient), including the morphology of the parasites in relation to the paroxysm. In the more extensive paper of 1889, he re-affirmed his earlier findings and presented figures of the development of the parasite in the red cell with amazing accuracy. Even though he clearly separated tertian from quartan malaria, he did not name the parasite of either one. In an addendum to a paper on the malaria of birds, Grassi and Feletti, 1890, gave the name *vivax* for the human tertian parasite under the genus *Haemamoeba*. In 1885, Marchiafava and Celli had proposed *Plasmodium* as the genus name for the malaria parasites with the result that the combination *Plasmodium vivax* (Grassi and Feletti, 1890) came into general use but lacked official status until the International Commission on Zoological Nomenclature, after much soul searching, made the historic decision, opinion 283, to validate the names of the human malaria parasites in common use (see Hemming, 1954).

Vivax malaria has a worldwide distribution but makes its greatest inroads in temperate climates. The disease is more or less confined to the lowlands, coastal areas, marshes, lake margins, and reclaimed sea beds. There are no known strains of the parasite which can complete their sporogonous development at temperatures below 15° C (59° F) and consequently vivax is stopped north and south of the equator, by summer isotherms of 15° or 16° C.

In the tropics, *P. vivax* may predominate over *P. falciparum*, as in the lower Amazon, but the absolute prevalence in any area may not be known because of the rapid build-up of immunity to all strains of the parasite, in areas of high transmission, with consequent suppression of parasitemia. This situation was well demonstrated by Missoroli (1932). The highest incidence under present conditions is probably in Asia where it extends as a wide belt across the entire continent.

In 1949, Brumpt mentioned what he called the "benign tertian mystery" in writing about the situation in Liberia, Gabon, Lagos, and Stanleyville where, in the presence of efficient vectors of *P. vivax*, no vivax malaria occurs.

Garnham (1966) enlarged upon this by including "most of West Africa in the belt between the Congo and Mauritania." The explanation may be that the indigenous population is highly refractory to this parasite. This phenomenon was ably investigated by Young *et al* (1955) who studied many different strains of *P. vivax* during some 20 years, and found that only 23 percent of American Negroes came down with developed infections as against 96 percent of Caucasians; even when massive numbers of parasites were introduced, the susceptibility rate remained the same.

The rule of thumb is that pronounced resistance to *P. vivax* is confined to the true Negro but like many such rules, there are exceptions, as the senior author learned when he encountered a very sick true Negro in the malaria ward at Fort Benning, Ga. in 1951. The record showed that the patient was infected with *P. vivax* acquired in Korea. This was questioned with some impatience; whereupon, a fresh smear was made, stained, and examined by the senior author. *It was P. vivax!* This was one of many American Negroes who acquired vivax malaria in Korea and in whom the natural history and clinical attacks appeared no different than the same infections in Caucasians (Hankey *et al*, 1953). It is interesting that on the same day the above episode was enacted at Fort Benning, the late Dr. Alf Alving had the exact same experience at Fort Dix, N.J.

Beginning in 1900, many investigators have studied different strains of *P. vivax* and among these, the ones which received the most attention were the Madagascar strain (James, 1931 and James *et al*, 1936), the Dutch strain (Schüffner *et al*, 1929), the McCoy strain (Boyd, 1940; Boyd and Kitchen, 1944), and the New Guinea strain (Fairley *et al*, 1945). In our own work, we have undertaken studies on many different strains from various parts of the world, but have concentrated our efforts on the St. Elizabeth (see Coatney and Young, 1941; Coatney and Cooper, 1948; Coatney *et al*, 1950a), and the Chesson strain (Ehrman *et al*, 1945; Coatney and Cooper, 1948). The last two, along with certain others, will be discussed more fully later in this chapter.

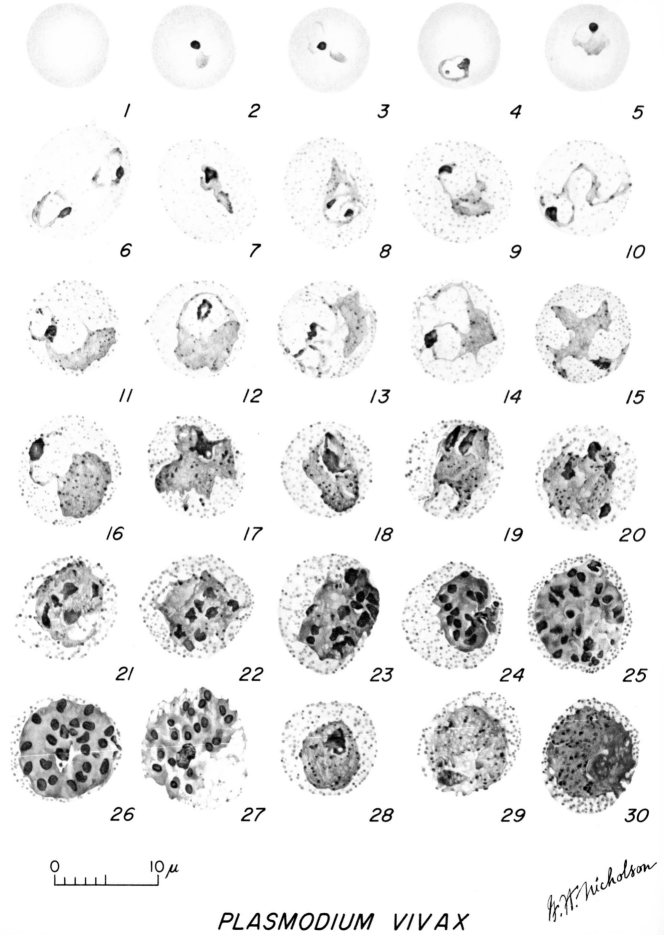

1 *2* *3* *4* *5*

6 *7* *8* *9* *10*

11 *12* *13* *14* *15*

16 *17* *18* *19* *20*

21 *22* *23* *24* *25*

26 *27* *28* *29* *30*

0   10 μ

G. W. Nicholson

PLASMODIUM VIVAX

Cycle in the Blood
PLATE 1

The young merozoite enters the red blood cell, generally a reticulocyte, as first reported by Craik (1920) and later verified by Kitchen (1938) and others, where it appears with a deep red nucleus and a whisp of cytoplasm (Fig. 2). As the parasite grows, a loop of cytoplasm forms enclosing a vacuole, with the circular nucleus at the anchor point (Fig. 3). Further growth produces a larger parasite with a distinct vacuole and sometimes with an accessory chromatin dot. Following this development, the red cell increases in size and displays Schüffner's stippling. The cytoplasm of the parasite is increased in amount, becomes decidedly amoeboid, and exhibits very small granules of light brown pigment. Multiple invasion of the host red cell is not uncommon (Figs. 4–10). The remainder of the development of the trophozoite consists of concentrating the cytoplasm with loss of the vacuole, the nucleus becomes larger and may assume grotesque shapes. Where only hours before, the trophozoite occupied a large part of the host cell, it now becomes compact, pigment granules become prominent, and stippling more intense (Figs. 11–18). The first stage of schizogony results in 2 nuclei and, then, in rather rapid succession, other divisions occur, to deliver up to 24 nuclei; the usual number is 16, although certain strains have 18 or more consistently. With the process of nuclear division other changes occur, too. The pigment granules come together to form larger chunks and then they coalesce into a single yellowish-brown lump. The maturing schizont occupies almost the whole red cell with the stippling forced into a rim-area. The host cell is enlarged and its cytoplasm appears depleted (Figs. 19–27).

The young gametocytes are easily separated from the asexual parasites because they are compact, lack a vacuole, are not amoeboid, and have a large nucleus with, sometimes, the suggestion of a halo. The enlarged host cell shows pronounced Schüffner's stippling. The immature macrogametocyte stains a deep blue. Dark pigment granules are scattered in the cytoplasm (Fig. 28). The mature macrogametocyte stains a lighter blue than the developing form and occupies most of the host cell. Its nucleus is generally eccentric and may show a darker portion inside the main body. Dark pigment grains are scattered in the cytoplasm. The host cell is enlarged, its cytoplasm appears pale and depleted (Fig. 29). The young microgametocyte resembles the immature macrogametocyte but as it approaches maturity, the staining of the cytoplasm is toward bluish-gray, the nucleus is larger, occupying about half or more of the parasite, and takes a reddish-purple stain. The dark pigment is confined to the area of the cytoplasm, leaving the nucleus free. The stippling of the host cell is forced toward its periphery (Fig. 30).

The asexual cycle takes 48 hours.

PLATE I.—*Plasmodium vivax*

Fig. 1.   Normal red cell.
Figs. 2–5.   Young trophozoites.
Figs. 6–16.   Growing trophozoites.
Figs. 17,18.   Mature trophozoites.
Figs. 19–21.   Early schizonts.
Figs. 22,23.   Developing schizonts.
Figs. 24–27.   Nearly mature and mature schizonts.
Figs. 28,29.   Nearly mature and mature macrogametocytes.
Fig. 30.   Mature microgametocyte.

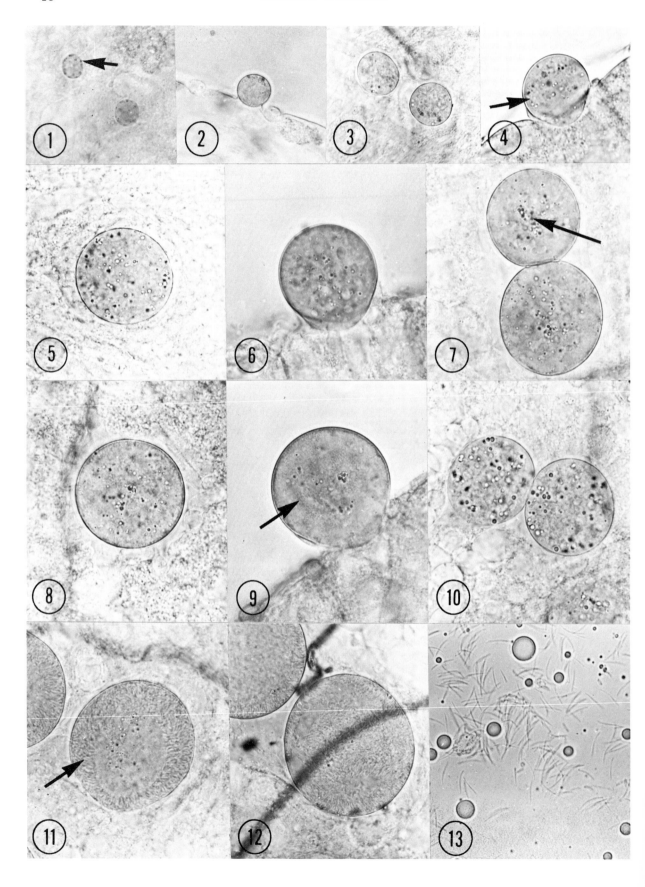

Sporogonic Cycle

PLATE II

Bano (1959) observed two small dot-like and two rod-like chromosomes in 49-hour oocysts of *P. vivax* in *Anopheles stephensi* mosquitoes. The haploid number of chromosomes was determined to be two. The size of oocysts at this time ranged from 11 to 14 μ in diameter. Although many workers have observed the oocysts of *P. vivax*, the studies of Shute and Maryon (1952) more nearly approximate our observations. These workers observed the development of oocysts of this parasite, at a temperature of 25° C, in *A. atroparvus* mosquitoes. They reported that the 50 to 100 greenish-brown pigment granules did not form a pattern in the very young oocysts. By days 4 and 5, however, there was a tendency toward chain formation, often in 3 lines. By day 6, the pigment was practically obscured and by day 7, only a few grains were observable. The oocysts were 10 to 46 μ in diameter. From day 3 to 6, the daily increase in diameter was about 7 μ; between the 6th and 7th day, however, growth became more rapid. Sporogony was completed in 9 days.

In our studies, observations were made on the oocyst development of the Chesson strain of *P. vivax*, in *A. b. balabacensis, A. freeborni, A. maculatus, A. stephensi,* and *A. quadrimaculatus*

mosquitoes incubated at a temperature of 25° C (Table 1).

In *A. b. balabacensis*, the oocysts, at day 4, ranged from 9 to 15 μ in diameter with a mean of 12 μ. The oocysts continued to grow so that by day 11, the size ranged from 18 to 59 μ with a mean of 46 μ. Sporozoites were present in the salivary glands by day 12. In *A. freeborni*, the mean oocyst diameters were generally greater than seen in the *A. b. balabacensis*; at day 11, the size of the oocysts ranged from 25 to 67 μ with a mean of 46 μ; sporozoites were present in the salivary glands. The oocyst diameters in the other species of mosquitoes fell within the range of these 2 mosquitoes. Sporozoites were present in the salivary glands of *A. maculatus* and *A. stephensi* by day 11 and in the salivary glands of *A. quadrimaculatus* by day 12.

In this, and in subsequent chapters, the growth of the oocysts is compared with those of *P. cynomolgi*. In each instance, the comparison is made from measurements made on the same species of mosquito. In this case, the comparison is between the growth curves of *P. vivax* and *P. cynomolgi* in *A. freeborni* mosquitoes (Fig. 6). *Plasmodium cynomolgi* has a larger mean oocyst diameter than *P. vivax* and much larger maximum oocyst diameter. Both of the parasites completed their development, as measured by the presence of sporozoites in the salivary glands, by day 11.

PLATE II

FIGURES 1–13.—Developing oocysts and sporozoites of *Plasmodium vivax* in *Anopheles maculatus, A. freeborni, A. quadrimaculatus,* and *A. b. balabacensis* mosquitoes. X 580.

Fig. 1. 4-day oocysts showing peripheral pigment.
Fig. 2. 5-day oocyst.
Fig. 3. 6-day oocysts.
Fig. 4. 7-day oocyst showing pigment and small vacuoles.
Fig. 5. 8-day oocyst.
Fig. 6. 9-day oocyst.
Fig. 7. 9-day oocysts showing concentration of vacuoles.

Fig. 8. 10-day oocyst.
Fig. 9. 10-day oocyst showing early formation of sporoblasts.
Fig. 10. 11-day oocysts showing prominent vacuolation.
Fig. 11. 12-day oocyst showing differentiation.
Fig. 12. Fully differentiated 12-day oocyst.
Fig. 13. Sporozoites present near salivary gland tissue 12 days after feeding.

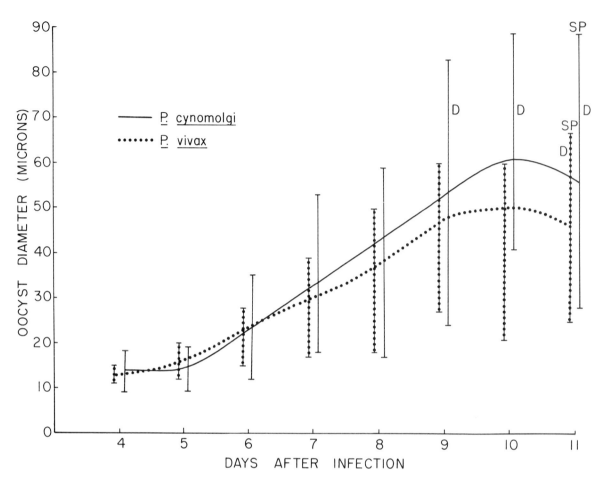

FIGURE 6.—A comparison of the mean oocyst diameter curve and ranges in oocyst diameters of *Plasmodium vivax* and *P. cynomolgi* in *Anopheles freeborni* mosquitoes. (D = oocyst differentiation; SP = sporozoites present in the salivary glands).

TABLE 1.—Oocyst diameters of *Plasmodium vivax* in *Anopheles b. balabacensis, A. freeborni, A. maculatus, A. stephensi,* and *A. quadrimaculatus* mosquitoes.

Days after infection	A. b. balabacensis			A. freeborni			A. maculatus			A. stephensi			A. quadrimaculatus		
	No.	Range	Mean*	No.	Range	Mean	No.	Range	Mean	No.	Range	Mean	No.	Range	Mean
4	100	9–15	12	100	11–15	13	100	11–17	13	56	11–15	13	102	11–14	12
5	100	12–19	16	76	12–20	16	53	11–19	15	100	12–18	14	36	12–18	15
6	100	12–26	22	92	15–28	23	17	18–26	22	100	14–27	22	64	13–25	22
7	100	13–32	25	100	17–39	30	100	15–35	27	100	18–42	31	100	18–31	25
8	100	18–40	32	100	18–50	36	100	‡	34	100	24–51	40	100	21–48	36
9	100	18–42	31	100	27–60	48	100	‡	40	100	30–59	47	100	18–52	41
10	100	18–61	45	100	21–60	50	100	‡	47	100	31–67	53	100	24–59	45
11	100	18–59	46†	95	25–67	46†**	100	26–66	47†**	100	24–65	48†**	100	21–59	49†
12			‡**			†**							100	27–59	47†**
Totals	800	9–61		763	11–67		670	11–66		756	11–67		802	11–59	

*   Measurements expressed in microns.
†   Oocyst differentiation.
** Sporozoites present in the salivary glands.
‡   Ranges in oocyst diameters not available.

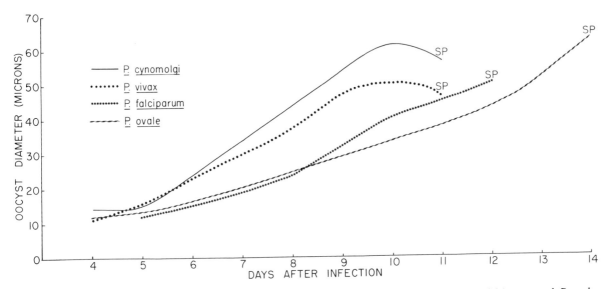

FIGURE 7—A comparison of the mean oocyst diameter curves of *Plasmodium cynomolgi*, *P. vivax*, *P. falciparum*, and *P. ovale* in *Anopheles freeborni* mosquitoes.

A comparison of the oocyst growth curves of the 3 human tertian malarias (*P. vivax*, *P. falciparum*, and *P. ovale*) with *P. cynomolgi* (Fig. 7) shows several distinct differences. Although *P. vivax* has a smaller mean diameter than *P. cynomolgi*, the shape of its growth curve is strikingly similar to that of *P. cynomolgi*. In contrast, *P. falciparum* and *P. ovale* have more of a straight line growth curve. Whereas sporozoites are present in the salivary glands of mosquitoes infected with *P. vivax* and *P. cynomolgi* by day 11, *P. falciparum* and *P. ovale* require 12 and 14 days, respectively for their development.

The sporozoites are narrow, elongate bodies, either straight or slightly curved, with one end more blunted than the other. The length of the living sporozoite is 14 μ and in dried preparations, is 1 to 2 μ less (Garnham, 1966). Using electron microscopy, Garnham *et al* (1963) gave detailed descriptions of the structures present in this form of the parasite which displays a complicated morphology.

We have readily transmitted the infection to man via the bites of *A. freeborni*, *A. quadrimaculatus*, *A. b. balabacensis*, and *A. maculatus* mosquitoes.

Cycle in the Tissue

The first tissue stages of a human malaria parasite, *P. vivax*, were demonstrated by Shortt and Garnham (1948). These tissue stages were found in a 7-day liver biopsy taken from a human volunteer upon whom approximately 1,728 anopheline mosquitoes, infected with *P. vivax*, were allowed to bite on 2 successive days. In addition, 200 pairs of salivary glands were dissected out from the same mosquitoes, and inoculated intravenously. Schizonts, considered to be 6- and 7-day forms, were described from the liver tissue taken at biopsy. The 6-day forms were ovoid masses similar to those seen in *P. cynomolgi* except that they were larger, about 42 μ in their greatest dimension. The various shapes, the vacuolation, the absence of tissue reaction, and the staining characteristics of the cytoplasm and chromatin were also similar to what they had first observed in *P. cynomolgi*. The 7-day stage, reported by these authors, consisted of a single, fully or nearly mature form, since merozoites were seen escaping from it.

The youngest *P. vivax* tissue stage was described by Rodhain in 1956 in liver biopsy material from a chimpanzee which had been inoculated with sporozoites of vivax malaria 7 and 4 days earlier. These 4-day forms (possibly 7-day tissue stages) ranged in size from 24 μ in diameter up to 47.7 by 35.2 μ. The nuclei, or chromatin masses, measured slightly over 2 μ and were rather sparsely distributed. Rodhain considered these forms to be similar to those described for man by Shortt and Garnham (1948).

Bray (1957) described 8- and 15-day tissue stages seen in liver biopsy material from a chimpanzee inoculated with sporozoites of *P. vivax* from *A. gambiae* mosquitoes. The 8-day *P. vivax* schizonts were similar to, but larger than, the 7-day forms demonstrated by Shortt and Garnham in 1948. He described two distinct stages of immature schizonts. The EE bodies averaged 52 by 44 μ and were almost always oval in shape. The immature stage contained 1 to 2 large vacuoles, cytoplasm was abundant and, at times, collected into darker staining aggregates. Occasionally, many small vacuoles were present, arranged around most of the periphery. Nuclei were relatively sparse. No clefts were observed. Bray also described premature and mature schizonts. In the premature stage, nuclei had completed their final division but with little or no change in their shape or size; the vacuoles had disappeared. The nuclei are elongate or form bars or loops; the cytoplasm breaks up and condenses upon the nuclei. This process of merozoite formation is completed in a very short time. The mature schizont is ovoid without any appreciable increase in size. They are packed with spherical merozoites which measure 1 to 1.4 μ in diameter. When the mature schizont ruptures, the merozoites are released. The size of the free merozoite is 0.8 to 1.2 μ.

Bray observed no patterns of nuclear arrangement or septal formation of the cytoplasm in any of the 8-day tissue stages of vivax malaria. There was no tissue reaction surrounding the EE bodies and no hypertrophic changes in the host-cell (hepatic) nuclei.

The tissue stages found in chimpanzee liver by Bray 15 days after exposure to infection appeared similar to the 8-day schizonts. There were no features which allowed for distinguishing these EE bodies as second generation forms. Secondary exoerythrocytic tissue stages were also found and described from a chimpanzee 9 months after inoculation with vivax sporozoites by Rodhain (1956a). Three of the 4 late tissue stages were elongate, irregular, or regular shaped ovals measuring 81, 61, and 49 μ in greatest dimension while the fourth form was lobulated.

The concensus is that there is a decided diminution in the number of tissue stages per measure of liver as the infection continues. Bray demonstrated this in his study of *P. vivax* in chimpanzees. With the inoculum used by him, Bray estimated a decrease from 20,000 primary exoerythrocytic forms (8-day biopsy) per mm³ of liver to 500 secondary exoerythrocytic forms in the 15-day biopsy material.

There can be no question that the liver cycle of vivax malaria persists for upwards of several years since many strains of vivax continue to exhibit true relapses through a minimum of 2 to 3 years. Ciuca *et al* (1955) observed relapses up to 8 years. It is doubtful that these latter were true relapses. Professor Gh. Lupascu, one of the late Dr. Ciuca's colleagues, has recently written one of us (PGC) that there was a good possibility of reinfection in their patients. Many of them had been released from the hospital for varying intervals and could easily have been re-exposed to infection because malaria was at that time endemic to the area.

Before we leave the discussion of the *P. vivax* cycle in the fixed tissue, mention should be made of Fairley's monumental work (1947) on the observations of various phases of the vivax life cycle. In this work, he subinoculated large volumes of blood (200 ml.) from individuals heavily exposed to infection with vivax malaria by mosquito bites. He observed that subinoculation during the first 30 minutes after exposure to infection resulted in eventual patent infection in the subinoculee. After 30 minutes and through 7 days, subinoculations were non-infective. On the 8th day subinoculation was infective, indicating that the tissue schizonts had liberated merozoites into the circulating blood on day 8.

Course of Infection

Fairley's experiments (1947) showed that the earliest prepatent period (i.e., the time from infection, day 0, to the time parasites become microscopically detectable in the circulating blood) could be as early as 8 days; this has been observed, but only rarely. In the last 10 years, we have encountered only one prepatent period of 8 days (Coatney *et al*,

1963). In addition, Boyd and Kitchen (1937) and Ciuca *et al* (1937) reported one 8-day prepatent period each in a large series of patients whose infections were induced by bites of infected mosquitoes. Putnam *et al* (1947) reported a 7-day prepatent period. However, this would be an 8-day period according to the manner in which all other investigators calculate the prepatent period. Kitchen (1949) reported 5 prepatent periods of 8 days in work with 9 different strains of vivax.

Generally, the duration of the prepatent period reported for many strains of *Plasmodium vivax* (Chesson, St. Elizabeth, Madagascar, McCoy, New Guinea, Roumanian, South Vietnam, Scanlon, West Pakistan, and Venezuelan) have ranged from 8 to 27 days, with medians or means ranging from 10.5 to 19 days (Boyd and Kitchen, 1937; Ciuca *et al*, 1937; Fairley *et al*, 1947; Coatney *et al*, 1950; Coatney *et al*, 1950a; Contacos and Coatney, 1963; Winckel, 1955).

Other strains of vivax malaria exhibit delayed prepatent periods, sometimes called protracted incubation periods, but probably more accurately described as delayed primaries.

The St. Elizabeth strain of vivax malaria (Coatney *et al*, 1950) is usually characterized by a short prepatent period of 11 to 18 days after infection. Only 3 volunteers out of 123 exhibited delayed primary attacks at 298 to 319 days after exposure to infection. Coatney and Cooper (1948) reviewed and described the characteristic of bimodal activity (parasitic and/or clinical) of a large number of vivax strains. They related the transmission studies of Sir Patrick Manson (1900) who exposed his son, P. Thurburn Manson, to infection with vivax malaria by bites of mosquitoes sent from Italy. A primary attack of malaria was experienced after 2 weeks and the attack was treated with quinine. Some 9 months later, a relapse of vivax malaria was experienced by Sir Patrick's son. There then followed many reports relating to 8- to 9-month intervals between primary and relapse activity, fitting more or less into a pattern for many strains of vivax in many countries. Hackett (1937) pointed out how this characteristic provided an explanation for spring malaria and for the overwintering of the parasite, and suggested, that strains of this type would have greatly enhanced chances for survival in temperate zones.

Yorke (1925) observed relapses in patients 6 to 13 months after exposure to infection. James (1931) and James *et al* (1936) observed late relapses with the Madagascar strain of vivax malaria. Schüffner *et al* (1929) observed prolonged "latency" in the form of delayed primary attacks in 8 of 8 patients exposed to infection with the Netherlands strain of vivax malaria. Boyd and Kitchen (1944) and Shannon *et al* (1948) observed the bimodal activity pattern (late relapses) with experimentally induced infections with the McCoy (U.S.) strain of vivax malaria. The Korean strain also exhibited the bimodal pattern of clinical activity and a period of long-term latency (Hankey *et al*, 1953).

Proof that such a consistently long period of time obtained between primary and relapse activity is common was furnished by studies of Coatney *et al* (1950) in volunteers who showed delayed relapse activity approximately 9 months after exposure to infection. They showed also that the time characteristic was independent of the season by exposing volunteers to infection during 9 months of the year. Relapses appeared only as a function of time with median periods of latency between 194 and 300 days.

Coatney and Cooper (1948) stated that morbidity statistics during World War II clearly showed that the vivax malarias from the Solomon Islands, New Guinea, and other areas of the Southwest Pacific did not exhibit consistent patterns of prolonged latency in their relapse mechanisms. Fairley (1945), working with vivax strains from New Guinea, reported no patterns of delayed relapse.

Coatney and Cooper (1948) summarized their studies with 2 strains of vivax malaria, used in drug evaluation studies in prisoner volunteers, the St. Elizabeth (U.S.A.) and the Chesson (New Guinea-South Pacific). The activity pattern of the St. Elizabeth strain is consistent with a relatively short prepatent period, between 7 and 14 days. This is followed by a period of many months when fixed-tissue stages remain quiescent, and then, by a late period of activity, with repeated spaced invasions of red blood cells which may continue for upwards of 2 years, sometimes, longer.

The Chesson strain pattern of activity is radically different from that of the St. Elizabeth strain. The former is characterized by fairly regular reinvasions of the blood stream, after the original attack, from fixed-tissue stages, gradually becoming more widely spaced. In heavy infections, relapses continue for upwards of 18 months, occasionally, longer.

The authors in commenting on the differences between the Chesson and the St. Elizabeth strains stated that the differences in relapse activity between the 2 strains was in keeping with the presumed tropical origin of the Chesson and the temperate zone origin of the St. Elizabeth strain.

Winckel (1955) presented material which appears to be somewhat paradoxical; namely, that the Netherlands strain under natural conditions produced delayed primary attacks, usually at about 8 months after infection. When infections were induced experimentally, however, the majority (51 out of 87) had early primary attacks (less than 21 days). However, on the basis of reports by Schüffner *et al* (1929) (obviously not their own data), Winckel stated that there are 3, not 2, types of vivax strains which can be separated by virtue of their life pattern; the tropical Chesson and Madagascar strains which have early primary attacks with frequent and early relapses; the temperate zone St. Elizabeth strain which has early primary attacks but late relapses; and the Netherlands temperate zone strain which displays delayed primary attacks followed by frequent relapses.

More recent studies tend to suggest that this classification of tropical versus temperate zone malaria is not all-inclusive. For example, we have studied a Central American (Panama), and certainly "tropical", strain of vivax and observed latent periods of approximately 5 months after exposure to infection or 4 months after treatment of the primary attack. In similar studies involving a Venezuelan strain of *P. vivax*, 5 of 6 volunteers who experienced relapse activity had their first relapse 110 to 335 days after exposure to infection. Only one of the 6 had a relapse as early as 29 days;

the latest was at day 609. These results would tend to indicate that long term relapses are not confined to temperate zone strains.

On the basis of life-pattern, Nikolaiev (1949) differentiated 2 subspecies of vivax malaria. One was characterized by short incubation periods of 7 to 23 days (from the southern part of U.S.S.R.), which he designated *P. vivax vivax*. The other subspecies (from northern and central areas of U.S.S.R.), characterized by long incubation periods (from 253 to 381 days), he called *P. vivax hibernans*. These designations failed to receive wide acecptance. Another Russian study in the same vein was that of Tiburskaya (1961) who described a strain isolated in 1953 from a patient who had never left Moscow. The author passed the strain for 5 years via *Anopheles labranchiae atroparvus* mosquitoes and in 103 infections the incubation periods were short (9 to 20 days), but in 13 they were extended (216 to 327 days). These data are somewhat reminiscent of our studies with St. Elizabeth vivax.

Most of the strains of vivax malaria studied to date have short prepatent periods. The greatest or most significant differences appear to lie in their relapse patterns; namely, a very short latent period or a very long latent period, between the primary attack and the first relapse.

We have purposefully omitted details of clinical human malaria because this work is concerned with the biology and parasitology of the primate malarias and, too, such information is well covered in numerous textbooks. We have included, however, the more general and pertinent aspects of human malaria.

Vivax malaria infections are considered to have relatively benign characteristics. Observations of large numbers of vivax infections, allowed to continue until terminated spontaneously, suggest that instances of death due to vivax malaria, in otherwise healthy adults, must indeed be very rare (Kitchen, 1949).

Whorton *et al* (1947) reported that prodromal symptoms before the primary attack in cases of Chesson vivax were almost never observed. Kitchen (1949) stated that prodromal symptoms are usually manifest in persons most susceptible to malaria. In our experience, with several strains of vivax malaria in non-immune volunteers, prodromal symptoms have not been commonly observed; but, when present, consisted mainly of headache and sometimes generalized malaise.

In non-immune individuals, the onset of the primary attack is usually characterized by a slight, rigorless paroxysm. Kitchen (1949) stated that the course, or sequence of events, of the uninterrupted attack of vivax is characterized by remittent fever, followed by intermittent fever, and then to remission or spontaneous termination of the primary attack. During the period of remittent fever, which lasts generally from 2 to 5 days, the continuous fever curve is characterized by quotidian fever spikes. These daily fever spikes exhibit progressively higher values reaching a maximum shortly after the appearance of intermittent fever. James (1926) reported that fever at the onset of primary attacks of Indian and Madagascar strains may be continuous or remittent over a period ranging from 1 to 3 days and that, if the early fever was intermittent, it was usually quotidian, rarely tertian. Kitchen (1949) emphasizes that this intermittent fever in the completely susceptible person is also quotidian. During the earliest intermittent paroxysms, certain characteristics are conspicuous: 1) the parasite density is mounting; 2) the paroxysms exhibit gradually increasing peak temperatures; 3) the duration of the paroxysm is protracted; and 4) a rigor does not introduce the first few intermittent paroxysms.

Whorton *et al* (1947) reported that in patients infected with Chesson strain vivax, 80 percent had remittent fever at the onset. Of the 20 percent who had intermittent fever at the beginning, 84 percent were quotidian and only 16 percent exhibited tertian fever spikes. The duration of remittent fever in that strain varied from 24 to 184 hours. They suggested that remittent fever, at the onset of the primary attack was probably related directly to irregular segmentation of the parasite. The more typical intermittent febrile paroxysms *are* directly related to the maturation and segmentation of one brood of parasites. During the initial remittent fever, segmentation occurs at irregular intervals (James, 1926; Boyd, 1941).

In our experience, with wholly susceptible

volunteers infected with Chesson vivax, the intermittent fever has been tertian as frequently as it has been quotidian. The characteristic of the fever pattern is a reflection of: 1) a single highly synchronous brood of parasites which produces sharp fever spikes, 2) an asynchronous single brood which produces plateau-like fever, and 3) multiple broods which produce daily paroxysms. If the infection is allowed to run, it is not unusual for multiple broods to get-in-step resulting in a tertian fever pattern; likewise, tertian patterns, sometimes, become quotidian for a time, only to revert to tertian again.

In a series of mosquito-induced infections with *P. vivax*, the mean duration of the primary attack was observed to be 19.3 days (Boyd *et al*, 1936a). Paroxysms accompanied by chills are indicative of a more severe paroxysm and usually attended by a greater degree of fever than those without chills. The mean maximum temperature for 654 paroxysms, with chills, was 104.2° F and for 346 paroxysms, without chills, was 102.5° F (Kitchen, 1949). Maximum paroxysmal temperatures are usually attained during the early part of the second week.

Kitchen and Putnam (1946), in a large series, noted that chills introduced up to 71 percent of all paroxysms. Chills were observed to last an average of 50 to 55 minutes. They stated that the temperature at the beginning of the chill was, as a rule, not in the febrile range; i.e., under 100° F and that, as a rule, fever appeared shortly after the onset of the chill, with an average increase of over 4° F (maximum increase was 7° F).

Boyd (1941) stated that chills are not observed at the onset of primary vivax infections and may not be evident for one or even 2 weeks. He reported that chills did occur in their patients during the period of remittent fever but were infrequent (only 26 percent of 144 patients). In a total 158 patients, only 46 percent had chills during any stage of the primary attack, with the first chill being observed as early as the 8th day. However, the incidence of chills might have been higher had primary attacks been allowed to continue.

Coatney and Young (1942) reported on detailed studies of 338 paroxysms in 21 infections with the St. Elizabeth strain of vivax malaria in Caucasian patients. They observed chills in only 201 (59 percent) of the paroxysms. They suggested that the absence of chills in as many as 41 percent of all paroxysms indicated that the term "chills and fever" does not adequately describe a malarial paroxysm. They found that the average temperature at the onset of each chill was 100.6° F. In addition, the average duration of the chill was 39 minutes; the average temperature rise was 2.3° F; the average time from onset of fever (100° F) to peak fever was 3 hours, 52 minutes; and the average duration of temperature 100° F and above, was 10 hours, 10 minutes. They observed that the average rate of fever rise was 3.3 times faster during the chill (1° F in 17 minutes) than during any other period of fever rise (1° F in 56 minutes). In the chill accompanied paroxysms, fever peaks averaged 0.7° F higher and duration of fever averaged 2 hours shorter than paroxysms without chills. It is generally thought that during this period, the patient is cold because he is shaking; but in truth, he is getting hotter all the time as can be seen in Figure 8. It is well recognized that the rise in a patient's temperature is associated with the maturation of the asexual parasites and that the peak of segmentation precedes the fever peak. It follows then, that the time between fever peaks (paroxysms) is a measure of the length of the asexual cycle which in a one-brooded infection of vivax is said to be 48 hours. However, when precise measurements of periodicity were carried out by Young (1944), it was discovered that the length of the paroxysmal interval for the St. Elizabeth strain was 43 hours, 25 minutes; with a New Hebrides strain the interval was 45 hours, 46 minutes; and with a Baltimore strain the interval was 41 hours, 31 minutes. Also, according to Young (loc. cit.) the fever charts published by Marchiafava and Bignami (1894) showed intervals of less than 48 hours. Kitchen (1949) was concerned with the total paroxysm-picture in contrast to Young's precise measurements and showed that only 28.9 percent were isochronous, 31.6 percent occurred more than 48 hours after the preceding paroxysm, and that 39.6 percent occurred less than 48 hours after the preceding paroxysm. In his experience, paroxysms less than 48 hours apart were more conspicuous during the early primary attack.

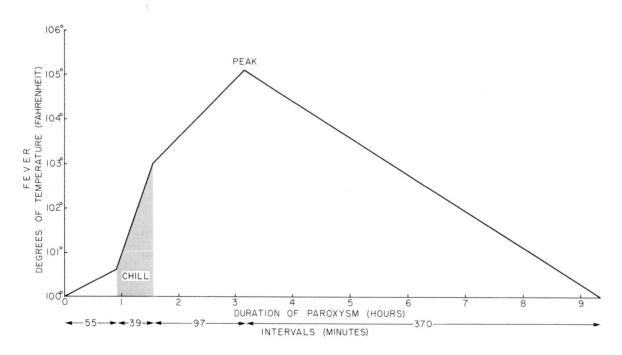

FIGURE 8—The temperature curve in relation to the chill in 201 paroxysms in *Plasmodium vivax* infections (after Coatney and Young, 1942).

Whorton *et al* (1947) reported the mean duration of fever over 103° F rectally in 235 paroxysms of Chesson vivax was 7.7 hours (only the first 3 paroxysms of the primary attack were measured). The maximum fever observed by them was 108.2° F rectally which occurred on the 10th day of a primary attack.

Fever in the experiences with vivax malaria reported by Kitchen (1949) frequently was found to exceed 106° F; temperatures of 107° F were uncommon. Kitchen (1949) reported an instance of a temperature recording of 107.6° F in a patient who reacted to this high temperature by convulsion—a rare occurrence.

As stated earlier, vivax infections are generally considered to have benign characteristics. In some patients, a pronounced exaggeration of one or more of the usual signs and/or symptoms may be evident and this phenomenon is probably related more to the variability of the host rather than to the parasite. Symptomatology generally includes headache, anorexia, backache, nausea with or without vomiting, myalgia, abdominal pain, and generalized malaise. Hepatomegaly and splenomegaly (up to 7 cm. below the left costal margin) with or without tenderness are not uncommon during the primary attack. Rarely, the spleen may extend into either the lower left or right quadrant. Tenderness is quite variable and not always proportional to the degree of enlargement (Kitchen, 1949).

Whorton *et al* (1947) found the subjective symptoms of Chesson vivax to be similar to those described for other strains. During the initial stage of remittent fever, malaise was almost universal. The other complaints were similar to those mentioned above. Headache was strikingly frequent, often very severe and persistent. They observed that the spleen can become palpable as early as the second day of illness. In most instances, the maximum parasite density is attained between the 7th and 14th days and maximum parasitemia rarely exceeds 50,000 parasites per mm^3 and usually remains below 25,000 per mm^3. Kitchen (1949) reported one vivax infection with a maximum parasite count of 96,000 per mm^3 which was not attended by any alarming symptoms.

Figure 9 shows the minimum and maximum parasitemia curves for 20 infections with the St. Elizabeth strain of *P. vivax* in our Caucasian patients. In addition, there are median parasitemia curves for blood-induced and sporozoite-induced infections. It can be seen that the median peak parasitemia for blood- and sporozoite-induced infections was reached on day 9 and 10 with maximum median counts of 8,365 and 6,775, respectively. After attaining peak parasitemia, the median curves gradually decreased so that by days 20, 30, 40, and 60, the median counts for the sporozoite-induced infections were approximately 3,000,

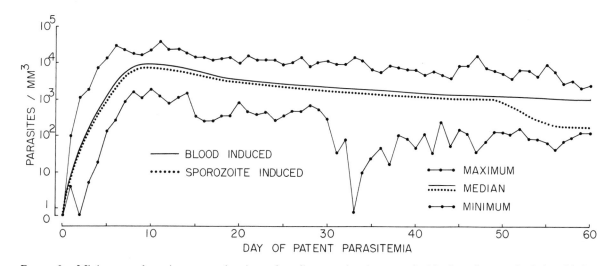

FIGURE 9.—Minimum and maximum parasitemias and median parasitemia curves for blood- and sporozoite-induced infections with St. Elizabeth strain *Plasmodium vivax* in Caucasian patients.

2,000, 1,000, and 100 parasites per mm³, respectively. This difference is evident in the figure at approximately 50 days. The parasitemia in blood-induced infections similarly decreased except that at days 40 and 60 the median counts were approximately 2,000 and 1,000 parasites per mm³, respectively. The maximum parasite counts for the blood-induced infections were 38,673 on day 11 and 23,232 on day 12 for the sporozoite-induced infections.

Figure 10 shows the parasitemia curves (minimum, median, maximum) for infections in 10 Negro patients with either the Chesson, St. Elizabeth, or Korean strain of vivax malaria. Exposure to infection was by the inoculation of parasitized blood or by sporozoites. It can be seen that the median peak parasitemia (6,850 parasites per mm³) obtained on day 7 and that the median parasitemia then very slowly but steadily declined. One of the most interesting facts evident in this figure is the maximum parasitemia of 45,844 per mm³ observed in one patient on day 7. Even more interesting, is the fact that this patient had experienced previous infections with ovale and malariae malaria. Six of the 10 Negro patients infected with vivax malaria had maximum parasitemias greater than 10,000 parasites per mm³. Three of the 10 Negro patients had experienced previous malaria infections.

An unexplained racial insusceptibility or resistance to infection with many strains of vivax malaria has been repeatedly reported for the Negro. Mayne (1932) first reported that American Negroes were relatively insusceptible to infection with vivax malaria. In 1933, Boyd and Stratman-Thomas also reported Negroes to be generally refractory to vivax malaria. Boyd (1934) showed the Negro was more immune to vivax than falciparum or malariae malaria. Young *et al* (1946, 1955) showed Negroes were more resistant than Caucasians to sporozoite induced vivax malaria. Whorton *et al* (1947a) observed that 6 of 8 Negroes inoculated with heavily parasitized blood failed to develop patent parasitemias. The other 2 showed evidence of partial refractoriness. Young *et al* (1955) reported that only 23 percent of American Negroes developed patent infections with vivax malaria as compared to a 96 percent infection rate in Caucasians. West African Negroes (Liberians) were found to be susceptible to infection with the Madagascar strain of vivax malaria in only 3.3 percent (1 out of 30) of the attempts (Bray, 1958).

Rhesus monkeys and other macaques have not been found susceptible to *P. vivax* either after the intravenous inoculation of heavily parasitized blood or large numbers of sporozoites and malariologists despaired of finding any of the monkeys susceptible to human

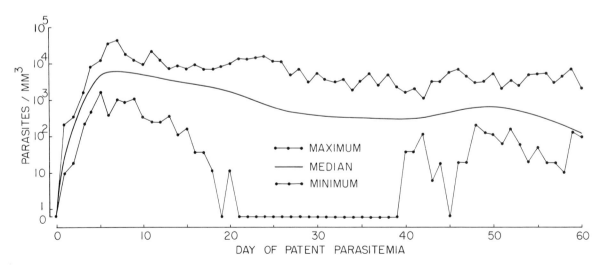

FIGURE 10.—Minimum, median, and maximum parasitemia curves in Negro patients infected with either Chesson, St. Elizabeth, or Korean strain vivax malaria.

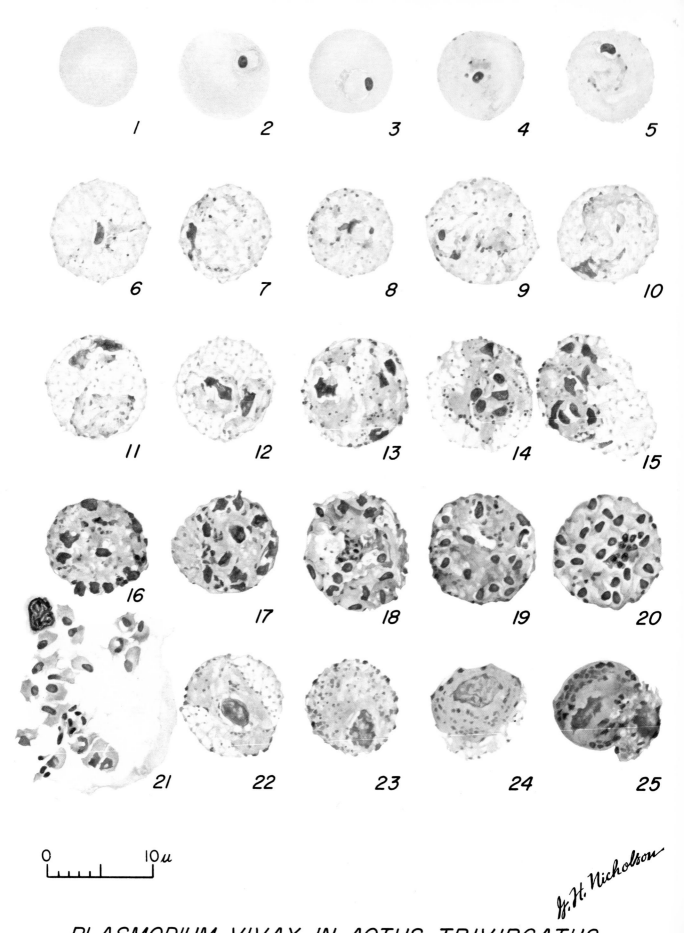

PLASMODIUM VIVAX IN AOTUS TRIVIRGATUS

malaria. However, in 1966, Young *et al* and Porter and Young reported that the owl or night monkey, *Aotus trivirgatus*, from Central America was susceptible to infection with *Plasmodium vivax*.

In our studies involving New World monkeys with human malarias, we have been able to establish 7 strains, or isolates, of vivax malaria in owl monkeys. In fact, 6 of the 7 strains were established in intact non-splenectomized animals. (Plate III depicts the appearance of *Plasmodium vivax* in the blood of this animal.) Once detectable parasites were present, the parasitemias rose fairly rapidly (Fig. 11) to a level of approximately 800 per mm^3 by day 11. After a drop in the median parasitemia by day 14, to approximately 100 per mm^3, the parasitemia rose to a level of approximately 1500 per mm^3 by day 18 and slowly declined thereafter. At the end of the 30-day observation period, the median para-

site count was approximately 500 per mm^3. Subsequent passage of the infections into splenectomized *A. trivirgatus* monkeys resulted in a more rapid rise in the median parasitemia curve to a maximum level of approximately 10,000 per mm^3 by day 23. At the end of the 30-day observation period, the median parasitemia was approximately 1500 per mm.^{3}

The parasitemia curve for an *A. trivirgatus* monkey infected with a strain of *P. vivax* from West Pakistan is presented in Figure 12. This animal was splenectomized prior to the intravenous inoculation of parasitized blood. On the 14th day after inoculation, daily feeding of *Anopheles freeborni* mosquitoes was initiated. Even though this was the first day gametocytes were found in the peripheral blood film, they were highly infectious to the mosquitoes. This high level of infection was maintained for the next 9 days followed by a gradual drop in the infection rate until day 32, when no mosquito

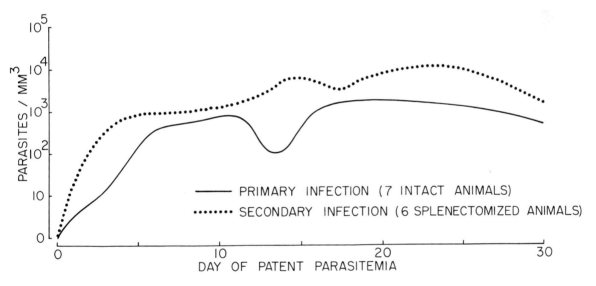

FIGURE 11.—Median parasitemia curves for primary (from man to monkey) and secondary (monkey to monkey) infections of *Plasmodium vivax* in *Aotus trivirgatus* monkeys.

PLATE III.—*Plasmodium vivax* in the night monkey, *Aotus trivirgatus*.

Fig. 1.   Normal red cell.
Figs. 2–5.   Young trophozoites.
Figs. 6–9.   Growing trophozoites.
Figs. 10, 11.   Mature trophozoites.

Figs. 12–17.   Developing schizonts.
Figs. 18–21.   Nearly mature and mature schizonts.
Figs. 22, 23.   Developing and mature macrogametocytes.
Figs. 24, 25.   Nearly mature and mature microgametocytes.

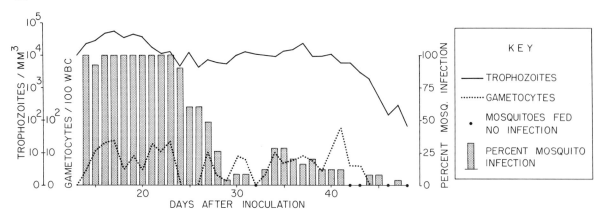

FIGURE 12.—Parasitemia and infectivity rates of *Anopheles freeborni* mosquitoes after feedings on an *Aotus trivirgatus* monkey (AO-91) infected with the West Pakistan strain of *Plasmodium vivax.*

infections were obtained. This was followed by a second period of lower-level infectivity of 9 days. The animal died 49 days after inoculation. The fact that an infection of *P. vivax* in the *Aotus trivirgatus* monkey could be infectious to mosquitoes over an extended period of time (in this case, 30 of 35 feeding days), indicates a great potential for their use in experiments necessitating large numbers of infected mosquitoes.

Rodhain (1956) and Bray (1957) have shown that chimpanzees are partially susceptible to *P. vivax*, in that the liver of the chimpanzee would support development of exoerythrocytic parasites but did not support the development of the erythrocytic stages well. However, when the animal, harboring the Madagascar strain, was splenectomized, a high parasitemia appeared in a short time. Prior to splenectomy, no erythrocytic parasites had been observed in smears of the peripheral blood. Subsequently, exposure of 2 splenectomized chimpanzees to infection with this same strain of *P. vivax* quickly resulted in patent infections which developed high parasitemias.

In 1956, Garnham *et al* infected a chimpanzee with fresh blood parasitized by the Madagascar strain of vivax. The parasite did not grow well in the chimpanzee but well enough so that *A. stephensi* mosquitoes could be

infected. After a suitable incubation period, the mosquitoes were allowed to bite one of the authors. He became infected. Parasitemia appeared on day 10 and when the patient was taken to the hospital on day 14, his temperature was 41.2° C. The infection was that of a typical vivax showing that the parasite had not been altered by its sojourn in the chimpanzee.

Cadigan *et al* (1968) were able to infect a gibbon with *P. vivax* even though only transient infection obtained.

Host Specificity

Man is apparently the only natural host for *Plasmodium vivax*. Experimental infections have been induced, however, in chimpanzees (Mesnil and Roubaud, 1917, 1920; Garnham *et al*, 1956) and in gibbons, *Hylobates lar*, (Cadigan *et al*, 1968). In 1966, Porter and Young reported the successful infection of owl monkeys, *Aotus trivirgatus*, and Geoffroy's tamarin, *Saguinus geoffroyi*, by the inoculation of parasitized blood from man. In addition, Young *et al* (1966) and Porter and Young (1966) reported the successful transmission of *P. vivax* from the owl monkey to man via the bites of *Anopheles albimanus* mosquitoes. These findings prompted intensive study of *P. vivax* in South American monkeys. Deane *et al* (1966) reported the experimental infection of splenec-tomized squirrel monkeys, *Saimiri sciureus*, with *P. vivax* and Young and Porter (1969) re-ported the infection of spider monkeys, *Ateles fusiceps* and *A. geoffroyi*, along with the white-faced monkey, *Cebus capucinus*, with *P. vivax* from *A. trivirgatus* donors.

Baerg *et al* (1969) reported transmission of *P. vivax* from *Aotus trivirgatus* and *Ateles fusiceps* to *Ateles fusiceps*, *A. trivirgatus*, and *S. geoffroyi* via the bites of *A. albimanus* mosquitoes, but only with some difficulty. However, Ward *et al* (1969) showed that the Chesson strain of *P. vivax* in the *Aotus trivirgatus* and the chimpanzee could be transmitted with relative ease to *Aotus trivirgatus* and the chimpanzee via the bites of *A. b. balabacensis*, *A. stephensi*, and *A. quadrimaculatus* mosquitoes.

The almost worldwide distribution of *P. vivax* is indicative of the large number of mos-quitoes capable of transmitting the parasite. Of the 5 species of *Anopheles* routinely used in our laboratory (Table 2), *A. stephensi* was the most susceptible to infection with it, followed by *A. b. balabacensis*, *A. freeborni*, *A. maculatus*, and, finally, *A. quadrimaculatus*.

In this and subsequent chapters, the relative susceptibility of a species of *Anopheles* to infec-tion with a particular species of *Plasmodium* is based on the determination of the average number of oocysts per 100 guts (Gut Infection Index) for a standard mosquito, either *A. freeborni*, *A. b. balabacensis*, or *A. maculatus*, fed simultaneously with the species being com-pared. The Gut Infection Index ratios are determined by the relationship of the GII of

the standard mosquito to that of the test mos-quito; the GII of the standard mosquito is then given an arbitrary rating of 100. In Table 2, *A. freeborni* is given the arbitrary rating of 100. If in a simultaneous feeding of this species and *A. stephensi*, the standard had 10 oocysts per gut, the *A. stephensi* would have had 13.19 oocysts per gut. By this method it is possible to determine the relative susceptibility of all the mosquitoes to each other by their relation-ship to the standard.

Immunity and Antigenic Relationships

In 1924, Yorke and Macfie demonstrated the existence of homologous strain immunity against *Plasmodium vivax* by showing that after the development of acquired immunity indi-viduals were refractory to superinfection by the same strain. Homologous strain immunity against vivax malaria has since been confirmed repeatedly by Boyd and Stratman-Thomas (1933a), Boyd *et al* (1936), Boyd and Mat-thews (1939), Boyd (1942), Boyd and Kitchen (1943, 1946), and Jeffery (1956). These inves-tigators were able to show that the develop-ment of the immunity obtained in subjects infected either by sporozoites or by parasitized blood. The phenomenon was manifest in the form of decreased parasite density, shorter duration of patent parasitemia, and/or de-creased clinical manifestations.

Boyd and Kitchen (1943, 1946) stated that abundant evidence, gathered by themselves and others, existed to show that persons con-

TABLE 2.—Comparative infectivity of *Plasmodium vivax* to *Anopheles freeborni*, *A. stephensi*, *A. b. balabacensis*, *A. maculatus*, and *A. quadrimaculatus*.

Mosq. species comparison*	Number tests	Number of mosquitoes		Percent infection		GII** ratio
		Standard	Other	Standard	Other	
F–1						100
F–1 : St–1	6	38	44	86.8	84.1	131.9
F–1 : Bal	11	88	61	68.2	82.0	109.3
F–1 : Mac	24	271	272	47.6	42.3	47.0
F–1 : Q–1	9	82	108	86.6	66.7	41.2

* F–1 = *Anopheles freeborni*; St–1 = *A. stephensi*; Bal = *A. b. balabacensis*; Mac = *A. maculatus*; Q–1 = *A. quadrimaculatus*.

** GII = Gut Infection Index = average number of oocysts per 100 guts; the GII ratio is the relationship of the GII of *A. freeborni* to another species where the GII of *A. freeborni* = 100.

valescing from an infection with vivax malaria had acquired potent immunity to the strain of parasite which produced their attack. While recovery from an attack of vivax malaria is indicative of acquired immunity to the strain which excited the attack, the same individual may be expected to exhibit a subclinical parasitemia subsequent to a reinoculation with the same strain of parasite. Boyd and Kitchen (1946) showed that the level of immunity in convalescing malarial infections could be increased by a series of subsequent reinoculations with the same strain of parasite. Oftentimes, a level of immunity (hyperimmunity) could be attained where the individual was able not only to withstand, but also to promptly destroy, large inocula of parasites, indeed, many million times greater than the minimal number required to infect a non-immune individual.

Boyd, Stratman-Thomas, and Kitchen (1936) reported that an effective homologous immunity to the McCoy strain of vivax malaria could persist for more than 3 years. Boyd and Matthews (1939) reported that 2 patients still showed signs or evidence of immunity 7 years after their primary experience with the homologous strain. The signs of immunity were diminished parasitemia, increased clinical tolerance, and accelerated activation of immune mechanisms.

Boyd and Kitchen (1943) made 2 attempts to transfer the hyperimmune state passively through the transfusion of large volumes of blood. Both attempts failed to prevent infection or modify the course of infection in susceptible persons.

Jeffery (1956) reported that patients reexposed to homologous strain infection of Chesson vivax, by bites of infected mosquitoes, were found to usually experience infections with a shorter and milder course, and, after treatment, a single relapse ensued which was usually asymptomatic.

Nicole and Steel (1926) reported that immunity may also exist between heterologous strains of vivax malaria. Boyd (1942) confirmed this observation with American strains of vivax malaria. Ciuca et al (1937) reported a relative cross-immunity in vivax malaria between imported strains, and strains indigenous to Roumania.

Boyd et al (1934), based on their studies with induced vivax malaria, reported that previous infections with malaria do reduce the severity of subsequent infections. They concluded that superinfections with heterologous strains of vivax malaria result in clinical attacks of milder intensity than the original ones.

Boyd et al (1939) reported that an absence of cross-immunity between species of malaria (P. vivax and P. falciparum) was observed whether super-infection occurred during the incubation period, during the acute primary attack, or shortly after recovery from the acute attack.

Whorton et al (1947a) in their studies with the Chesson strain of vivax malaria discussed innate or natural immunity as well as acquired immunity. They reported that of 8 Negroes inoculated intravenously with blood parasites of the Chesson strain, all were partially or completely refractory to infection. Four of the patients developed neither patent parasitemia nor fever. This phenomenon has been reported by many investigators. For example, Young et al (1955) in their studies of induced human malaria in patients reported that Negroes generally demonstrated a refractoriness to infections with many domestic and foreign strains of vivax malaria under conditions in which Caucasian patients were wholly susceptible.

Tobie and Coatney (1961) were the first to report that antisera to P. vivax and to P. cynomolgi would cross-react with the heterologous antigens. Voller (1962) showed that such cross-reactions would also occur between P. vivax and P. bastianellii (= B strain P. cynomolgi), P. gonderi, and P. osmaniae (= OS strain P. inui). Further studies by Tobie et al (1962) indicated that although considerable cross-reaction was obtained, the maximum antibody titer tended to be the homologous antigen. Diggs and Sadun (1965) studied the cross-reactivity of sera from volunteers infected with P. falciparum and others infected with P. vivax, using the IFA technique, and found that sera from patients with P. falciparum had geometrical mean reciprocal titers of 1:28.2 against the homologous antigen in contrast to 1:6.3 against the P. vivax antigen. In a reverse study, sera from patients with P. vivax infections had homologous geometrical mean titers of 1:17.2 and heterologous mean titers of 1:9.3.

REFERENCES

BAERG, D. C., PORTER, J. A., JR., and YOUNG, M. D., 1969. Sporozoite transmission of *Plasmodium vivax* to Panamanian primates. Am. J. Trop. Med. & Hyg. *18* : 346–350.

BANO, L., 1959. A cytological study of the early oocysts of seven species of *Plasomdium* and the occurrence of post-zygotic meiosis. Parasitology *49* : 559–585.

BOYD, M. F., 1934. Observations on naturally induced malaria. Southern Med. Jour. *27* : 115–159.

BOYD, M. F., 1940. On strains or races of the malaria parasites. Am. J. Trop. Med. *20* : 69–80.

BOYD, M. F., 1941. The infection in the intermediate host: symptomatology, general considerations. Am. Assoc. Adv. Sci. (No. 15), 163–182.

BOYD, M. F., 1942. Criteria of immunity and susceptibility in naturally induced vivax malaria infections. Am. J. Trop. Med. *22* : 217–226.

BOYD, M. F. and STRATMAN-THOMAS, W. K., 1933. Studies on benign tertian malaria. 4. On the refractoriness of Negroes to inoculation with *Plasmodium vivax*. Am. J. Hyg. *18* : 485–489.

BOYD, M. F. and STRATMAN-THOMAS, W. K., 1933a. Studies on benign tertian malaria. I. On the occurrence of acquired tolerance to *Plasmodium vivax*. Am. J. Hyg. *17* : 55–59.

BOYD, M. F. and MATTHEWS, C. B., 1939. Further observations on the duration of immunity to the homologous strain of *Plasmodium vivax*. Am. J. Trop. Med. *19* : 63–67.

BOYD, M. F. and KITCHEN, S. F., 1937. A consideration of the duration of the intrinsic incubation period in vivax malaria in relation to certain factors affecting the parasites. Am. J. Trop. Med. *17* : 437–444.

BOYD, M. F. and KITCHEN, S. F., 1943. On attempts to hyperimmunize convalescents from vivax malaria. Am. J. Trop. Med. *23* : 209–225.

BOYD, M. F. and KITCHEN, S. F., 1944. Renewed clinical activity in naturally induced vivax malaria. Am. J. Trop. Med. *24* : 221–234.

BOYD, M. F. and KITCHEN, S. F., 1946. An attempt at active immunization with *Plasmodium vivax* killed in vivo. Am. J. Trop. Med. *26* : 749–752.

BOYD, M. F., STRATMAN-THOMAS, W. K., and KITCHEN, S. F., 1936. On the duration of acquired homologous immunity to *Plasmodium vivax*. Am. J. Trop. Med. *16* : 311–315.

BOYD, M. F., STRATMAN-THOMAS, W. K., and MUENCH, H., 1934. Studies on benign tertian malaria. 6. On heterologous tolerance. Am. J. Hyg. *20* : 482–487.

BOYD, M. F., KITCHEN, S. F., and MUENCH, H., 1936a. Seasonal variations in the characteristics of vivax malaria. Am. J. Trop. Med. *16* : 589–592.

BOYD, M. F., KITCHEN, S. F., and MATTHEWS, C. B., 1939. Consecutive inoculations with *Plasmodium vivax* and *Plasmodium falciparum*. Am. J. Trop. Med. *19* : 141–150.

BRAY, R. S., 1957. Studies on malaria in chimpanzees. II. *Plasmodium vivax*. Am. J. Trop. Med. Hyg. *6* : 514–520.

BRAY, R. S., 1958. The susceptibility of Liberians to the Madagascar strain of *Plasmodium vivax*. J. Parasit. *44* : 371–373.

BRUMPT, E., 1949. The human parasites of the genus *Plasmodium*. Malariology. Vol. I, edited by Mark F. Boyd W. B. Saunders Co., Phila.

CADIGAN, F. C., JR., WARD, R. A., and PUHOMCHAREON, S., 1968. Transient infection of the gibbon with *Plasmodium vivax* malaria. Trans. Roy. Soc. Trop. Med. & Hyg. *62* : 295–296.

CELLI, A. and SANFELICE, F., 1891. Sui parassiti del globulo rosso nell'uoms et negli animali. Quar. Ist. Igene Sper. Univ. Roma, 1 (N.S.) 33–63 and Ueber die Parasiten des Rothen Blutkorpercheres im Menschen und in Thieren. Fortsch. Med. *9* : 581–586.

CIUCA, M., BALLIF, L., CHELARESCU, M., and LAVRINENKU, M., 1937. A l'étude de l'infection expérimentale au *Plasmodium vivax*. Arch. Roum. de Pathol. Expér. et Mikrobiol. *10* : 217–265.

CIUCA, M., CHELARESCU, M., SOFLETEA, A., CONSTAN-TINESCU, P., TERITEANU, E., CORTEZ, P., BALANOVSCHI, G., and ILIES, M., 1955. Expérimentale à l'étude de l'immunité dans le paludisme. Editions De L'académie de al Republique Populaire Roumaine (Bucharest), 61–108.

COATNEY, G. R. and COOPER, W. C., 1948. Recrudescence and relapse in vivax malaria. Proc. 4th Int. Cong. Trop. Med. & Mal. *1* : 629–639.

COATNEY, G. R. and YOUNG, M. D., 1941. The taxonomy of the human malaria parasites with notes on the principal American strains. Am. Assoc. Adv. Sci. (No. 15), 19–24.

COATNEY, G. R. and YOUNG, M. D., 1942. A study of the paroxysms resulting from induced infections of *Plasmodium vivax*. Am. J. Hyg. *35* : 138–141.

COATNEY, G. R., COOPER, W. C., RUHE, D. S., YOUNG, M. D., and BURGESS, R. W., 1950. Studies in human malaria. XVIII. The life pattern of sporozoite-induced St. Elizabeth strain vivax malaria. Am. J. Hyg. *51* : 200–215.

COATNEY, G. R., COOPER, W. C., and YOUNG, M. D., 1950a. Studies in human malaria. XXX. A summary of 204 sporozoite-induced infections with the Chesson strain of *Plasmodium vivax*. J. Natl. Mal. Soc. *9* : 381–396.

COATNEY, G. R., CONTACOS, P. G., LUNN, J. S., KILPATRICK, J. W., and ELDER, H. A., 1963. The effect of a repository preparation of the dihydrotriazine metabolite of chlorguanide, CI–501, against the Chesson strain of *Plasmodium vivax* in man. Am. J. Trop. Med. & Hyg. *12* : 504–508.

CONTACOS, P. G. and COATNEY, G. R., 1963. The relapse activity of a Venezuelan strain of *Plasmodium vivax*. Unpublished data.

CRAIK, R., 1920. A note on the erythrocytes in malaria. Lancet *1* : 1110–1112.

DEANE, L. M., NETO, J. F., and SILVEIRA, I. P. S., 1966. Experimental infection of a splenectomized squirrel-monkey, *Saimiri sciureus*, with *Plasmodium vivax*. Trans. Roy. Soc. Trop. Med. & Hyg. *60* : 811–812.

DIGGS, C. L. and SADUN, E. H., 1965. Serological cross reactivity between *Plasmodium vivax* and *Plasmodium falciparum* as determined by a modified fluorescent antibody test. Exp. Parasit. *16* : 217–223.

EHRMAN, F. C., ELLIS, J. M., and YOUNG, M. D., 1945.

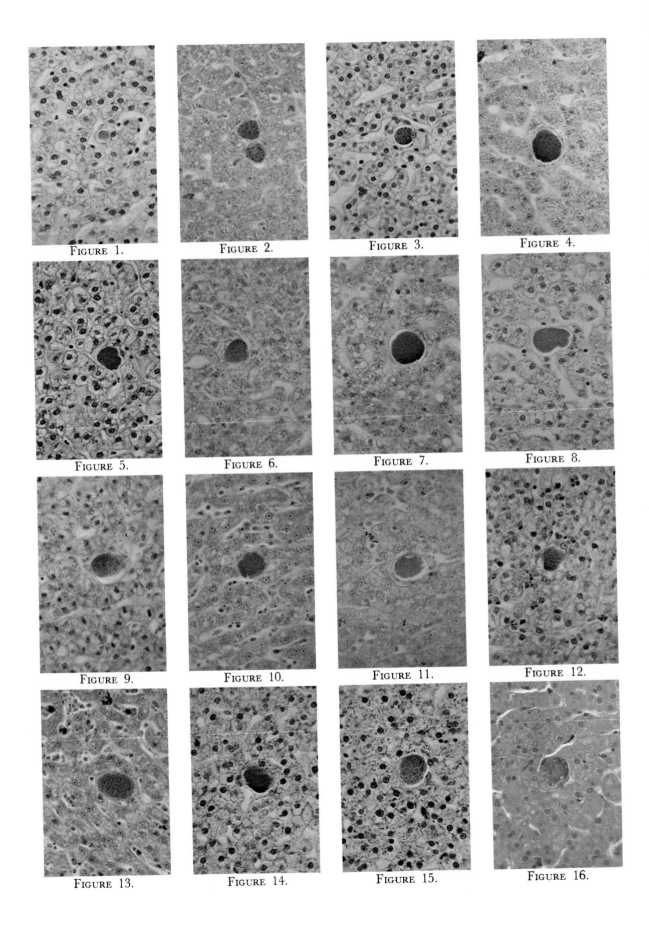

FIGURE 1.

FIGURE 2.

FIGURE 3.

FIGURE 4.

FIGURE 5.

FIGURE 6.

FIGURE 7.

FIGURE 8.

FIGURE 9.

FIGURE 10.

FIGURE 11.

FIGURE 12.

FIGURE 13.

FIGURE 14.

FIGURE 15.

FIGURE 16.

Cycle in the Tissue

PLATE VI

The discovery of an exoerythrocytic stage in primate malaria was announced by Shortt and Garnham on 24 January, 1948. Prior to the actual discovery it was agreed generally that contrary to Schaudinn's convincing "dream", of the sporozoite going directly into the host red cell, there had to be a fixed tissue stage to account for prepatent periods and for relapses. In fact, in speaking of the latter, Thayer (1897) in a series of lectures on human malaria, at the Johns Hopkins University, agreed with earlier investigators that there must be some undiscovered form of the parasite; he wrote "the organism may remain perhaps within the cell body of certain phagocytes for long periods of time, only to be set free again as a result of some insult, the nature of which is not yet appreciable to us." Fifty-one years later, it did become "appreciable to us." In the interim, pre-erythrocytic stages of many of the bird malaries were described, mainly by the Huff school of investigators (see Huff and Coulston, 1944 and Huff, 1947). Also, during this period, there were various doubtful records of a corresponding stage in human malaria (see Angelini, 1947 and Huff, 1947).

Fairley *et al* (1945, 1947) transferred from 200 to 500 ml. of blood from patients bitten by infected mosquitoes to clean test subjects. Recipients became infected when blood was taken within 30 minutes of mosquito biting but after that, all results were negative until day 7 in falciparum infections, and day 8 in vivax infections. The evidence was clear, that wherever the sporozoites and subsequent schizogonies occurred, it was not in the peripheral blood. Similarly, our own studies carried out in March of 1945 (Cooper, Ruhe, and Coatney, 1949) showed that with the St. Elizabeth strain of *P. vivax* the blood is not infectious during the latent period in patients whose infections relapsed subsequently. These authors transferred 250 ml. of blood from patients 181 days after the primary infection to other volunteers. Only one of 6 recipients developed malaria and his donor experienced a relapse 7 days after blood was drawn for transfer. The other 5 volunteers were shown to be susceptible to infection when homologous strain parasitized blood was inoculated into them. These and similar experiments did not prove the presence of EE stages in primate malaria but as indirect evidence the stage was set for the Shortt and Garnham discovery.

The initial announcement told of finding 6- and 7-day EE bodies and subsequent papers through 1954 (Shortt and Garnham, 1948, 1948a; Shortt, Garnham, and Malamos, 1948; Hawking, Perry, and Thurston, 1948; Shortt, 1948; Shortt and Garnham, 1948b; and Shortt, Bray, and Cooper, 1954) filled in the primary exoerythrocytic schizogony from day 2 through day 12 and certain older forms including one at day 104.

As shown by Fairley *et al* (loc. cit.) the sporozoite leaves the peripheral blood shortly after it is introduced into the host and probably enters a parenchyma cell of the liver. The earliest

PLATE VI.—Exoerythrocytic bodies of *Plasmodium cynomolgi* in liver of *Macaca mulatta* monkeys. X 240. Figs. 1–5, 11, 12, 14–16 are B strain; Figs. 6, 10, and 13 are M strain; Figs. 7 and 9 are RO strain; Fig. 8 is PT strain. Figs. 1–15 EE bodies stained by Giemsa-Colophonium technique; Fig. 16 EE body stained with Hematoxylin-Eosin.

Fig. 1. 5 day body.
Fig. 2. 6 day bodies showing prominent flocculi.
Fig. 3. 6 day body showing host cell nucleus.
Fig. 4. 7 day body.
Fig. 5. 7 day body.
Fig. 6. 8 day body.
Fig. 7. 9 day body.
Fig. 8. 10 day body showing numerous nuclei.
Fig. 9. 11 day body.

Fig. 10. 12 day body.
Fig. 11. 14 day body.
Fig. 12. 17 day body.
Fig. 13. 18 day body.
Fig. 14. 60 day body.
Fig. 15. 105 day body.
Fig. 16. 143 day body; this figure courtesy of
Dr. Leon Schmidt.

stage seen, a 2-day form, is a spherical to ovoid body about 2.3 to 2.45 μ in diameter. The cytoplasm stains blue; the nucleus is single and stains red. (The authors were not unmindful of the difficulties connected with recognizing this minute stage and that of day 3, also; however, their illustrations appear convincing.) The 3-day form is spherical or ovoid and measures 4.5 to 5.9 μ in diameter. It occupies a more or less peripheral position in the cell. The cytoplasm stains blue and there are 8 or more nuclei which stain reddish-violet. The 4-day forms are about twice the size of those of the previous day, about 10 μ in diameter. The cytoplasm stains a pastel blue. The nuclei have increased to about 20 and stain a reddish-mauve. The periphery of the schizont is marked by a fine membrane. By the next day, the 5th, the schizont is about 14 μ in diameter and houses up to 70 nuclei. The host cell nucleus is pushed to one side but otherwise the host cell shows no sign of being invaded; staining is typical.

Up to this point, the development of the tissue parasite is more or less routine but by the 6th day there is a decided change. The size is now up to 29 μ in diameter, the host cell is much enlarged, and its nucleus is pushed toward the periphery. The cytoplasm of the parasite stains a pastel blue. The nuclei are difficult to count but the number is over 100. Vacuoles are a new development and become more prominent as growth proceeds. Seven day forms may assume various shapes, other than the characteristic oval, due to tissue resistance, but irrespective of the shape the internal structure is constant. The cytoplasm stains light-blue or mauve and is somewhat granular. The chromatin particles stain magenta, tend to be spherical, rod- or boat-shaped and measure about 0.75 μ in diameter. The 8-day EE bodies average about 38 μ in diameter. They are spherical to oval. The tendency for vacuolization seems to be a feature connected with parasites from some monkeys and absent from others. The cytoplasm stains blue as in the younger forms, the nuclei red. Some of the schizonts are mature by this time because parasites may appear in the peripheral blood. By the 9th day, the maturation of the EE bodies is definitely in force but since there

is a lack of complete synchronicity, remaining first generation schizonts continue their development. These slower-growing forms are compact and entire. The merozoites appear as if composed entirely of chromatin but there is surely a cytoplasmic envelope, too. Bray (1957) found these forms measured 46 μ in diameter and Eyles (1960a) found them to measure about 49.8 μ with extremes of 35 to 62.5 μ. Ten day forms generally contain differentiated merozoites. Ruptured forms, when seen, appear to have lost their compact regular outline. Older first generation schizonts have been seen but except for their large size, up to 108 μ, they appear about like the 8 to 10 day forms.

Secondary schizonts have been seen at 60 and 105 days (see Plate VI, Figs. 15 and 16) 143 days by Schmidt and at 378 days by Warren. Secondary schizonts is an arbitrary designation for there is no proof that these older forms, probably responsible for relapse, arise from the rare parasite of the first or succeeding generations and, for reasons of their own, re-enter a liver cell. Certainly these liver schizonts do not originate from circulating blood forms—for if they did, blood-induced infections would relapse, also. They do not. Relapse, in the true sense, is a part of the life-pattern of *P. cynomolgi* as it is of *P. vivax*, *P. fieldi*, and certain others, but the process responsible for producing the tissue schizonts which initiate it is still a matter for speculation. It is not impossible that these continuing EE bodies are derived from the original sporozoites which lie dormant for a time, and then, through some urge, not appreciable to us, are moved to complete their destiny. A fuller discussion is found in an earlier section (Chapter 4).

The secondary schizonts, found at 60 days and/or later, resemble the initial forms in all respects including active division. This latter characteristic shows that they are not latent or retarded forms. Garnham (1966) believes that these forms can be separated from earlier forms because their contour is generally "markedly convoluted." This has not been our experience as may be seen by examining Figs. 15 and 16 (60- and 105-day parasites) and the same is true for the 143- and the 378-

day forms. As the evidence stands now we doubt that the contour of the parasite can be relied upon as an indication of the age of the EE body.

There were no reports on the ultrastructure of the EE bodies of any of the primate malarias until the paper by Sodeman *et al* (1970) on 7-day forms of the B strain of *Plasmodium cynomolgi* (Plate VII). They studied 4 of these bodies which had an average size of 28 x 17μ. The liver cell border, with its organelles, surrounds the EE body completely. The host cell is enlarged and its nucleus is pushed to one side. There appear to be no degenerative changes in the cell as a result of the parasitism.

The lobulated EE body has a two-layered membrane which lies close to the cytoplasm of the parasite. Mutliple irregularly shaped nuclei, 1.1 x 1.6μ, are scattered throughout the body. The nucleus is homogenous and granular with a clear space surrounding it. The cytoplasm of the EE body contains densely packed free ribosomes. Some of these appear in a linear fashion. Mitochondria are present.

There are 2 types of vacuoles: Type 1 is 0.3 to 3.5μ, round, and with a distinct membrane. They appear empty but some contain membrane-like structures; Type 2 vacuoles are smaller, homogeneous, and more electron dense. They are generally round, but may be crescent-shaped.

It is hoped that these authors will continue

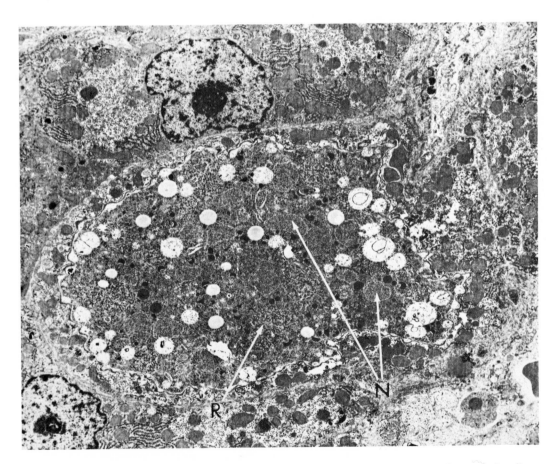

PLATE VII.—Midsection of a 7-day-old exoerythrocytic body of *Plasmodium cynomolgi* in rhesus monkey liver. The parasitized hepatic cell surrounds the EE body. A wavy outer membrane and a thin inner membrane enclose the EE body. Several areas of linear arranged ribosomes are seen (R). Nuclei (N) have a clear space surrounding them. (X 4600). Electron-photomicrograph courtesy of Dr. Thomas Sodeman.

their investigations so that we may learn more about the ultrastructure of this and other primate malaria EE bodies.

Course of Infection

Plasmodium cynomolgi is readily transmitted by a number of species of mosquitoes. In our studies, there was a total of 132 successful transmissions out of 136 attempts (Table 4). These transmissions were initiated by the inoculation of sporozoites, by mosquito bite, or by intravenous and/or intrahepatic injection. The prepatent periods ranged from 7 to 16 days with a mean of 9.8 days. In general, slightly shorter prepatent periods were obtained when large numbers of sporozoites were inoculated intravenously and/or intrahepatically than were obtained by mosquito bite.

The two strains of *P. cynomolgi* which have received the greatest attention are the Mulligan or M strain and the subspecies *bastianellii*

TABLE 4.—Summary of transmissions for seven strains of *Plasmodium cynomolgi* using six species of *Anopheles*.

Strain	Transmissions/Attempts						Total trans.	Prepatent Period (Days)	
	Fre*	Qua	Ste	Mac	Atr	Bal		Range	Mean
B†	10/10	23/23	1/1	44/47		8/8	86/89	7–16	9.8
M		2/2		4/4			6/6	8–11	10.0
Camb	2/2	1/1					3/3	9–13	11.0
Berok	1/1	6/6		2/2			9/9	8–12	9.7
Gombak	1/2	1/1	1/1	2/2		1/1	6/7	8–14	10.0
RO	2/2	11/11	1/1		1/1		15/15	8–12	9.4
C	3/3	1/1	1/1	2/2			7/7	8–16	10.7
Totals	19/20	45/45	4/4	54/57	1/1	9/9	132/136	7–16	9.8

* Fre = *Anopheles freeborni*, Qua = *A. quadrimaculatus*, Ste = *A. stephensi*, Mac = *A. maculatus*, Atr = *A. atroparvus*, Bal = *A. b. balabacensis*.

† B = Bastianellii strain, M = Mulligan strain, Camb = Cambodian strain, Berok = Berok strain, Gambok = Gambok strain, RO = Rossan strain, C = Ceylonensis strain.

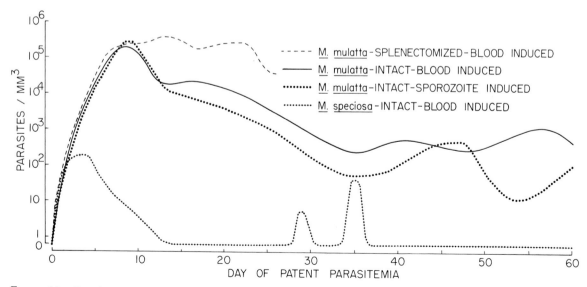

FIGURE 14.—Parasitemia curve for 1 *Macaca speciosa* and median parasitemia curves for 102 *M. mulatta* monkeys infected with the B strain of *Plasmodium cynomolgi*.

or the B strain. The histories of these two isolates were ably discussed by Eyles (1963).

Our efforts have been primarily directed towards study of the B strain, the results of which are shown in Figure 14. In 8 splenectomized *M. mulatta* monkeys infected by inoculation of parasitized blood, the median parasitemia reached a level of approximately 200,000 per mm³ by day 8, followed by rises to approximately 400,000 and 300,000 per mm³ on days 13 and 22, followed by a sudden drop in parasite levels. Maximum parasitemias as high as 1,200,000 were obtained in some animals during the 26 day observation period. In 44 intact *M. mulatta* monkeys similarly inoculated, the peak median parasitemia of approximately 200,000 per mm³ was obtained on day 8, also. However, in these animals, the parasitemia fell rapidly to a level of 18,000 per mm³ by day 13 and after several succeeding fluctuations, reached a level of approximately 500 per mm³ by day 60. In 50 intact *M. mulatta* monkeys, infected by inoculation of sporozoites, the peak median parasitemia was about the same as that encountered in the blood-induced infections. However, the parasitemia dropped to a lower level by day 35 (50 per mm³) followed by a rise in parasite level by day 47 and, then, by another drop in the parasitemia. The median parasite count

after 60 days was only 100 per mm³. The inoculation of one *M. speciosa* monkey resulted in a peak parasitemia of 200 per mm³, 4 days after inoculation. This was followed by a drop to an undetectable level. Two recrudescenses were observed 28 and 35 days after inoculation.

In order to examine the normal parasitemias of infections with both the M and the B strains, Dr. Leon Schmidt of the Southern Research Institute, Birmingham, Ala., supplied the data, from 174 *M. mulatta* monkeys, used in preparing Figures 15 through 19.

The B strain infections, induced by the inoculation of parasitized blood (Fig. 15), gave a mean peak parasitemia, by the 8th day of patency, of approximately 1,000 per 10,000 RBC. After the peak, the parasite level rapidly declined to approximately 80 per 10,000 RBC by day 12. This was followed by successive decreasing waves in the parasite count until day 45 when the parasitemia had fallen to 2.6 per 10,000 RBC. Thereafter, the parasitemia rose and was 10 per 10,000 RBC at the end of the 60 day observation period. In the monkeys infected by inoculation of sporozoites (Fig. 16), the peak mean parasitemia was again, on the 8th day of patency, at a level of approximately 700 per 10,000 RBC. The parasite level then declined rapidly to approxi-

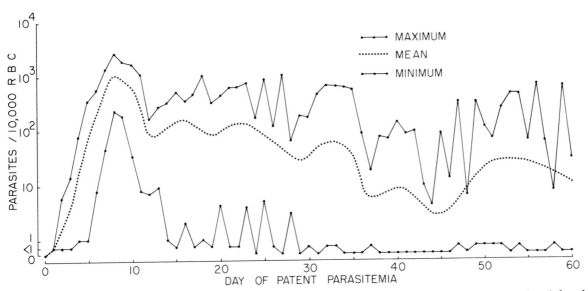

FIGURE 15.—Mean parasitemia curve, with minimum and maximum parasite counts, for 29 *Macaca mulatta* monkeys infected with B strain *Plasmodium cynomolgi* by the inoculation of parasitized blood. (Data courtesy Dr. Leon Schmidt).

mately 90 per 10,000 RBC on day 14. This was followed by a declining parasite count to a level of approximately 5 per 10,000 RBC by day 60.

The M strain infections, initiated by the inoculation of parasitized blood (Fig. 17) resulted in a peak mean parasitemia on day 9 with a count of approximately 600 per 10,000

RBC. The parasite level declined rapidly to a much lower level than encountered with the B strain, approximately 4 per 10,000 RBC by day 23. The mean parasitemia remained at this low level for the remainder of the 60-day observation period. In monkeys infected with the M strain, by sporozoite inoculation (Fig. 18), the peak mean parasitemia was on day 10

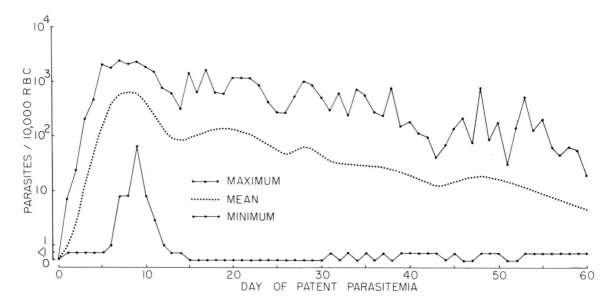

FIGURE 16.—Mean parasitemia curve, with minimum and maximum parasite counts, for 60 *Macaca mulatta* monkeys infected with B strain *Plasmodium cynomolgi* by inoculation of sporozoites. (Data courtesy Dr. Leon Schmidt).

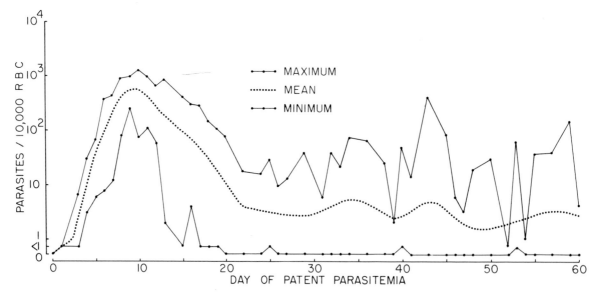

FIGURE 17.—Mean parasitemia curve and mimimum and maximum parasite counts for 25 *Macaca mulatta* monkeys infected with M strain *Plasmodium cynomolgi* by the inoculation of parasitized blood. (Data courtesy of Dr. Leon Schmidt).

at a level of approximately 500 per 10,000 RBC. The parasite level then declined to approximately 1.4 per 10,000 RBC by day 30. After a subsequent rise, the parasitemia eventually fell to approximately 1 per 10,000 RBC by day 60.

As shown in Figure 19, sporozoite-induced infections with the B strain peak slightly sooner than do those with the M strain parasite. The main difference between the 2 isolates lies in the subsequent parasite levels. After day 15, the B strain maintains a consistently higher level of parasitemia throughout the 60-day observation period. That this characteristic is attributable to this particular strain is evidenced by the fact that the same difference in the parasitemia occurred with animals infected by blood inoculation. Only in the period between day 35 and day 50, when the curve of the blood induced infections with the B strain dropped, was there a joining of the curves for the 2 strains. It appears clear that

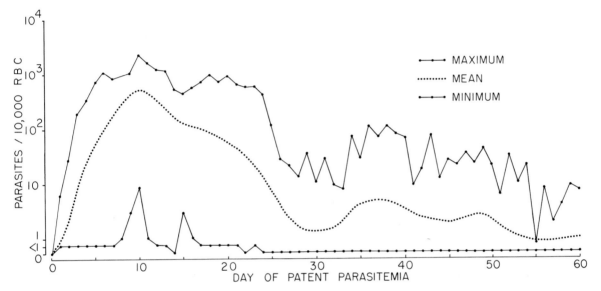

FIGURE 18.—Mean parasitemia curve and minimum and maximum parasite counts for 60 *Macaca mulatta* monkeys infected with M strain *Plasmodium cynomolgi* by inoculation of sporozoites. (Data courtesy of Dr. Leon Schmidt).

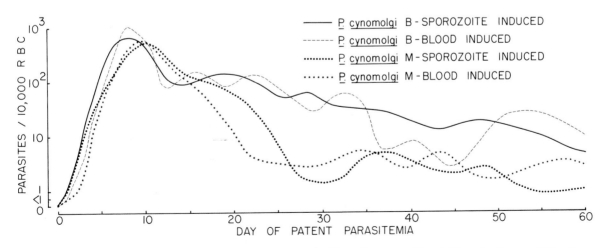

FIGURE 19.—Mean parasitemia curves for infections of B strain *Plasmodium cynomolgi* and M strain *P. cynomolgi* in *Macaca mulatta* monkeys.

the B strain parasitemias were consistently maintained at a higher level than were those of the M strain.

It has long been established that *P. cynomolgi* is a relapsing malaria in the true sense. In monkeys infected with the M strain, via mosquito bite, during a one-year period of observation, there were from 2 to 17 relapses (Fig. 20). In one monkey (T-445), the appearance of relapses was frequent and, in some ways, predictable; in another (T-495), relapses occurred only twice, 40 and 120 days after exposure to infection. The total number of relapses which an animal, such as T-445, is capable of having would appear to be large since there appeared to be little diminution in frequency of relapses at the end of the observation period.

We have been concerned for a long time about the most propitious time for feeding mosquitoes in order to obtain good infections. Studies have been carried out on both blood- and sporozoite-induced infections. The latter is the natural mode of infection and, for that reason, the results of one of the studies is presented in Figure 21. The initial feeding on day 5 of parasitemia (15 days after sporozoite inoculation) revealed that mosquito infection was already taking place. This continued through day 36 followed by 5 days in which mosquitoes failed to become infected. Subsequent mosquito infections appeared to be correlated with rises in the parasitemia (re-

lapses or recrudescenses of the infection). Of considerable interest was the presence of a pattern of every-other-day infectivity which persisted often for many days; for example, between days 26 and 37, days 42 and 63, and days 78 and 89. This pattern of infectivity to mosquitoes was also seen in similar studies with other *P. cynomolgi* infections. Since the highest level of infection was correlated with the predominance of very young trophozoite forms in the blood, it is postulated that the gametocytes mature at approximately the same time as the schizonts; and, that they are more infectious in this early period than 24 hours later. It appears that gametocytes lose their infectivity fairly rapidly. Whether this infectivity is subsequently restored is doubtful since a day of high level infectivity (for example day 34) may be followed by several days (in this case 7 days) of low level infectivity. Restoration of infectivity is associated with a rise in parasitemia. The infectivity to mosquitoes 113 days after exposure to infection, or, after 103 days of almost continuous patent parasitemia, indicates that infectivity can continue for an extended period of time with *P. cynomolgi* in *M. mulatta* monkeys.

In man. Up to 1960, the attitude among malariologists generally was: "Monkey malaria is for monkeys, and human malaria is for humans." That attitude took a shattering blow on 5 May 1960 when the senior author (GRC), on answering a telephone call from Dr. Don

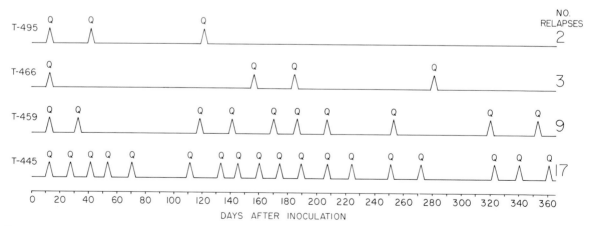

FIGURE 20.—Frequency of relapse activity in 4 *Macaca mulatta* monkeys infected with M strain of *Plasmodium cynomolgi* by the inoculation of sporozoites via the bites of *Anopheles maculatus* mosquitoes. (Drug regimen: 300 mgm. quinine x 5 days with each appearance of parasites).

E. Eyles, head of the Section on Cytology, Laboratory of Parasite Chemotherapy, NIH, in Memphis, Tennessee, heard him say, "Bob, I have monkey malaria." I was incredulous—had it really happened? The remainder of the conversation went about as follows:

GRC: If you have monkey malaria, don't take any drugs.

DEE: I thought you would say that so I took chloroquine before I placed this call to you.

GRC: I hope you drew blood for inoculation into a clean rhesus.

DEE: I did, and the blood has been given to the monkey. Now all we have to do is wait for the monkey to come down.

(It did—8 days later: Eyles *et al*, 1960).

This was the first recognized instance of a simian malaria infection transmitted to man by natural means and, therefore, what happened during the next two months was a prelude to the developments of the next 10 years.

Dr. Eyles' illness was due to an accidental infection in connection with the study of the effect of drugs on the exoerythrocytic stages of the B strain of *P. cynomolgi* (Eyles and Coatney, 1962). Because it was thought, "man could not be infected with monkey malaria" and because the object was to get sporozoites from as many mosquitoes as possible during a single day, Dr. Eyles and his technician (Mrs. N.C.O.) paid scant attention to the occasional mosquito that escaped into the room. Two days after Dr. Eyles recognized the cause of his illness, 7 May, the technician (N.C.O.) became ill with fever. Five ml. of her blood was given to a clean rhesus monkey; parasites were present 10 days later, and a normal infection ensued. On the same day, another 20 ml. of blood was drawn from N.C.O. and divided between two inmate volunteers. Each of the volunteers developed clinical malaria, but neither one had anything but minimal parasite counts.

At the time of the subinoculations, there was no proof that the parasite involved was *P. cynomolgi* and, if it were *P. cynomolgi*, that it was transferred by mosquito bite. To answer

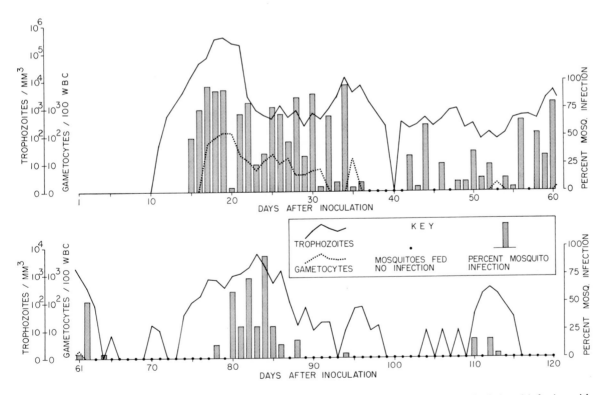

FIGURE 21.—The infectivity of *Anopheles quadrimaculatus* mosquitoes during the course of a sporozoite-induced infection with B strain *Plasmodium cynomolgi*, with its parasitemia curve, in a *Macaca mulatta* monkey.

these points, two staff members allowed mosquitoes (*A. freeborni*) infected with *P. cynomolgi* to bite them. H.A. became ill after 11 days but parasites could not be demonstrated. Blood was taken from him and injected into a clean monkey. The animal was positive for the infection 6 days later. The second man (C.S.S.), also bitten by infected *A. freeborni* mosquitoes, was positive for the infection 14 days later. It was thus proved that *P. cynomolgi* can be transmitted to man by mosquito bite. Surprisingly, almost at the same time, R.G. in Dr. Leon Schmidt's laboratory at the Christ Hospital, in Cincinnati, Ohio, came down with an accidental infection. The infecting parasite was again the B strain of *P. cynomolgi* (see Eyles *et al*, 1960; Schmidt *et al*, 1961).

After this rash of accidental infections, it was evident that mosquitoes infected with this parasite should be handled with the same respect accorded those infected with the human malarias. We did not expect further accidents, but in this we were mistaken. In mid-May, Dr. Schmidt sent mosquitoes infected with the B strain cynomolgi parasites to Dr. Clay Huff at the Naval Medical Research Institute in Bethesda, Maryland. Mrs. D.M., with wide experience in handling infected mosquitoes, took charge of them. On 4 July, she became ill with a high fever and was taken to a local hospital. On the second day following admission, when the attending physician was not sure of the diagnosis, D.M. suggested to him that she might have monkey malaria. The physician had never heard of monkey malaria, and, because she had a high fever, he assumed she was delirious. The patient was confident that she had simian malaria, a fact soon confirmed. Mrs. D.M. was transferred to the NIH Clinical Center where the infection was treated and the patient made an uneventful recovery.

Faced with this remarkable series of accidents so close together, one is moved to inquire as to why they occurred and why they had been absent previously. The explanation possibly lies with the fact that prior to 1959 work had been limited to the M strain, isolated by Mulligan in 1935, and maintained, generally by blood-inoculation, in widely scattered laboratories here and abroad. The M strain was transmitted to man with some difficulty (Coat-

ney *et al*, 1961, and Schmidt *et al*, 1961), and when initially successful, it produced a mild disease. The B strain, however, possibly due to its recent isolation, was more readily acceptable to the human host. Also, the vector may have played an important role. *Anopheles quadrimaculatus*, the old standby in this country, is a relatively poor vector, but *A. freeborni* is highly efficient. Interestingly enough, similar accidents have been few or absent during the last 10 years, probably due to more careful handling of infected mosquitoes.

This brace of accidents, coupled with the intentional natural infections in man, indicated a zoonosis of unknown proportions, but one which might have a profound effect on the emerging world-wide program of malaria eradication, toward which the U.S. was appropriating some 60 million dollars per annum. It was considered imperative that we have information on this subject without delay. To obtain such information, studies would have to be carried out in the area where *P. cynomolgi* is endemic, namely—Malaya.

The logical one to inaugurate these studies was Dr. Eyles. When offered the chance to carry out a study of simian malaria in depth, he accepted with enthusiasm. He arrived in Kuala Lumpur, Malaya on 17 August 1960 to head the Far East Research Unit (FERU), LPC, NIH, and to work cooperatively with personnel of the Malayan Institute of Medical Research (IMR). The productivity of Eyles and his coworkers was prodigious. Their work and that of the LPC workers in this country is the basis for this monograph.

With the knowledge that *P. cynomolgi* infects and produces disease in man, it was felt desirable to embark on a more intensive study involving both the M and B strains of the parasite, with special emphasis on parasitological and clinical aspects in man. As a result of this effort, three papers appeared in rapid succession: Beye *et al*, 1961, Schmidt *et al*, 1961, and Contacos *et al*, 1962. In addition, Schneider (1961) in France, and Garnham *et al* (1962) in England, reported less extensive studies with the B strain of *P. cynomolgi*.

The results of our effort which involved some 56 patients (34 B strain, 22 M strain) infected via mosquito bite (*A. freeborni* or *A.*

quadrimaculatus) or by the inoculation of para-sitized blood, can be summarized about as follows:

(1) Negroes are refractory to infection with this parasite as are some Caucasians.

(2) Monkey to man, man to man, and man to monkey transmission of the infection via mosquito bite is not only possible, but, at times, relatively easy to accomplish. The bite of a single infected mosquito resulted in a patent infection in one of 3 volunteers. The prepatent period was 19 days. The patient experienced 4 tertian fever cycles with a maximum temperature of 103° F. (Contacos and Coatney, 1963). Also, the same authors showed that the infection in a monkey (PT strain) brought directly from the field, in con-trast to the long laboratory-residence of the M strain and the 3 year laboratory-residence of the B strain, could be transferred to man by mosquito bite at the first attempt. The prepatent period was 20 days.

(3) The prepatent period with either strain is about 19 days, with a range of 15 to 20 days for the B strain and 16 to 37 days, with one exception of 82 days, for the M strain.

(4) The maximum parasitemia is somewhat higher with the M strain, about 300 parasites per mm³ as against 150 per mm³ for the B strain. (One M strain patient, infected by blood-inoculation, developed a parasite count of 8,300 per mm³.)

(5) There were no differences in the dura-tion of parasitemia in the 2 strains.

(6) The first fever appeared between 16 and 19 days.

(7) The maximum temperature was 105.2° F.

(8) Tertian fever patterns were not the rule but prominent in some patients.

Clinical symptoms in patients infected with either strain consisted of cephalgia, anorexia, myalgia, and nausea, in that order. The symptoms were usually present only during febrile episodes, were of moderate severity, and easily controlled by simple medications. The most prominent physical findings were splenomegaly and hepatomegaly.

We have produced infections in many vol-unteers with *P. cynomolgi* and from them we have selected 29 B strain infections (13 spo-rozoite- and 16 blood-induced) (Fig. 22), and 26 M strain infections (11 sporozoite- and 15 blood-induced) (Fig. 23), none of which re-ceived treatment, whose parasite counts were known for the first 50 days (an arbitrary cutoff point) of their infection. Perusal of these figures will show that the parasitologic picture coincides with what was described earlier. The clinical manifestations in these patients were in the same vein.

Schneider (loc. cit.) had 3 patients, one infected by sporozoites and the other 2 by the inoculation of parasitized blood. He reported mild fever episodes, none higher than 100° F, accompanied by very low parasitemias.

The following year, Garnham *et al* (loc. cit.)

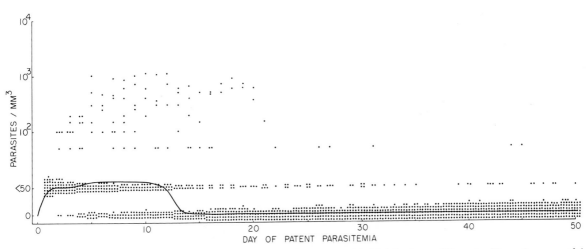

FIGURE 22.—Individual parasite counts and median parasitemia curve for 29 infections of B strain *Plasmodium cynomolgi* in man (13 sporozoite- and 16 blood-induced).

reported on sporozoite-induced infections in 14 patients (8 by mosquito bites and 6 by intravenous injections of sporozoites). The maximum temperature recorded was 104° F. The earliest prepatent period was 11 days and the average incubation period was 13 days. The infections exhibited the typical behavior of relatively severe symptoms with low parasitemias. All the infections were treated early, but there is little doubt that had they been allowed to continue, they would have exhibited the usual pattern of the untreated infection.

These studies of the early sixties convinced the most skeptical that *P. cynomolgi* was a zoonosis of unknown potential. In fact, the senior author had gone so far as to predict that *P. cynomolgi* would be the first field-acquired simian malaria in man; it was not to be (see Chapter 26).

Later attempts to infect man with *P. cynomolgi* experimentally embrace work in 2 different areas of the Orient. Dissanaike *et al* (1965) gave blood parasitized with *P. cynomolgi ceylonensis* (= our strain C) to each of 4 patients; 2 other patients were bitten by heavily infected *A. atroparvus* mosquitoes. (The primate host was not given.) None of these patients became infected. The length of the observation period was not given. In the same year, Dissanaike (1965) reported giving parasitized blood to 4 other patients; 2 received *P. cynomolgi* and *P. shortti* (= our OS strain *P. inui*) and the other

2 got *P. cynomolgi ceylonensis* (= our C strain) and *P. fragile*. None of the patients evidenced infection during an observation period of 30 days. Here, and probably in the earlier cases, too, the observation period was only 30 days. It is not unlikely that a longer period of observation would have turned up an infection in some of the recipients.

Bennett and Warren (1965) using a strain of *P. cynomolgi* isolated from an *M. irus* monkey taken in Cambodia found it infective to man via the bites of *A. maculatus* mosquitoes. The prepatent period was 21 days. In 1970, Cheong and Coombs transmitted *P. cynomolgi* to man by mosquito bite.

In our own studies we have transmitted the Gombak strain to one of 2 men exposed on one occasion, the prepatent period was 52 days; and the Smithsonian to each of two men, the prepatent periods were 25 and 26 days, respectively.

Host Specificity

Plasmodium cynomolgi naturally infects *Macaca irus* (= *fascicularis*), *M. nemestrina* (Eyles *et al*, 1962), *M. radiata* (Prakash and Chakrabarti, 1962), *M. cyclopis* (Inoki *et al*, 1951), *M. sinica* (Dissanaike, 1963), *M. mulatta* (Schmidt personal communication), *Presbytis cristatus* (Eyles *et al*, 1962a), and *P. entellus* (Dissanaike *et al*, 1965).

Experimentally, infections have been ob-

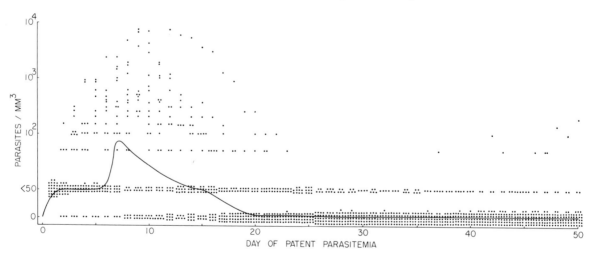

FIGURE 23.—Individual parasite counts and median parasitemia curve for 26 infections of M strain *Plasmodium cynomolgi* in man (11 sporozoite- and 15 blood-induced).

tained in *M. mulatta*, *Cercopithecus aethiops* (Huff and Coulston, 1944), *Cebus capucinus* (Garnham, 1959), *Papio papio* (Garnham, 1959), and in man (Eyles *et al*, 1960; and others).

Plasmodium cynomolgi is considered to be an oligoxenous parasite since it is infective to and transmitted by a wide variety of coindigenous and exotic species of mosquitoes. Because of this, it has been used extensively in experimental studies. In Table 5, we have listed those anopheline mosquitoes which have been tested for their susceptibility to infection with this parasite. In addition, *Mansonia uniformis*

TABLE 5.—Anopheline mosquitoes tested for susceptibility to infection with *Plasmodium cynomolgi* and those shown to be vectors experimentally.

Mosquito species	Level of susceptibility	Transmission	References
Anopheles annularis	High	−	Mulligan, 1935
A. annularis	Moderate	−	Ind. Res. Fund. As., 1947
A. aconitus	Low	−	Warren *et al*, 1963
A. aconitus	Low	−	Bennett *et al*, 1966
A. albimanus	Low	+	Eyles, 1960b
A. albimanus	Low	−	Omar, 1968
A. albimanus	Low	−	Omar, 1968a
A. argyropus	Low	−	Bennett *et al*, 1966
A. aztecus	High	−	Garnham and Lainson, 1957
A. aztecus	High	+	Garnham, 1959
A. aztecus	High	−	Dissanaike *et al*, 1965
A. atroparvus	Refractory	−	Mayer, 1908
A. atroparvus	Unknown	−	Weyer, 1937
A. atroparvus	High	−	Rodhain and van Hoff, 1940
A. atroparvus	High	+	Hawking *et al*, 1948
A. atroparvus	High	+	Shortt and Garnham, 1948
A. atroparvus	High	+	Collins *et al*, 1965
A. atroparvus	High	+	Dissanaike *et al*, 1965
A. atroparvus	High	−	Omar, 1968
A.b. balabacensis	High	+	Collins, 1969
A.b. introlatus	Moderate	+	Bennett *et al*, 1966
A.b. introlatus	Low	−	Warren *et al*, 1963
A. barbirostris	High	−	Ind. Res. Fund. As., 1947
A. barbirostris	Refractory	−	Warren *et al*, 1963
A. barbirostris	Low	−	Warren and Wharton, 1963
A. barbirostris	Moderate	−	Bennett *et al*, 1966
A. baezai	Refractory	−	Warren *et al*, 1963
A. baezai	Refractory	−	Bennett *et al*, 1966
A. campestris	Moderate	−	Bennett *et al*, 1966
A. campestris	Low	−	Warren *et al*, 1963
A. crawfordi	Low	−	Warren *et al*, 1963
A. crawfordi	Low	−	Bennett *et al*, 1966
A. culicifacies	High	−	Mulligan, 1935
A. culicifacies	Moderate	−	Ind. Res. Fund. As., 1947

TABLE 6.—Comparative infectivity of *Plasmodium cynomolgi* to 23 species of anophelines.

Mosq. species comparison*	Number tests	Number of mosquitoes		Percent infection		GII** ratios
		Standard	Other	Standard	Other	
Mac						100
Mac : Bal	30	225	190	81.8	81.1	148.7
Mac : F–1	58	405	365	80.5	83.6	116.6
Mac : St–1	28	316	269	49.4	68.8	102.8
Mac : Sun	11	102	89	92.2	75.3	100.1
Mac : Q–1	56	489	515	65.6	58.8	78.2
Mac : Koc	15	257	92	84.4	79.3	76.2
Mac : Bar	14	137	111	91.2	22.5	35.3
Mac : Les	6	59	62	84.7	54.8	27.8
Mac : Phi	10	123	70	74.0	75.7	21.5
Mac : Vag	22	263	168	83.3	46.4	17.0
Mac : Hod	3	49	9	65.3	11.0	9.9
Mac : Let	14	150	208	79.3	47.6	8.7
Mac : Sep	3	34	14	50.0	14.3	5.0
Mac : Sin	10	107	56	95.3	32.1	4.6
Mac : Atr	7	90	29	81.1	44.8	4.4
Mac : Cam	3	22	10	100.0	30.0	1.7
Mac : Ped	12	158	166	72.8	4.2	0.8
Mac : Umb	3	11	79	100.0	29.1	0.8
Mac : Arg	7	75	126	100.0	11.5	0.6
Mac : Alb	18	204	313	71.6	3.2	0.3
Mac : Don	10	107	71	83.2	12.7	0.2
Mac : Rop	2	15	12	100.0	8.3	0.1

* Mac = *A. maculatus*, Bal = *A. b. balabacensis*, F–1 = *A. freeborni*, St–1 = *A. stephensi*, Sun = *A. sundaicus*, Q–1 = *A. quadrimaculatus*, Koc = *A. kochi*, Bar = *A. barbirostris*, Les = *A. lesteri*, Phi = *A. philippinensis*, Vag = *A. vagus*, Hod = *A. hodgkini*, Let = *A. letifer*, Sep = *A. separatus*, Sin = *A. sinensis*, Atr = *A. atroparvus*, Cam = *A. campestris*, Ped = *A. peditaeniatus*, Umb = *A. umbrosus*, Arg = *A. argyropus*, Alb = *A. albimanus*, Don = *A. donaldi*, Rop = *A. roperi*.

** GII = Gut Infection Index = average number of oocysts per 100 guts; the GII ratio is the relationship of the GII of *A. maculatus* to another species where the GII of *A. maculatus* = 100.

has been experimentally infected with several strains of *P. cynomolgi* (Warren *et al*, 1962). Both oocyst and sporozoite infections were demonstrated but no transmissions were obtained (Warren and Wharton, 1963; Bennett *et al*, 1966). *Culex vishnui* (Mulligan, 1935), *C. tritaeniorhynchus* (Warren and Wharton, 1963) and *Aedes butleri* (Warren and Wharton, 1963; Bennett *et al*, 1966) have been reported susceptible to infection as far as the oocyst stage only.

In our own studies, 23 species of anophelines have been compared for susceptibility to infection with *P. cynomolgi* (Table 6). The most readily infected was *A. b. balabacensis* and the least susceptible was *A. roperi*.

Immunity and Antigenic Relationships

Mulligan and Sinton (1933) demonstrated that immunity produced by a given strain of the parasite in monkeys appears to be specific mainly for the same strain. There was some evidence, however, to suggest a slight degree of common immunity. Chronic infections with *P. cynomolgi* conferred effective immunity against the clinical effects of superinfection with the same strain of parasite. They were unable, however, to demonstrate any cross-immunity between infections due to *P. knowlesi* and *P. cynomolgi*. Singh and Singh (1940) found that chronic infections due to *P. cynomolgi* and *P. inui* failed to prevent, or modify, the course of infection with heterologous parasites. It was also shown that *P. cynomolgi* produces an immunity to homologous superinfection which remains effective for at least 18 months.

In 1966, Voller *et al* reported on cross-immunity studies with a number of species of monkey malaria. They demonstrated that infections with *P. cynomolgi bastianellii* and *P. cynomolgi ceylonensis* produced no cross-immunity either to each other or to *P. knowlesi*, *P. coatneyi*, *P. fragile*, *P. inui*, *P. inui shortti*, and *P. gonderi*. In a later extensive immunological study, Voller and Rossan (1969, 1969a, 1969b) demonstrated that *M. mulatta* monkeys with chronic infections due to *P. knowlesi* were still susceptible to infection with *P. cynomolgi bastianellii*. Animals with chronic infections with *P. cynomolgi bastianellii* were immune to challenge with the homologous parasite and to a high degree to *P. cynomolgi ceylonensis*. In contrast, monkeys with chronic infections of *P. cynomolgi bastianellii* produced severe infections when challenged with *P. cynomolgi ceylonensis*. Their studies also indicated that parasite populations isolated from a late relapse of *P. cynomolgi* were immunologically different from those isolated from the primary infection and from an early relapse. They concluded that these variants arose from different antigenic variants released from the liver.

The first observations on the serologic cross reactions between *P. cynomolgi* and *P. vivax* were made, using the fluorescent antibody test, by Tobie and Coatney (1961) and Tobie *et al* (1962). They found that when antisera to *P. cynomolgi* from human volunteers was allowed to react with the homologous and heterologous parasites, considerable cross reaction was obtained. They noted, however, that the maximum antibody titers were obtained with the homologous parasite. Voller (1962) demonstrated a strong IFA cross reaction between *P. bastianellii* (= *P. cynomolgi bastianellii*) and *P. vivax*, *P. gonderi*, and *P. osmaniae* (= *P. inui shortti*). Subsequent studies indicated that antisera to *P. falciparum*, *P. malariae*, and *P. ovale* would also cross react with the *P. cynomolgi* antigen (Kuvin and Voller, 1963; Collins *et al*, 1966a; Meuwissen, 1968).

In our studies (Collins *et al*, 1966), antisera to *P. cynomolgi* gave a fluorescent antibody cross reaction at a high level to *P. fieldi* antigen (mean reciprocal titer ratio of 100:76) and lesser reactions to *P. knowlesi*, *P. gonderi*, and *P. brasilianum* (mean reciprocal titer ratios of 100 : 54, 100 : 36, and 100 : 31, respectively). In the reverse procedure, *P. cynomolgi* antigen gave the highest cross reaction to *P. inui*, *P. knowlesi*, *P. fragile*, and *P. fieldi* (mean reciprocal titer ratios of 100 : 46, 100 : 41, 100 : 33, and 100 : 31, respectively).

El-Nahal (1967), using the exoerythrocytic stages of *P. cynomolgi* as antigen in a fluorescent antibody test, showed that whereas the homologous antisera responded well, the heterologous antisera to *P. inui* and *P. malariae* failed to respond.

REFERENCES

ANGELINI, G., 1947. Incertezza dei reperti di "forme esoeritrocitiche" dei plasmodi della malaria umana nel midollo osseo. Riv. di Parassit. *8* : 5–18.

BANO, L., 1959. A cytological study of the early oocysts of seven species of *Plasmodium* and the occurrence of post-zygotic meiosis. Parasitology. *49* : 559–585.

BENNETT, G. F. and WARREN, McW., 1965. Transmission of a new strain of *Plasmodium cynomolgi* to man. J. Parasit. *51* : 79–80.

BENNETT, G. F., WARREN, McW., and CHEONG, W. H., 1966. Biology of the simian malarias of Southeast Asia. II. The susceptibility of some Malaysian mosquitoes to infection with five strains of *Plasmodium cynomolgi*. J. Parasit. *52* : 625–631.

BENNETT, G. F., WARREN, McW., and CHEONG, W. H., 1966a. Biology of the simian malarias of Southeast

Asia. III. Sporogony of the Cambodian strain of *Plasmodium cynomolgi*. J. Parasit. *52* : 632–638.

BENNETT, G. F., WARREN, McW., and CHEONG, W. H., 1966b. Biology of the simian malarias of Southeast Asia. IV. Sporogony of four strains of *Plasmodium cynomolgi*. J. Parasit. *52* : 639–646.

BEYE, H. K., GETZ, M. E., COATNEY, G. R., ELDER, H. A., and EYLES, D. E., 1961. Simian malaria in man. Am. J. Trop. Med. & Hyg. *10* : 311–316.

BRAY, R. S., 1957. Studies on the exo-erythrocytic cycle in the genus *Plasmodium*. London School of Hyg. & Trop. Med. Memoir 12. H. K. Lewis & Co. Ltd. London.

BRAY, R. S., 1963. Malaria infections in primates and their importance to man. Ergebnisse Mikrobiol. Immunitätsf. u. Exp. Therapie *36* : 168–213.

BRAY, R. S. and GARNHAM, P. C. C., 1964. *Anopheles* as

REFERENCES—Continued

vectors of animal malaria parasites. Bull. Wld. Hlth. Org. *31* : 143–147.

CHEONG, W. H. and COOMBS, G. L., 1970. Transmission of *Plasmodium cynomolgi* (Perlis strain) to man. Se. Asian J. Trop. Med. Pub. Hlth. *1* : 302.

CHOUDHURY, D. S., MOHAN, B. N., PRAKASH, S., and RAMAKRISHNAN, S. P., 1963. Experimental susceptibility of anopheline mosquitoes to simian malaria in the Nilgiris, Madras state, South India. Ind. J. Malariol. *17* : 237–242.

CHOUDHURY, D. S., WATTAL, B. L., and RAMAKRISHNAN, S. P., 1963a. Incrimination of *Anopheles elegans* James (1903) as a natural vector of simian malaria in the Niligiris, Madras state, India. Ind. J. Malariol. *17* : 243–247.

COATNEY, G. R., ELDER, H. A., CONTACOS, P. G., GETZ, M. E., GREENLAND, R., ROSSAN, R. N., and SCHMIDT, L. H., 1961. Transmission of the M strain of *Plasmodium cynomolgi* to man. Am. J. Trop. Med. & Hyg. *10* : 673–678.

COGGESHALL, L. T., 1941. Infection of *Anopheles quadri-maculatus* with *Plasmodium cynomolgi*, a monkey malaria parasite, and with *Plasmodium lophurae*, an avian malaria parasite. Am. J. Trop. Med. *21* : 525–530.

COLLINS, W. E., 1969. Some observations on the transmission of simian malaria. Proc. New Jersey Mosq. Extermination Assoc. *56* : 152–158.

CONTACOS, P. G., ELDER, H. A., COATNEY, G. R., and GENTHER, C., 1962. Man to man transfer of two strains of *Plasmodium cynomolgi* by mosquito bite. Am. J. Trop. Med. & Hyg. *11* : 186–193.

COLLINS, W. E., JONES, F. E., and DOBROVOLNY, C. G., 1965. Transmission of the RO strain of *Plasmodium cynomolgi* by *A. stephensi*, *A. quadrimaculatus* and *A. labranchiae atroparvus*. Mosq. News *25* : 389–392.

COLLINS, W. E., SKINNER, J. C., and GUINN, E. G., 1966. Antigenic variations in the plasmodia of certain primates as detected by immuno-fluorescence. Am. J. Trop. Med. & Hyg. *15* : 483–485.

COLLINS, W. E., JEFFERY, G. M., GUINN, E. G., and SKINNER, J. C., 1966a. Fluorescent antibody studies in human malaria. IV. Cross-reactions between human and simian malaria. Am. J. Trop. Med. & Hyg. *15* : 11–15.

CONTACOS, P. G. and COATNEY, G. R., 1963. Experimental adaptation of simian malarias to abnormal hosts. J. Parasit. 49 : 912–918.

COOPER, W. C., RUHE, D. S., and COATNEY, G. R., 1949. Studies in Human Malaria. XVI. Results of massive subinoculation during latency from patients infected with St. Elizabeth strain vivax malaria. Am. J. Hyg. *50* : 189–193.

COULSTON, F., 1949. Exoerythrocytic stages of *Plasmodium cynomolgi* in the *Macaca mulatta*. Proc. Soc. Exper. Biol. & Med. *70* : 360–364.

DISSANAIKE, A. S., 1963. *Plasmodium* infection in Ceylon monkeys. Trans. Roy. Soc. Trop. Med. & Hyg. *57* : 488–489.

DISSANAIKE, A. S., NELSON, P., and GARNHAM, P. C. C., 1965. Two new malaria parasites, *Plasmodium cynomolgi ceylonensis* subsp. nov. and *Plasmodium fragile* sp. nov., from monkeys in Ceylon. Ceylon J. Med. Sci. (D) *14* : 1–9.

DISSANAIKE, A. S., 1965. Simian malaria parasites of Ceylon. Bull. Wld. Hlth. Org. *32* : 593–597.

EL-NAHAL, H. M. S., 1967. Study of serological cross-reactions of exoerythrocytic schizonts of avian, rodent and primate malaria parasites by the fluorescent antibody technique. Bull. Wld. Hlth. Org. *37* : 154–158.

EYLES, D. E., 1960. *Anopheles freeborni* and *Anopheles quadrimaculatus* as experimental vectors of *Plasmodium cynomolgi* and *P. inui*. J. Parasit. 46 : 540.

EYLES, D. E., 1960a. The exoerythrocytic cycle of *Plasmodium cynomolgi* and *P. cynomolgi bastianellii* in the rhesus monkey. Am. J. Trop. Med. & Hyg. *9* : 543–555.

EYLES, D. E., 1960b. Susceptibility of *Anopheles albimanus* to primate and avian malarias. Mosq. News 20 : 368–371.

EYLES, D. E., COATNEY, G. R., and GETZ, M. E., 1960. Vivax-type parasite of macaques transmissible to man. Science *132* : 1812–1813.

EYLES, D. E., 1963. The species of simian malaria: taxonomy, morphology, life cycle, and geographical distribution of the monkey species. J. Parasit. *49* : 866–887.

EYLES, D. E. and COATNEY, G. R., 1962. Effect of certain drugs on exoerythrocytic parasites of *Plasmodium cynomolgi*. Am. J. Trop. Med. & Hyg. *11* : 175–185.

EYLES, D. E., LAING, A. B. G., and DOBROVOLNY, C. G., 1962. The malaria parasites of the pig-tailed macaque, *Macaca nemestrina nemestrina* (Linnaeus), in Malaya. Ind. J. Malariol. *16* : 285–298.

EYLES, D. E., LAING, A. B. G., WARREN, McW., and SANDOSHAM, A. A., 1962a. Malaria parasites of Malayan leaf monkeys of the genus *Presbytis*. Med. J. Malaya *17* : 85–86.

EYLES, D. E., WARREN, McW., GUINN, E., WHARTON, R. H., and RAMACHANDRAN, C. P., 1963. Identification of *Anopheles balabacensis introlatus* as a vector of monkey malaria in Malaya. Bull. Wld. Hlth. Org. *28* : 134–135.

FAIRLEY, N. H. *et al*, 1945. Chemotherapeutic suppression and prophylaxis in malaria. Trans. Roy. Soc. Trop. Med. & Hyg. *38* : 311–366.

FAIRLEY, N. H. *et al*, 1947. Sidelights on malaria in man obtained by subinoculation experiments. Trans. Roy. Soc. Trop. Med. & Hyg. *40* : 621–676.

FREYVOGEL, T. A., 1966. Shape, movement *in situ* and locomotion of plasmodial ookinetes. Acta Tropica *23* : 201–222.

GARNHAM, P. C. C., 1959. A new sub-species of *Plasmodium cynomolgi*. Riv. di Parassit. *20* : 273–278.

GARNHAM, P. C. C. and LAINSON, R., 1957. *Anopheles aztecus* as a highly efficient vector of malaria parasites. Trans. Roy. Soc. Trop. Med. & Hyg. *51* : 6.

GARNHAM, P. C. C., MOLINARI, V., and SHUTE, P. G., 1962. Differential diagnosis of bastianellii and vivax malaria. Bull. Wld. Hlth. Org. *27* : 199–202.

GARNHAM, P. C. C., BIRD, R. G., and BAKER, J. R., 1963. Electron microscope studies of motile stages of malaria. IV. The fine structure of the sporozoite of four species of *Plasmodium*. Trans. Roy. Soc. Trop. Med. & Hyg. *57* : 27–31.

REFERENCES—Continued

GARNHAM, P. C. C., 1966. Malaria parasites and other haemosporidia. Blackwell Scientific Publications. Oxford. pp. 1114.

GREEN, R., 1932. A malaria parasite of Malayan monkeys and its development in anopheline mosquitoes. Trans. Roy. Soc. Trop. Med. & Hyg. 25 : 455–477.

HALBERSTAEDTER, L. and PROWZEK, S., 1907. Untersuchungen über die malariaparasiten der affen. Arb. K. Gesundh. -Amte (Berl.) 26 : 37–43.

HAWKING, F., PERRY, W. L. M., and THURSTON, J. P., 1948. Tissue forms of a malaria parasite, Plasmodium cynomolgi. Lancet 1 : 783–789.

HAWKING, F., WORMS, M. J., GAMMAGE, K., and GODDARD, P. A., 1966. The biological purpose of the blood-cycle of the malaria parasite Plasmodium cynomolgi. Lancet 2 : 422–424.

HAWKING, F., WORMS, M. J., and GAMMAGE, K., 1968. 24- and 48-hour cycles of malaria parasites in the blood; their purpose, production and control. Trans. Roy. Soc. Trop. Med. & Hyg. 62 : 731–760.

HSIEH, H. C., 1960. Malaria parasites of the Taiwan monkey. Formosan Science 14 : 477–487.

HUFF, C. G. and COULSTON, F., 1944. The development of P. gallinaceum from sporozoite to erythrocytic trophozoite. J. Infect. Dis. 75 : 231–249.

HUFF, C. G., 1947. Life cycle of malarial parasites. Ann. Rev. Microbiol. 1 : 43–60.

HUFF, C. G. and COULSTON, F., 1948. A search for pre-erythrocytic stages of Plasmodium vivax and P. cynomolgi. J. Parasit. 34 : 264–274.

Indian Research Fund Assoc., 1947. Report of the scientific advisory board for 1st January to the 31st December, 1946. 9–14.

INOKI, S., TAKEMURA, S., MAKIURA, Y., and HOTTA, F., 1942. A malaria parasite, Plasmodium inui var. cyclopis Inoki, Takemura, Makiura, and Hotta 1941 in Macaca cyclopis Swinhoe. (Japanese text). Osaka Igakkai Zassi 41 : 1327–1343. (NS).

INOKI, S., 1951. Studies on the exoerythrocytic schizogony of the malaria parasite. Exoerythrocytic forms of the Formosan monkey malaria parasite, Plasmodium inui var. cyclopis. Med. J. Osaka Univ. 2 : 45–53.

INOKI, S., OKUNO, Y., and AOYAMA, A., 1951. On the length of the asexual life cycle of Plasmodium inui var. cyclopis. Med. J. Osaka Univ. 2 : 37–43.

KUVIN, S. F. and VOLLER, A., 1963. Malarial antibody titres in West Africans in Britain. Brit. Med. Jour. 2 : 477–479.

MAYER, M. 1907. Ueber malaria beim affen. Med. Klin, Berl. 3 : 579–580.

MAYER, M., 1908. Über malariaparasiten bei affen. Arch. f. Protist. 12 : 314–321.

MEUWISSEN, J. H. E. TH., 1968. Antibody responses of patients with natural malaria to human and simian Plasmodium antigens measured by the fluorescent antibody test. Trop. georg. Med. 20 : 137–140.

MULLIGAN, H. W. and SINTON, J. A., 1933. Studies in immunity in malaria. II. Superinfection with various strains of monkey malarial parasites. Rec. Mal. Surv. India 3 : 529–568.

MULLIGAN, H. W., 1935. Descriptions of two species of monkey plasmodium isolated from Silenus irus. Arch. f. Protist. 84 : 285–314.

OMAR, M. S., 1968. Die empfänglichkeit verschiedener Anopheles-Arten für den erreger der affenmalaria Plasmodium cynomolgi bastianellii. Zschr. Tropenmed. Parasit. 19 : 152–170.

OMAR, M. S., 1968a. Vergleichende beobachtungen über die entwicklung von Plasmodium cynomolgi bastianellii im Anopheles stephensi und Anopheles albimanus. Zschr. Tropenmed. Parasit. 19 : 370–389.

PRAKASH, S. and CHAKRABARTI, S. C., 1962. The isolation and description of Plasmodium cynomolgi (Mayer, 1907) and Plasmodium inui (Halberstadter and Prowazek, 1907) from naturally occurring mixed infections in Macaca radiata radiata monkeys of the Nilgiris, Madras state, India. Ind. J. Malariol. 16 : 303–311.

RAMAKRISHNAN, S. P. and MOHAN, B. N., 1962. An enzootic focus of simian malaria in Macaca radiata radiata Geoffroy of Nilgiris, Madras state, India. Ind. J. Malariol. 16 : 87–94.

RODHAIN, J. and VAN HOFF, T., 1940. Contribution à l'étude des Plasmodium des singes africains. Le comportement différent des Pl. gonderi et Pl. kochi chez les moustiques. Bull. Soc. Path. Exot. 33 : 107–113.

ROSSAN, R. N., FISHER, K. F., GREENLAND, R. D., GENTHER, C. S., and SCHMIDT, L. H., 1964. The localization of infective pre-erythrocytic forms of Plasmodium cynomolgi. Trans. Roy. Soc. Trop. Med. & Hyg. 58 : 159–163.

SCHMIDT, L. H., FRADKIN, R., SQUIRES, W., and GENTHER, C. S., 1948. Malaria chemotherapy: II. The response of sporozoite-induced infections with Plasmodium cynomolgi to various antimalarial drugs. Fed. Proc. 7 : 253–254.

SCHMIDT, L. H., GREENLAND, R., and GENTHER, C. S., 1961. The transmission of Plasmodium cynomolgi to man. Am. J. Trop. Med. & Hyg. 10 : 679–688.

SCHMIDT, L. H., GREENLAND, R., ROSSAN, R., and GENTHER, C., 1961a. Natural occurrence of malaria in rhesus monkeys. Science 133 : 753.

SCHMIDT, L. H., ROSSAN, R. N., and FISHER, K. F., 1963. The activity of a repository form of 4,6-Diamino-1-(p-chlorophenyl)-1,2-dihydro-2,2-dimethyl-s-triazine against infections with Plasmodium cynomolgi. Am. J. Trop. Med. & Hyg. 12 : 494–503.

SCHMIDT, L. H., ROSSAN, R. N., FRADKIN, R., WOODS, J., SCHULEMANN, W., and KRATZ, L., 1966. Studies on the antimalarial activity of 1,2-Dimethoxy-4-(bis-diethylaminoethyl)-amino-5-bromobenzene. Bull. Wld. Hlth. Org. 34 : 783–788.

SCHMIDT, L. H., HARRISON, J., ELLISON, R., and WORCESTER, P., 1970. The activities of chlorinated lincomycin derivatives against infections with Plasmodium cynomolgi in Macaca mulatta. Am. J. Trop. Med. & Hyg. 19 : 1–11.

SCHNEIDER, J., 1961. P. cynomolgi bastianelli: Hématozoaire du singe transmissible à l'homme. Essai d'impaludation thérapeutique. Bull. Soc. Path. Exot. 54 : 7–11.

SHORTT, H. E., 1948. The pre-erythrocytic cycle of

REFERENCES—Continued

Plasmodium cynomolgi. 4th Int. Cong. Trop. Med. & Malaria *1* : 607–617.

SHORTT, H. E. and GARNHAM, P. C. C., 1948. Pre-erythrocytic stage in mammalian malaria parasites. Nature *161* : 126.

SHORTT, H. E. and GARNHAM, P. C. C., 1948a. The pre-erythrocytic development of *Plasmodium cynomolgi* and *Plasmodium vivax.* Trans. Roy. Soc. Trop. Med. & Hyg. *41* : 785–795.

SHORTT, H. E. and GARNHAM, P. C. C., 1948b. Demonstration of a persisting exo-erythrocytic cycle in *Plasmodium cynomolgi* and its bearing on the production of relapses. Brit. Med. Jour. *1* : 1225–1228.

SHORTT, H. E., GARNHAM, P. C. C., and MALAMOS, B., 1948. The pre-erythrocytic stage of mammalian malaria. Brit. Med. Jour. *1* : 192–194.

SHORTT, H. E., BRAY, R. S., and COOPER, W., 1954. Further notes on the tissue stages of *Plasmodium cynomolgi.* Trans. Roy. Soc. Trop. Med. & Hyg. *48* : 122–131.

SINGH, J. and SINGH, H., 1940. Observations on immunity in monkey malaria as evidenced by the results of super-infections. J. Malar. Inst. Ind. *3* : 99–114.

SODEMAN, T., SCHNITZER, B., CONTACOS, P. G., and DURKEE, T., 1970. The fine structure of the exoerythrocytic stage of *Plasmodium cynomolgi.* Science. *170* : 340–341.

THAYER, W. S., 1897. Lectures on the malarial fevers. D. Appleton & Co., New York, pp. 326.

TOBIE, J. E. and COATNEY, G. R., 1961. Fluorescent antibody staining of human malaria parasites. Exp. Parasit. *11* : 128–132.

TOBIE, J. E., KUVIN, S. F., CONTACOS, P. G., COATNEY, G. R., and EVANS, C. B., 1962. Fluorescent antibody studies on cross reactions between human and simian malaria in normal volunteers. Am. J. Trop. Med. & Hyg. *11* : 589–596.

VOLLER, A., 1962. Fluorescent antibody studies on ma-laria parasites. Bull. Wld. Hlth. Org. *27* : 283–287.

VOLLER, A., GARNHAM, P. C. C., and TARGETT, G. A. T., 1966. Cross immunity in monkey malaria. J. Trop. Med. Hyg. *69* : 121–123.

VOLLER, A. and ROSSAN, R. N., 1969. Immunological studies with simian malarias. I. Antigenic variants of *Plasmodium cynomolgi bastianellii* Trans. Roy. Soc. Trop. Med. & Hyg. *63* : 45–56.

VOLLER, A. and ROSSAN, R. N., 1969a. Immunological studies with simian malarias. II. Heterologous immunity in the "*cynomolgi*" group. Trans. Roy. Soc. Trop. Med. & Hyg. *63* : 57–63.

VOLLER, A. and ROSSAN, R. N., 1969b. Immunological studies on simian malaria parasites. IV. Heterologous superinfection of monkeys with chronic *Plasmodium knowlesi* infections. Trans. Roy. Soc. Trop. Med. & Hyg. *63* : 837–845.

WARREN, McW., EYLES, D. E., and WHARTON, R. H., 1962. Primate malaria infections in *Mansonia uniformis.* Mosq. News *22* : 303–304.

WARREN, McW., EYLES, D. E., WHARTON, R. H., and OW YANG CHEE KONG, 1963. The susceptibility of Malayan anophelines to *Plasmodium cynomolgi bastianellii.* Ind. J. Malariol. *17* : 85–105.

WARREN, McW. and WHARTON, R. H., 1963. The vectors of simian malaria: identity, biology, and geographical distribution. J. Parasit. *49* : 892–904.

WEYER, F., 1937. Versuche zur Übertragung der affen-malaria durch stechmücken. Arch. f. Schiffs- u. Trop. -Hyg. *41* : 167–172.

WOLFSON, F. and WINTER, M. W., 1946. Studies of *Plasmodium cynomolgi* in the rhesus monkey, *Macaca mulatta.* Am. J. Hyg. *44* : 273–300.

(NS) = Not seen.

7

Plasmodium eylesi Warren, Bennett, Sandosham, and Coatney, 1965

T HIS was the second species of malaria described from Malayan gibbons and the third described for the world. A mature male *Hylobates lar* was taken in the Kedah-Perlis area of the country and made available to the authors for study. It was found infected with a malaria parasite (Warren *et al*, 1965, 1965a) which was studied subsequently in five other gibbons. There was no doubt in the minds of the authors as to its being a new species. They gave it the name *Plasmodium eylesi* in honor of the late Dr. Don E. Eyles who contributed so much to our knowledge of malaria in general and to simian malaria in particular.

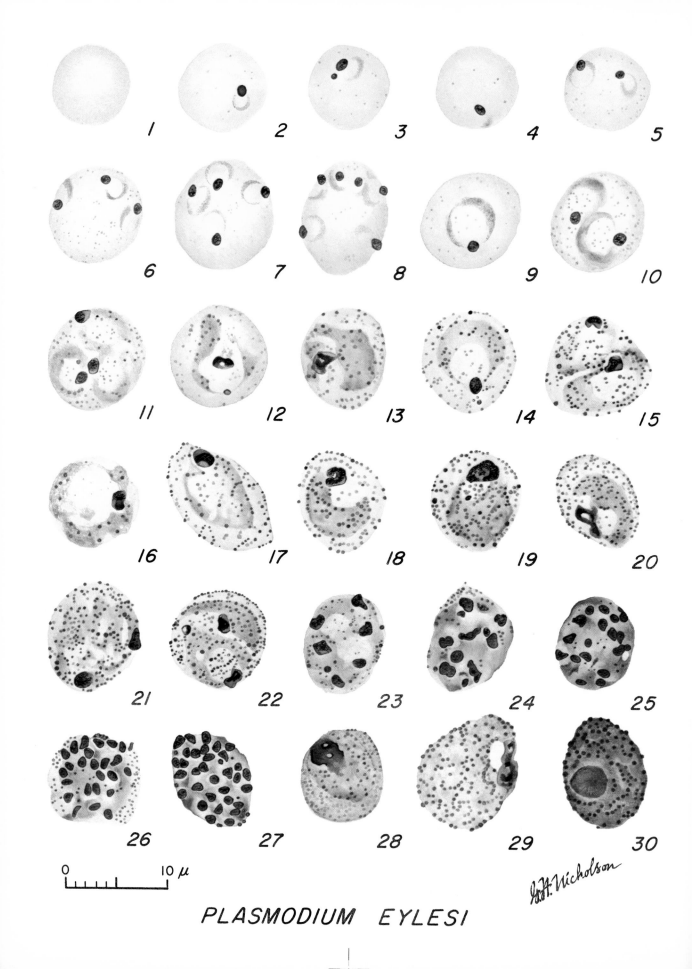

PLASMODIUM EYLESI

Cycle in the Blood

PLATE VIII

Immediately after the young parasite enters an erythrocyte, the cell becomes enlarged. Schüffner's stippling becomes evident even with the youngest forms but is not pronounced (Figs. 2–10). Amoeboid forms may occur, but ring forms are by far the most common aspect of the early part of the asexual cycle. Not only are multiple infections present but they are common with as many as six rings in a single cell (Fig. 8). The red-staining nucleus is generally single. The older trophozoites do not fill the cell; they may be slightly amoeboid (Fig. 13) and may surround a vacuole (Fig. 16). Pigment is scarce, granular, and yellowish-brown; Schüffner's stippling continues. The mature trophozoites exhibit a more dense blue-staining cytoplasm (Fig. 19); they are not amoeboid; pigment is granular, and is a yellow-brown to gray. Stippling is scattered and coarse. The host cell is enlarged and sometimes distorted (Fig. 17).

Young schizonts almost fill the enlarged host cell except for small areas where Schüffner's inclusion bodies may be prominent (Fig. 24). The cytoplasm remains dense grayish-blue as schizogony progresses. Pigment remains granular and difficult to distinguish; oval-shaped forms are not uncommon (Fig. 23). Older schizonts are frequently oval (Figs. 25, 27) and the cytoplasm stains a deep bluish-red. The chromatin bodies are randomly distributed (Figs. 26, 27); pigment is yellowish-brown and not clumped. The number of chromatin bodies ranges from 20 to 34 with an average of 25. Fully differentiated mature schizonts have not been observed.

The gametocytes are distinctive, especially the microgametocytes. The fully mature macrogametocytes fill the much enlarged host cell (Fig. 29). They stain a grayish-blue and exhibit coarse, granular pigment which is scattered rather evenly throughout the parasite. The deep staining, generally oval, nucleus may have a vacuole adjacent to it (Fig. 29). The mature microgametocytes are in an enlarged, circular to oval, host cell which takes a deep brilliant reddish-purple stain with a slightly deeper staining nucleus. The pigment is somewhat prominent and scattered throughout the cytoplasm. Once this parasite is seen, the trained eye will "not forget it" (Fig. 30).

One of the most striking features of this parasite is its tendency for multiple invasion of the host red blood cells, a phenomenon probably associated with the parasites' predilection for reticulocytes. This multiple development in a single host cell is responsible for a second characteristic feature of *P. eylesi*, namely the consistent appearance of parasitized cells with as many as 33 merozoites (Fig. 27).

The parasite has a highly synchronous tertian periodicity.

Sporogonic Cycle

The natural vector of this parasite is unknown. However, the sporogonic cycle has been studied in three laboratory reared species of mosquitoes indigenous to peninsular Malaysia (*Anopheles kochi*, *A. maculatus*, and *A. sundaicus*). Observations began 36 hours after the mosquitoes fed and continued through 14.5 days. Extrinsic incubation took place in an insectary maintained at approximately 27° C. The oocyst measurements are presented in Table 7.

In *A. kochi*, at day 1.5, the mean oocyst diameter was 7.5 μ with a range of 7 to 9 μ.

PLATE VIII.—*Plasmodium eylesi.*

Fig. 1.   Normal red cell.
Figs. 2–8.   Young trophozoites.
Figs. 9–15.   Growing trophozoites.
Figs. 16–20.   Mature trophozoites.
Figs. 21–25.   Developing schizonts.

Figs. 26–27.   Mature or nearly mature schizonts.
Fig. 28.   Young macrogametocyte.
Fig. 29.   Mature macrogametocyte.
Fig. 30.   Mature microgametocyte.

The oocysts continued to grow so that on day 9.5, they had an average size of 53 μ with a range of 27 to 69 μ. Sporozoites were first seen in the salivary glands on day 9.5.

The examination of oocysts in *A. maculatus* and *A. sundaicus* mosquitoes indicated that the growth rate of the parasite was similar in all three species. Sporozoites were present in the salivary glands of each species by day 9.5.

A comparison of the growth rate of *P. eylesi* with that of *P. cynomolgi* in *A. maculatus* mosquitoes (Fig. 24) shows the mean oocyst diameters were quite similar and that sporozoites of each of the parasites were present in the salivary glands at 9.5 days.

The sporozoites in *A. kochi* were infective as shown by their ability to initiate an infection in a gibbon. The prepatent period was 12 days.

Cycle in the Tissue

This part of the cycle is unknown.

Course of Infection

Infections, induced by the inoculation of parasitized blood, have been studied in four gibbons (Fig. 25). Beginning on the first day of patent infection the parasitemia increased rapidly, so that by the end of the first week the count was 20,000 per mm^3 where it remained, more or less, until day 20. From then until day 40, the count averaged about 10,000 parasites per mm^3 of blood, and thereafter declined slowly. The details of the actual infection in each animal were different; i.e., gibbon G 19, whose parasitemia reached 90,000 per mm^3, was treated and then survived a second episode of above 100,000 per mm^3. It was finally cleared of the infection by a curative dose of chloroquine on the 128th day of the patent infection, whereas the other animals exhibited more moderate parasitemias and were able to handle their infections without treatment.

The original investigators were able to study a single infection induced by the inoculation of sporozoites from *A. kochi* fed on G 19. This was accomplished in gibbon G 8 on 30 May 1964; young parasites appeared in the blood 12 days later. The parasite count increased from a second day count of 401 per mm^3 of blood to a count of 40,900 on day 8 which was the highest count encountered during an observation period of 32 days.

Because of the possible zoonotic nature of these malarias in the higher apes one is always tempted to inquire of Nature whether she will

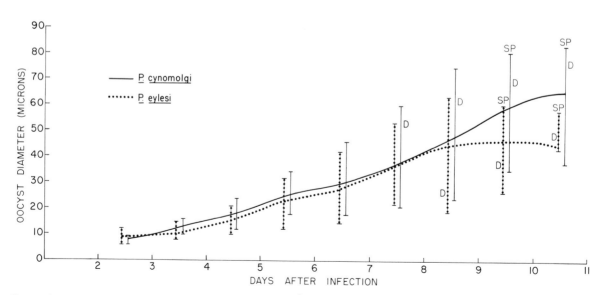

FIGURE 24.—Mean oocyst growth curve and ranges in oocyst diameters of *Plasmodium eylesi* and *P. cynomolgi* in *Anopheles maculatus* mosquitoes. Incubation temperature 27° C. (D = oocyst differentiation; SP = sporozoites present in the salivary glands). (Data courtest of Dr. Gordon Bennett).

accept such a parasite in man. With *A. kochi* mosquitoes harboring sporozoites of *P. eylesi* in their salivary glands and lacking certified human volunteers the only hope of a trial in man was for one of the investigators to act as a volunteer. This Dr. Gordon F. Bennett (1968) did. He was bitten by *A. kochi* mosquitoes, known to be infected. On the 15th post exposure day, he exhibited pronounced clinical symptoms comparable to those he had previously experienced when infected with *P. cynomolgi*. The symptoms persisted for about two weeks. During this time, parasites were evident at a very low level for about one week. There is reasonable doubt that Bennett's symptoms, although real, were due to infection with

P. eylesi because blood passaged from him to a parasite-free gibbon failed to produce an infection in the animal and, also, because the *P. eylesi* infection, if that is what it was, was too low to allow positive identification from parasites encountered in the blood smears.

Host Specificity

The natural host of *P. eylesi* is the white-handed gibbon, *Hylobates lar*. The parasite is not transferable to the rhesus monkey (*Macaca mulatta*) by the inoculation of infected blood.

The natural invertebrate host of *P. eylesi* is unknown. On an experimental basis, 12 species of anopheline mosquitoes indigenous to its area

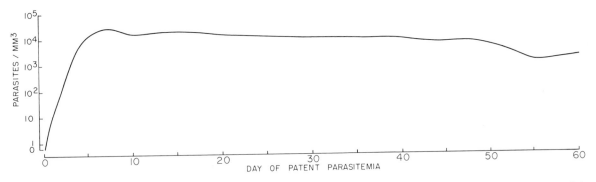

FIGURE 25.—Median parasitemia curve for infections of *Plasmodium eylesi* (4 blood-induced and one sporozoite-induced) in five gibbons, *Hylobates lar*.

TABLE 7.—Oocyst diameters of *Plasmodium eylesi* in *Anopheles kochi*, *A. maculatus*, and *A. sundaicus*.

Days after infection	A. kochi			A. maculatus			A. sundaicus		
	No.	Range	Mean*	No.	Range	Mean	No.	Range	Mean
1.5	6	7–9	7.5						
2.5	48	7–12	9	17	6–12	9	52	6–14	10
3.5	76	8–17	12	62	8–15	10	60	10–15	12
4.5	204	11–24	18	112	10–21	15	96	12–24	18
5.5	188	12–35	24	215	12–32	26	113	15–39	25
6.5	279	15–50	33	65	14–42	26	98	21–57	36
7.5	268	23–63	42†	81	22–53	38	111	24–56	45
8.5	334	21–68	48†	151	19–63	45†	50	41–68	52†
9.5	210	27–69	53†**	100	27–60	46†**	211	29–75	54†**
10.5	128	26–71	54†**	12	43–58	44†**	138	30–71	54†**
11.5							110	38–65	52†**
Totals	1741	7–71		815	6–63		1039	6–75	

* Measurements expressed in microns.

† Oocyst differentiation.

** Sporozoites present in the salivary gland.

of the world became infected when allowed to feed on a gibbon parasitized with *P. eylesi*. These were *A. kochi*, *A. maculatus*, *A. sundaicus*, *A. leucosphyrus*, *A. umbrosus*, *A. roperi*, *A. letifer*, *A. b. introlatus*, *A. riparis macarthuri*, *A. vagus*, *A. sinensis*, and *A. lesteri*. All but the latter three species delivered sporozoites to the salivary glands. The intensity of the infections varied from one species to another (Table 8). *Anopheles vagus* was the most susceptible followed by *A. kochi*, *A. maculatus*, *A. sundaicus*, *A. umbrosus*, and *A. lesteri*. Comparative feedings were not made with the other species.

Infections were obtained in *A. kochi*, *A. maculatus* and *A. sundaicus* mosquitoes when they were allowed to feed on two different gibbons (G 11 and G 19) between the 6th and the 18th days of patent parasitemia (Fig. 26). Maximum infection (100 percent) was obtained, from feedings on both animals, on day 10.

A comparison of the salivary gland infection rates (Table 9) shows that when the gut infection levels are comparable, the percentage and intensity of infection of the salivary glands is greater in *A. kochi* than in *A. maculatus*.

It is possible that a single human infection was obtained through the agency of mosquito bites (*A. kochi*) but further work is needed before this observation can be inserted into the realm of fact.

Antigenic Relationships and Immunity

Not much is known about antigenic relationships and immunity as applied to this species, although it is well to point out that the animal in which *P. eylesi* was induced by sporozoite inoculation was already carrying a low grade infection with *P. youngi*. This may show that infection with *P. youngi* did not exclude infection with *P. eylesi*, although it must be recognized that the previous and current *P. youngi* infection may have modified the course of the superimposed *P. eylesi* infection.

TABLE 8.—Comparative infectivity of *Plasmodium eylesi* in: *Anopheles kochi*, *A. vagus*, *A. maculatus*, *A. sundaicus*, *A. umbrosus*, and *A. lesteri*.

Mosq. species comparison*	Number tests	Number of mosquitoes		Percent infection		GII** ratios
		Standard	Other	Standard	Other	
Kochi						
Kochi : Vagus	1	10	10	60.0	30.0	110
Kochi : Mac	3	156	179	59.0	55.3	113.3
Kochi : Sund	1	10	21	100	100	47.0
Kochi : Umb	1	35	7	77.1	28.6	36.0
Kochi : Les	2	18	12	100	50.0	3.6
						1.4

* Kochi = *Anopheles kochi*, Vagus = *A. vagus*, Mac = *A. maculatus*, Sund = *A. sundaicus*, Umb = *A. umbrosus*, Les = *A lesteri*.

** GII = Gut Infection Index = average number of oocysts per 100 guts; the GII ratio is the relationship of the GII of *A. kochi* to another species where the GII of *A. kochi* = 100.

TABLE 9.—Comparison of salivary gland infection rates of *Plasmodium eylesi* in *Anopheles kochi* and *A. maculatus* (gut infection rates were 27 oocysts per gut for each species).

Days after infection	A. kochi		A. maculatus	
	Positive/Dissected	PGI*	Positive/Dissected	PGI
8.5	0/24		0/10	
9.5	16/34	3.4	7/45	2.1
10.5	24/36	3.3	7/18	2.1
11.5	22/37	3.2	21/32	2.4
12.5	15/20	2.7	18/35	2.9
13.5	7/17	3.7	8/23	3.0
14.5	6/14	2.5	2/10	1.5
Totals	90/182	3.2	63/173	2.5

* PGI = Positive Gland Index = Average gland rating of salivary glands found to be positive.

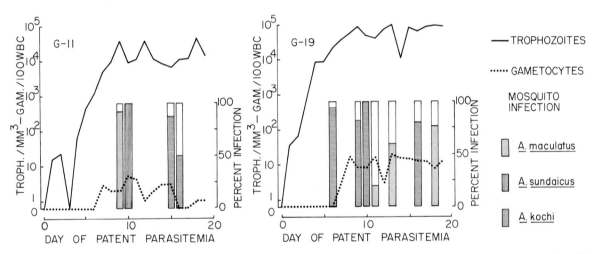

FIGURE 26.—Relationship of parasitemia to mosquito infection in two different gibbons, *Hylobates lar*, infected with *Plasmodium eylesi*.

REFERENCES

BENNETT, G. F., 1968. Personal communication.

WARREN, McW., BENNETT, G. F., and SANDOSHAM, A. A., 1965. A new malaria parasite from the white-handed gibbon, *Hylobates lar lar* in Malaya. Singapore Med. J. *6* : 50.

WARREN, McW., BENNETT, G. F., SANDOSHAM, A. A., and COATNEY, G. R., 1965a. *Plasmodium eylesi* sp. nov., a tertian malaria parasite from the white-handed gibbon, *Hylobates lar*. Ann. Trop. Med. Parasit. *59* : 500–508.

8

Plasmodium gonderi Sinton and Mulligan, 1933

THIS parasite was first seen by Gonder and von Berenberg-Gossler (1908) in the blood of a mangabey, *Cercocebus fuliginosus* (= *C. atys*), housed in the Hamburg Zoo. These authors identified the organism as *Plasmodium kochi*. Berenberg-Gossler saw the parasite again in 1909 in the same host, and, in two long-tailed green monkeys which Sinton and Mulligan (1933) identified as *Cercopithecus* (*C. sabaeus*). Each of the Berenberg-Gossler papers concerned with this parasite was illustrated with beautiful colored plates comprising some 72 figures. In 1910, Gonder and Rodenwalt again studied the parasite in the natural host and pointed out its morphological resemblance to *P. vivax* and its tertian periodicity.

Sinton and Mulligan in 1932–33 did a complete review of all the known malarias from the lower monkeys (*Cercopithicidae* and *Colobidae*) and concluded that the parasite described by Gonder and von Berenberg-Gossler was a true *Plasmodium* allied to the *P. inui* group. They proposed the name *P. inui gonderi*. At that time, it was not recognized that *P. inui* had a 72-hour cycle. Rodhain and van den Berghe (1936) isolated the parasite from a *Cercocebus galeritus agilus* from the Congo and proceeded to study it. They, as Gonder and Rodenwalt before them, found its periodicity to be tertian. This being true, it could not be considered as belonging to the inui group of malaria parasites and, therefore, they raised it to specific rank under the name *Plasmodium gonderi*.

According to Garnham *et al* (1958), Duke, in 1956, found a malaria parasite in a drill (*Mandrillus leucophaeus*), taken in the Cameroons, and succeeded in infecting other drills with it. An infected animal was eventually sent to Garnham who, after careful study, concluded that the parsite was *P. gonderi*. The significance of this find was that it expanded the range of the parasite some one thousand miles northwest of its then known habitat. The following year (1959) Bray encountered the same parasite in mangabeys (*Cercocebus fuliginosus*) in Liberia which further extended its range to include the west coast of Africa from the mouth of the Congo river to Liberia.

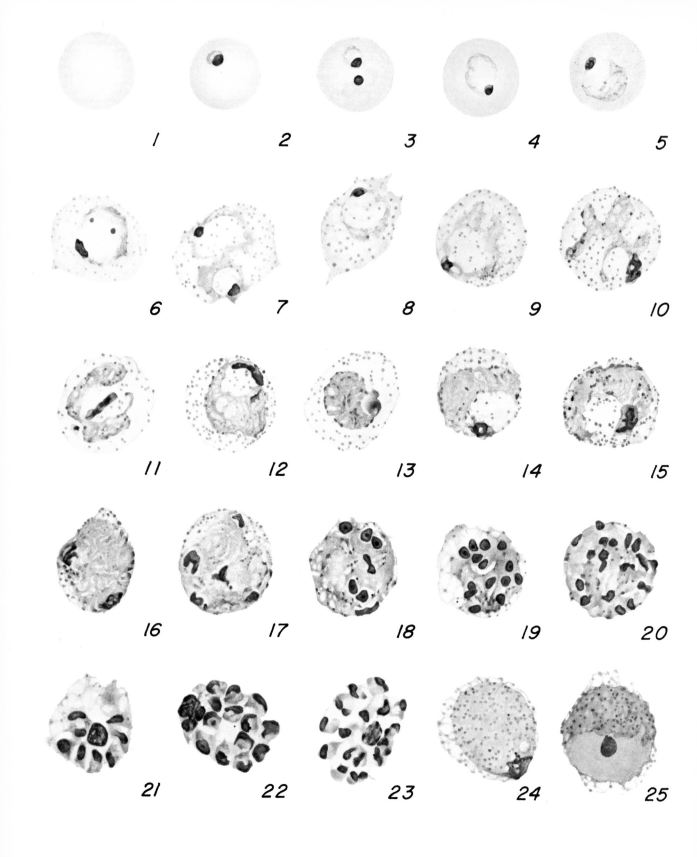

1 *2* *3* *4* *5*

6 *7* *8* *9* *10*

11 *12* *13* *14* *15*

16 *17* *18* *19* *20*

21 *22* *23* *24* *25*

0   10 *u*

PLASMODIUM GONDERI

G. H. Nicholson

A clear circular vacuole is generally present in the cytoplasm; the nucleus is not too well defined.

Bano (1959) studied the early sporogony of *P. gonderi* in *Anopheles aztecus* and reported that at 50 hours the oocysts measured about 12 μ in diameter. At 58 hours, as a result of mitosis, the haploid number of chromosomes was shown to be three (two large and one small). Growth proceeds rapidly at 28° C. At 6 days, the oocysts measured 25 μ, at 7 days 40 μ and when mature, up to 60 μ. Nine days after the blood meal, sporozoites, measuring about 10 μ in dried films, were in the salivary glands.

We have observed the oocyst growth in six species of anophelines when incubated at 25° C (Table 10). In *A. freeborni*, the mean oocyst diameter at day 4 was 13 μ with a range of 9 to 19 μ. The oocysts continued to grow so that by day 12, the mean diameter was 65 μ, with a range of 41 to 94 μ, and sporozoites were present in the salivary glands.

In the other mosquitoes, *A. stephensi*, *A. maculatus*, *A. b. balabacensis*, *A. quadrimaculatus*, and *A. atroparvus*, the oocyst diameters were within the limits found in *A. freeborni*. Sporozoites were present in the salivary glands of the *A. quadrimaculatus* and *A. atroparvus* on day 12; in *A. maculatus* on day 13; and in *A.*

stephensi on day 15. Although the oocyst development appeared to be normal in the *A. b. balabacensis*, sporozoites did not appear in the salivary glands until day 16, and in some lots, not until day 20.

A comparison of the oocyst growth curve of *P. gonderi* with that of *P. cynomolgi* (Fig. 27) indicates that these species in *A. freeborni* are similar in size through 11 days of incubation. However, sporozoites were present in the salivary glands of mosquitoes infected with *P. cynomolgi* two days earlier than with *P. gonderi*.

The sporozoites were shown to be infective because the infection was transmitted to rhesus monkeys by the bites of *A. freeborni* (3 times), *A. maculatus* (once), *A. stephensi* (3 times), and *A. b. balabacensis* (twice). The prepatent periods of these nine transmissions ranged from 9 to 17 days with a mean of 12.7 days. Garnham *et al* (1958) reported prepatent periods of 8 days in each of two *M. mulatta* monkeys infected by the intravenous inoculation of infected salivary glands from *A. aztecus* mosquitoes.

Cycle in the Tissue

We have tried to demonstrate the EE cycle of *P. gonderi* on one occasion but met with

TABLE 10.—Oocyst diameters of *Plasmodium gonderi* in *Anopheles freeborni*, *A. stephensi*, *A. masculatus*, *A. b. balabacensis*, *A. quadrimaculatus*, and *A. atroparvus*.

Days after infection	A. freeborni			A. stephensi			A. maculatus			A. b. balabacensis			A. quadrimaculatus			A. atroparvus		
	No.	Range*	Mean	No.	Range	Mean	No.	Range	Mean	No.	Range	Mean	No.	Range	Mean	No.	Range	Mean
4	100	8–19	13	100	9–25	14	100	8–18	13	100	8–19	13	100	9–26	16			
5	100	11–25	19	100	12–31	22	100	12–27	20	100	12–26	20	100	12–26	19	8	14–18	16
6	204	12–34	23	100	18–32	25	222	12–32	23	216	12–33	23	102	18–33	25	49	18–31	24
7	100	13–30	22				88	15–27	21	111	18–35	28	100	14–28	22			
8	100	18–51	37				100	21–54	38	121	18–59	39	101	18–50	32	99	20–55	40
9	100	30–64	50	41	22–41	33	100	24–61	44	100	24–57	42	101	24–53	39	158	24–63	44
10	100	24–72	58	100	30–77	53	100	24–72	45	100	24–77	50	100	24–72	50	8	40–59	48
11	100	30–85	56†	100	41–89	62†	100	30–65	50	100	41–85	61†	100	35–83	60†	100	33–70	49†
12	100	41–94	65†**	100	30–77	55†	100	35–89	61†	100	41–94	63†	100	35–85	63†**	100	30–80	57†**
13	100	41–89	68†**	100	22–89	59†	100	41–107	70†**	90	35–104	71†	100	18–100	61†**			
14	100	35–100	71†**	100	30–94	65†	100	33–94	63†**	100	34–94	66†	100	51–98	71†**			
15	100	44–81	67†**			**												
Totals	1304	8–100		841	9–94		1210	8–107		1238	8–104		1104	9–100		431	14–80	

* Measurements expressed in microns.
† Oocyst differentiation.
** Sporozoites present in the salivary glands.

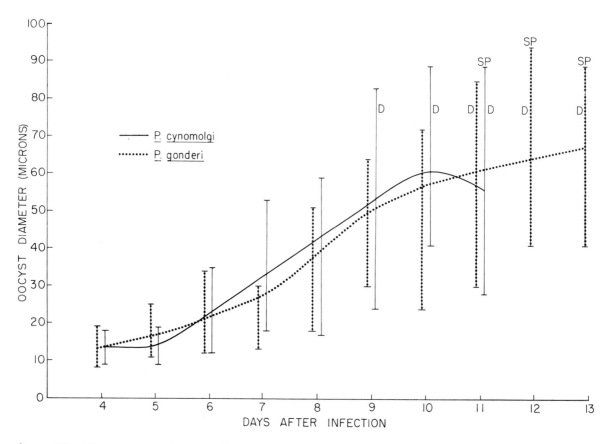

FIGURE 27.—Mean oocyst growth curve and ranges in oocyst diameters of *Plasmodium cynomolgi* and *P. gonderi* in *Anopheles freeborni* mosquitoes. (D = oocyst differentiation; SP = sporozoites present in the salivary glands).

failure even though the test animal developed an infection after a suitable prepatent period. Garnham *et al* (1958) were able to demonstrate the EE cycle in the rhesus monkey on days 5, 7, and 8 and reported that the 5-day schizonts were within a definite limiting membrane surrounding a granular cytoplasm with about 20 nuclei. The largest schizont measured 13 by 19 μ. Seven-day forms were generally oval in shape with a regular outline. The largest ones measured 18 to 27 μ. These forms showed numerous large dense spherical to rod-shaped nuclei; the cytoplasm was granular and without vacuoles.

The eight-day forms represented nearly mature, mature, and post-mature parasites. They expressed no decided increase in size over the 7-day forms but there were many more nuclei packed closely together. The nuclei were small and appeared as densely stained granules in a paler matrix. Some of the schizonts showed lobations. The cytoplasm

was granular and contained in an oval outline. The size of these bodies was variable, the largest was 27 by 32 μ, and estimated to carry about two thousand merozoites.

It is not known if there are secondary EE bodies in the life-cycle of *P. gonderi*.

Course of Infection

According to Garnham *et al* (1958), blood-induced infections in the rhesus monkey are characterized by initial high parasitemias which decline slowly during the following weeks and then persist; parasites were found easily, in thin films, after twelve months. The peak of schizogony was found to occur about mid-day. Infected animals showed no signs of illness. Zuckerman (1960), on the other hand, reported that *P. gonderi* produced an excessive degree of anemia in these animals.

In our studies, the course of infection was followed in 25 *M. mulatta* monkeys; 17 were infected by the inoculation of parasitized blood and 8 by the inoculation of sporozoites (Fig. 28). In the former animals, the peak parasitemia (approximately 140,000/mm³) occurred after about 10 days of parent parasitemia. The parasite count then declined slowly to a more or less persistent level. After 60 days of patent parasitemia, the median count was about 5,000/mm³.

In the 8 monkeys infected by sporozoite-inoculation, the peak parasite count obtained on the 10th day of patent parasitemia (approximately 190,000/mm³). The parasite count then declined but to a lower level than found in the blood-induced infections. The median parasite count at 60 days was about 350/mm³. None of the animals required chemotherapy for survival.

Host Specificity

The natural hosts of *P. gonderi* are the mangabeys and drills found on the west coast of Africa and in the Cameroons. It was reported from mangabeys, *Cercocebus fuliginosus* (= *atys*) by Gonder and von Berenberg-Gossler (1908), and from *C. galeritus*, *C. aterrimus*, and *C. atys* by Bray (1963). Garnham *et al* (1958) reported it from the drill, *Mandrillus leucophaeus*.

Numerous investigators have successfully transferred *P. gonderi* to the rhesus monkey, *M. mulatta*, via blood and by sporozoites. It was passaged by blood to *Papio anubis*, *P. jubilaeus*, and *Cercopithecus aethiops* by Rodhain and van den Berghe (1936). We have also infected *M. radiata* by blood inoculation.

Rodhain and van den Berghe (1936) made one attempt to transfer *P. gonderi* to man by blood inoculation but without success. We attempted to transmit this species to 8 volunteers by mosquito bite; all attempts failed with observation continued for 180 days.

The natural vector of *P. gonderi* is unknown, but being an African-based parasite, it would be expected that *A. gambiae* would transmit the infection readily. However, Bray (1959), given favorable conditions was unable to obtain infections. Rodhain and van Hoof (1940) successfully transmitted the infection using *A. atroparvus*. Garnham *et al* (1958) obtained transmission using *A. aztecus*. We have been able to infect *A. freeborni*, *A. maculatus*, *A. b. balabacensis*, *A. stephensi*, *A. quadrimaculatus*, *A. atroparvus*, *A. sundaicus*, and *A. albimanus*. The level of susceptibility varied (Table 11), with *A. freeborni*, *A. b. balabacensis*, *A. maculatus*, *A. stephensi*, and *A. quadrimaculatus* being readily susceptible whereas the other species were not.

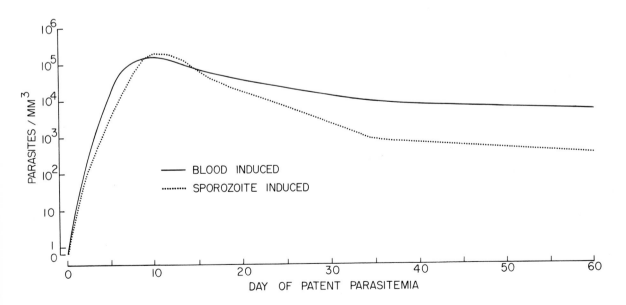

FIGURE 28.—Median curves of the parasitemia of blood-induced (17 animals) and sporozoite-induced (8 animals) infections of *Plasmodium gonderi* in *Macaca mulatta* monkeys.

Immunity and Antigenic Relationships

Garnham and Bray (1955) reported no cross-immunity between *P. gonderi* and *P. cynomolgi* in that a monkey cured of one infection was completely susceptible to infection with the other species. Voller *et al* (1966) reported that monkeys originally infected with *P. cynomolgi* or with *P. knowlesi* could be infected with *P. gonderi* and that a normal infection developed.

Data from serology show that antisera to *P.* *gonderi* give a fluorescent antibody cross-reaction at only a low level to *P. fieldi* antigen (mean reciprocal titer ratio of 100:41) and much lower levels of reactivity to other primate malaria antigens (Collins *et al*, 1966). In the reverse procedure, *P. gonderi* antigen produces low level responses to *P. cynomolgi*, *P. fragile*, and *P. inui* antisera (mean reciprocal titer ratios of 100:36, 100:35, and 100:32, respectively).

Although antisera to *P. falciparum* and *P. malariae* responded to the *P. gonderi* antigen, the cross reactions were much lower than the homologous responses (Collins *et al*, 1966a).

TABLE 11.—Comparative infectivity of *Plasmodium gonderi* to eight species of *Anopheles*.

Mosq. species comparison*	Number tests	Number of mosquitoes		Percent infection		GII** ratios
		Standard	Other	Standard	Other	
F–1						100
F–1 : Bal	11	121	106	50.4	44.3	87.0
F–1 : Mac	22	245	236	58.8	64.4	84.7
F–1 : St–1	9	69	82	73.9	75.6	55.4
F–1 : Q–1	28	563	569	59.0	43.8	50.6
F–1 : Atro	7	210	186	58.6	8.6	6.5
F–1 : Sund	7	178	143	64.0	9.8	2.6
F–1 : Alb	9	124	117	25.8	2.6	0.3

* F–1 = *Anopheles freeborni*, Bal = *A. b. balabacensis*, Mac = *A. maculatus*, St–1 = *A. stephensi*, Q–1 = *A. quadrimaculatus*, Atro = *A. atroparvus*, Sund = *A. sundaicus*, Alb = *A. albimanus*.

** GII = Gut Infection Index = average number of oocysts per 100 guts; the GII ratio is the relationship of the GII of *A. freeborni* to another species where the GII of *A. freeborni* = 100.

REFERENCES

BANO, L., 1959. A cytological study of the early oocysts of seven species of *Plasmodium* and the occurrence of postzygotic meiosis. Parasitol. *49* : 559–585.

BERENBERG-GOSSLER, VON H. V., 1909. Beitrage zur naturgeschichte der malariaplasmodien. Arch. f. Protist (Jena) *16* : 245–280.

BRAY, R. S., 1959. Range of *Plasmodium gonderi*. Trans. Roy. Soc. Trop. Med. & Hyg. *53* : 300.

BRAY, R. S., 1963. Malaria infections in primates and their importance to man. Ergeb. Mikrob. Immunit. Experim. Therap. *36* : 168–213.

COLLINS, W. E., SKINNER, J. C., and GUINN, E. G., 1966. Antigenic variations in the plasmodia of certain primates as detected by immuno-fluorescence. Am. J. Trop. Med. & Hyg. *15* : 438–485.

COLLINS, W. E., JEFFERY, G. M., GUINN, E., and SKINNER, J. C., 1966a. Fluorescent antibody studies in human malaria. IV. Cross-reactions between human and simian malaria. Am. J. Trop. Med. & Hyg. *15* : 11–15.

GARNHAM, P. C. C. and BRAY, R. S., 1955. Absence of cross-immunity between *Plasmodium cynomolgi* and *Plasmodium gonderi*. Ind. J. Malariol. *9* : 255–260.

GARNHAM, P. C. C., LAINSON, R. and COOPER, W., 1958. The complete life cycle of a new strain of *Plasmodium gonderi* from the drill (*Mandrillus leucophaeus*), including its sporogony in *Anopheles aztecus* and its pre-erythrocytic schizogony in the rhesus monkey. Trans. Roy. Soc. Trop. Med. & Hyg. *52* : 509–517.

GARNHAM, P. C. C., 1966. Malaria parasites and other haemosporidia. Blackwell Scientific Publications. Oxford.

GONDER, R. and BERENBERG-GOSSLER, VON H. V., 1908. Untersuchungen über malaria-plasmodien der affen. Malaria-Intern. Arch., Leipzig *1* : 47–56.

GONDER, R. and RODENWALDT, E., 1910. Experimentelle untersuchungen über affenmalaria. Centralbl. f. Bakt. I. Abt. Orig. *54* : 236–240.

RODHAIN, J., and VAN DEN BERGHE, L., 1936. Contribution à l'étude des plasmodiums des singes africains. Ann. Soc. Belg. Med. Trop. *16* : 521–531.

RODHAIN, J. and LASSMAN, P., 1939. Le comportement

REFERENCES—Continued

différent de *Plasmodium cynomolgi* Mayer et de *Plasmodium gonderi* Rodhain et van den Berghe vis-a-vis des réticulocytes. C. R. Soc. Biol. *132* : 71–75.

RODHAIN, J. and VAN HOOF, T., 1940. Contribution a l'étude des *Plasmodium* des singes africains. Le comportement différent des *Pl. gonderi* et *Pl. kochi* chez les moustiques. Bull. Soc. Path. Exot. *33* : 107–113.

RUDZINSKA, M. A., BRAY, R. S. and TRAGER, W., 1960. Intracellular phagotrophy in *Plasmodium falciparum* and *Plasmodium gonderi*. J. Protozool. *7* : 24–25.

SINTON, J. A., and MULLIGAN, H. W., 1932 and 1933. A critical review of the literature relating to the identification of the malarial parasites recorded from monkeys of the families Cercopithecidae and Colobidae. Rec. Malar. Surv. India *III:* 357–380; 381–444.

VOLLER, A., GARNHAM, P. C. C., and TARGETT, G. A. T., 1966. Cross immunity in monkey malaria. J. Trop. Med. & Hyg. *69* : 121–123.

ZUCKERMAN, A., 1960. Blood loss and replacement in plasmodial infections. III. *Plasmodium cynomolgi*, *Plasmodium gonderi*, and *Plasmodium knowlesi* in *Macaca mulatta mulatta*, the rhesus monkey. J. Infec. Dis. *106* : 123–140

9

Plasmodium hylobati Rodhain, 1941

ON the 2nd of June 1939, Dr. Jerome Rodhain examined the blood of a gibbon, *Hylobates lensciscus* Geoff. from Java and in the blood, he found a few parasites of a malaria. He made a second examination five days later and saw that the parasites were more numerous. They then disappeared and he never saw them again. From the material collected on those two occasions, Rodhain described the parasite and named it *Plasmodium hylobati* in 1941. His description lacked completeness, in that he did not see microgamecocytes; but, it does allow for the recognition of the parasite. He predicted that the asexual cycle was quartan. According to Garnham (1966), Wenyon saw a similar parasite in other species of gibbons which had died in the London Zoo in 1946 and he, Garnham, saw it in films sent to him from Sarawak. This extra material was evidently used by Garnham in writing his description of the parasite.

The parasite has not been found in peninsular Malaysia or in Thailand and none of us had ever seen it. In fact, we despaired of locating material for a colored plate, and other studies, when a fortunate happening occurred. A mature male *Hylobates moloch* from North Borneo was received at the University of Singapore and found to be infected with a malaria tentatively identified as *P. hylobati*. Dr. Zaman, knowing the rarity of the parasite, sent the infected animal to Professor Garnham at the London School of Hygiene & Tropical Medicine so that further studies could be carried out. Professor Garnham also believed the parasite to be the long-sought *P. hylobati* and, anxious to have a demonstration of the exoerythrocytic stages, he sent the animal to us in Chamblee, Georgia, because we maintained a colony of *A. b. balabacensis* believed to be a potential vector. The gibbon was received at Chamblee in good health and carrying a low-grade infection of a malaria. Later, the animal was splenectomized; and with increased parasitemia, it was evident that the parasite was *P. hylobati*. Under those favorable conditions, mosquitoes were allowed to feed on the animal. At the same time, there was ample material for studying the periodicity of the asexual cycle and for transfer of parasitized blood to monkeys. Five species of mosquitoes were allowed to feed on the gibbon whereupon, its malaria was eliminated by treatment with chloroquine. When the test mosquitoes were found infected, they were dissected and their sporozoites inoculated intravenously into the original gibbon and, intrahepatically at laparotomy, into an owl monkey (*Aotus trivirgatus*). Following exposure to infection, liver biopsies were done on day 7 and 14 in the gibbon and on day 7 in the owl monkey. Exoerythrocytic parasties were found in each of the animals. Human volunteers were exposed to infection through bites of infected mosquitoes.

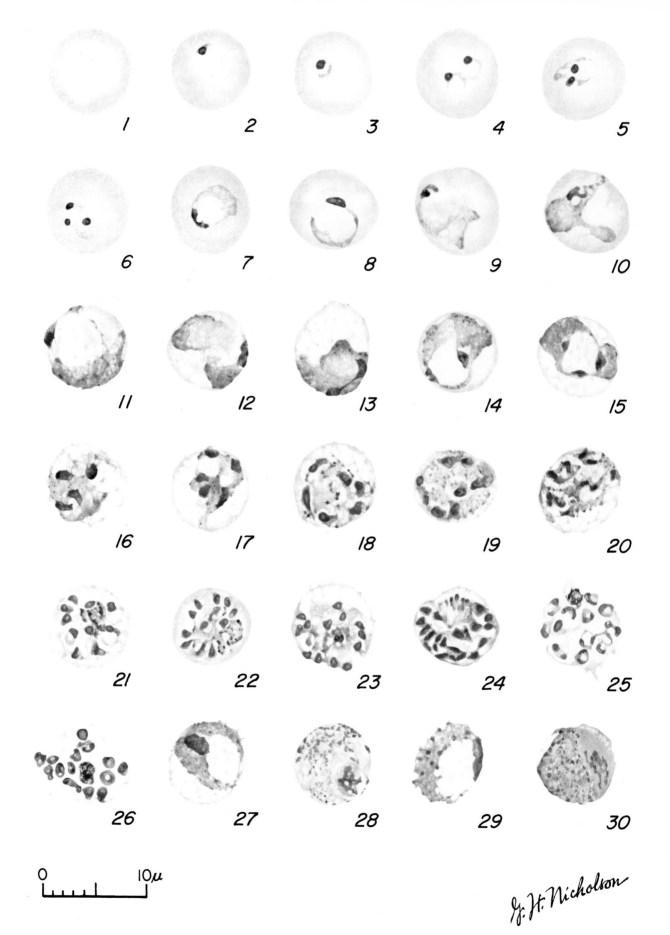

G. H. Nicholson

PLASMODIUM HYLOBATI

Cycle in the Blood
PLATE XI

The youngest erythrocytic parasites consist of a prominent nucleus and a small fragment of cytoplasm (Fig. 2). As the young parasite grows, the nuclear mass remains essentially unchanged while the cytoplasm increases both in volume and in the area of the host cell it occupies (Figs. 3–6). Multiple chromatin masses are not uncommon (Figs. 5, 6). Dual invasion of a single host cell has been observed (Fig. 4) but the condition is not considered characteristic of the parasite. The nucleus begins to change as the trophozoite continues to develop, stretching around the periphery of the vacuole or branching as it grows (Figs. 7–10). Pigment first appears as one or two accumulations of very fine, grayish-black granules causing areas of the cytoplasm to appear more gray than blue in the Romanowsky-stained young trophozoite (Fig. 10). The pigment becomes identifiable though not prominent in the young adult forms (Fig. 11). As the trophozoite approaches maturity, the cytoplasm thickens, takes a deeper stain, and the nucleus becomes more dense (Figs. 10–12). The pigment remains scarce and frequently hard to identify. There is no obvious host cell enlargement. Schüffner's stippling or other types of inclusions in the host cell have not been observed. Schizogony is unremarkable except that the host cell cytoplasm sometimes appears greatly depleted, leaving the parasite enmeshed in a network of fine cytoplasmic threads (Figs. 16–18, 20, 23). In some cases, the nuclear material is dominated by thick, tortuous threads or globs (Figs. 20, 24). As the schizont approaches maturity the pigment be-comes more abundant and begins to accumulate into groups of moderately coarse, yellowish-black granules (Figs. 21, 23, 24). The mature schizont has from 12 to 20 merozoites, which may be arranged to form what Rodhain called a rosette; 14 to 16 is the most common number. When the merozoites are completely formed, the pigment assumes a single dense yellowish-black mass (Figs. 25, 26).

Young gametocytes are difficult to distinguish from young and mature trophozoites. However, the young microgametocyte does show some of the rare staining qualities of the cytoplasm fairly early (Fig. 29).

The mature macrogametocyte fills the host cell and displays smooth, uniformly staining blue cytoplasm. The pigment is in moderately coarse, randomly distributed granules. The nucleus is circular to oval, dense, and usually located at the periphery of the cell (Fig. 28).

The fully adult microgametocyte fills the host cell and the cytoplasm as well as the nucleus stains a bright rose-pink. The nucleus is large and diffuse with a dense central mass. Frequently, the nucleus and the cytoplasm stain a uniform pink. Separation is achieved because pigment granules are randomly distributed through the cytoplasm but they are absent from the nucleus (Fig. 30).

The asexual cycle in the blood occupies 48 hours.

Sporogonic Cycle
PLATE XII

The natural vector of this parasite is unknown. However, we were able to study the sporogonic cycle in five laboratory reared species of mosquitoes: *A. b. balabacensis* from

PLATE XI.—*Plasmodium hylobati*.

Fig. 1.   Normal red blood cell.
Figs. 2–13.   Developmental stages of the trophozoite.
Figs. 2–4.   Ring stages.
Figs. 5, 6.   Young trophozoites.
Figs. 7–9.   Adolescent trophozoites.
Fig. 10.   Young adult trophozoite.
Figs. 11, 12.   Mature or adult trophozoites.
Fig. 13.   Mature trophozoite with dividing nucleus.

Figs. 14–24.   Schizogonic stages.
Fig. 25.   Submature schizont.
Fig. 26.   Mature schizont.
Figs. 27–30.   Gametocytes.
Fig. 27.   Immature macrogametocyte.
Fig. 28.   Mature macrogametocyte.
Fig. 29.   Immature microgametocyte.
Fig. 30.   Mature microgametocyte.

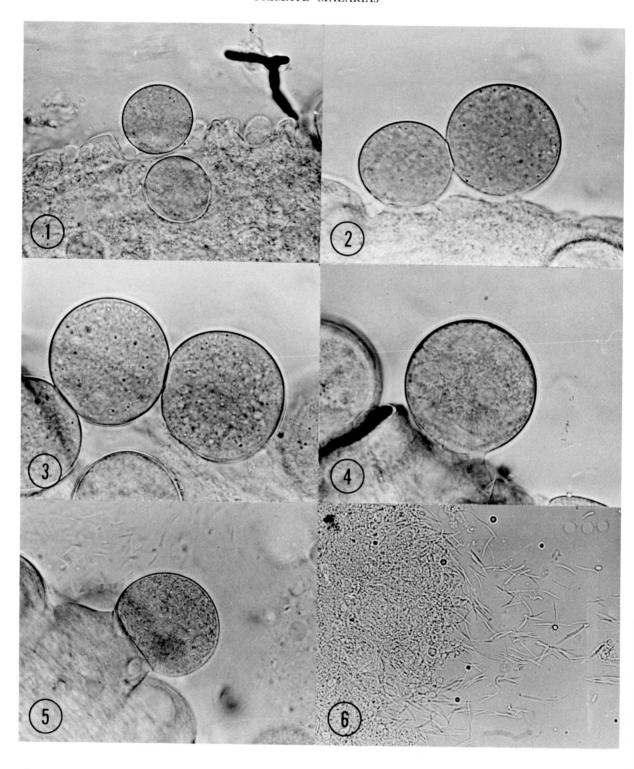

PLATE XII.—Developing oocysts and sporozoites of *Plasmodium hylobati* in *Anopheles b. balabacensis* mosquitoes. X 580.

Fig. 1. 8-day oocysts.
Fig. 2. 9-day oocysts.
Fig. 3. 10-day oocysts.
Fig. 4. 11-day oocyst showing differentiation.

Fig. 5. 12-day differentiated oocyst. Sporozoites free in fluid near gut.
Fig. 6. Sporozoites present near salivary gland tissue 12 days after feeding.

Thailand, *A. stephensi* from India, *A. maculatus* from Malaysia, *A. freeborni* and *A. quadrimaculatus* from the United States. Observations began 6 days after feeding and continued through day 13. The extrinsic incubation temperature was 25° C.

The results of the oocyst measurements are presented in Table 12. In *A. b. balabacensis*, on day 6, the mean oocyst diameter was 15 μ with a range of 11 to 20 μ. The oocysts continued to grow so that by day 12, the average size was 53 μ with a range of 30 to 70 μ. Sporozoites were first seen in the salivary glands on day 12.

The examination of the oocyst diameters in the other test mosquitoes indicated that the growth rate of the parasite was similar in each of the five species. Sporozoites were present in the salivary glands of *A. stephensi* on day 12 and in *A. freeborni* and *A. maculatus* on day 13. No sporozoites were found in the salivary glands of the *A. quadrimaculatus* through day 16.

In comparing the extrinsic development of *P. hylobati* in *A. b. balabacensis* with *P. cynomolgi*, from the rhesus monkey (Fig. 29), and *P. jefferyi*, from the gibbon (Fig. 30) one finds that the *P. cynomolgi* oocysts are much larger and that its sporozoites appear in the salivary glands two days earlier. *Plasmodium jefferyi* oocysts are considerably smaller than those of *P. hylobati* and its sporozoites appear in the glands one day later.

Comparison studies with *P. eylesi* could not be made because the growth studies with it were made at a different extrinsic incubation temperature.

The sporozoites of *P. hylobati* in *A. b. balabacensis* were infective because they initiated infection in a gibbon. The prepatent period was nine days.

Cycle in the Tissue

PLATE XIII

Sodeman *et al* (1971) ably described the tissue stages of *Plasmodium hylobati* found on day 7 and 14 in the gibbon and those seen on day 7 in the owl monkey.

The EE bodies were round to elliptical in shape with smooth edges. Some were retracted from their surrounding liver cell, probably as a result of fixation. The nuclei were round, although, infrequent bar-shapes were seen. The nuclei stained magenta, measured 0.5–1.5 μ in diameter, and were evenly distributed through the cytoplasm. The latter was granular in texture and stained pale blue. In many of the parasites irregular shaped, dark blue aggregates ("flocculi") were scattered diffusely through the cytoplasm but this feature was not universal. The flocculated material contained small holes. Parasitized liver cells were enlarged and their nuclei displaced peripherally. There was no nuclear enlargement of the parasitized liver cells; and, vacuolation of the cytoplasm was seen only occasionally. No mononu-

TABLE 12.—Oocyst diameters of *Plasmodium hylobati* in *Anopheles b. balabacensis*, *A. stephensi*, *A. freeborni*, *A. maculatus*, and *A. quadrimaculatus*.

Days after Infection	A. b. balabacensis			A. stephensi			A. freeborni			A. maculatus			A. quadrimaculatus		
	No.	Range*	Mean	No.	Range	Mean	No.	Range	Mean	No.	Range	Mean	No.	Range	Mean
6	150	11–20	15												
7	100	12–30	21	90	13–25	19	107	12–25	17	105	12–26	16	117	12–27	20
8	100	15–33	26	111	17–35	24	105	13–35	25	113	14–35	24	128	18–40	29
9	100	18–47	35	124	19–45	33	135	13–42	30	111	14–37	24	109	18–45	34
10	100	25–55	41†	100	27–55	42†	100	19–47	35	114	20–52	34	150	21–55	37
11	100	28–59	45†	100	24–65	39†	110	20–47	34	111	19–63	46†	100	21–61	41†
12	100	30–70	53†**	108	22–65	45†**	100	26–68	51†**	114	20–64	45†**	100	32–72	51†
Totals	750	11–70	†**	633	13–25	†**	657	12–68	†**	668	12–64	†**	704	12–72	†

* Measurements expressed in microns; incubation temperature 25° C.

† Oocyst differentiation.

** Sporozoites present in the salivary glands.

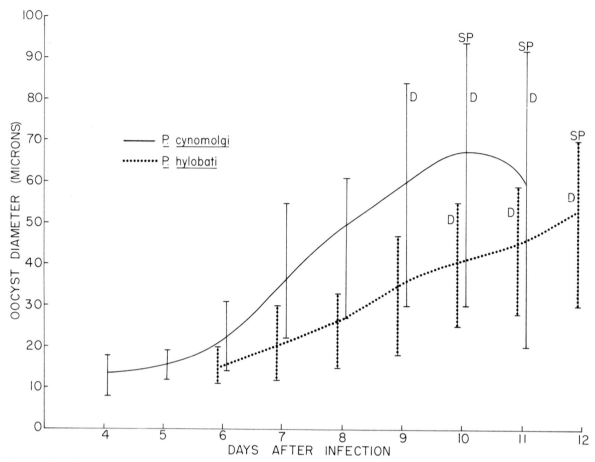

FIGURE 29.—Range in oocyst diameters and the mean oocyst diameter curve of *Plasmodium hylobati* and *P. cynomolgi* in *Anopheles b. balabacensis* mosquitoes. (D = oocyst differentiation; SP = sporozoites present in the salivary glands).

clear cell or acute inflammatory cell infiltrate was present.

The seven day forms (Figs. 1 & 2) sectioned at 3 μ extended through 5 sections; those sectioned at 6 μ, through 2.6 sections. The average size was 15.2 μ in length and 11.3 μ in width. The space occupied by the EE bodies averaged 15.8 μ in length and 11.7 μ in width. The limiting membrane was thin but distinct. Only two vacuoles were seen in fifty specimens examined; they measured 5 μ in diameter and were clear.

Only four EE bodies were seen in the 14-day material (Figs. 3 & 4). In the 6 μ sections they extended through 4 sections. Their average size was 26.1 μ in length and 18.6 μ in width. The space occupied by the parasites in the liver cell averaged 26.4 μ in length and 19.5 μ in width. A limiting membrane was distinct and flocculi were present, however, they were

small and less frequent than in the 7-day forms. No vacuoles were present and vague clefts were observed in only one body.

Only two exoerythrocytic bodies were seen in the 7-day material from the owl monkey (Figs. 5 & 6). In the 6 μ sections one body was complete. It extended through 4 sections and measured 25.2 μ by 14.4 μ. Sections of the EE body measured up to 22.8 μ by 19.2 μ. There was a distinct limiting membrane. Flocculi were large and more frequent than in the gibbon material. The parasites exhibited small, clear vacuoles. The nuclei were round and measured 1–1.5 μ. Clefts were present in the cytoplasm.

It seems safe to say that the morphology of *P. hylobati* is not unlike that of the other primate malarias (Held *et al*, 1967). If one compares the 6-day parasite of *P. jefferyi*, the only other EE parasite of a gibbon so far described

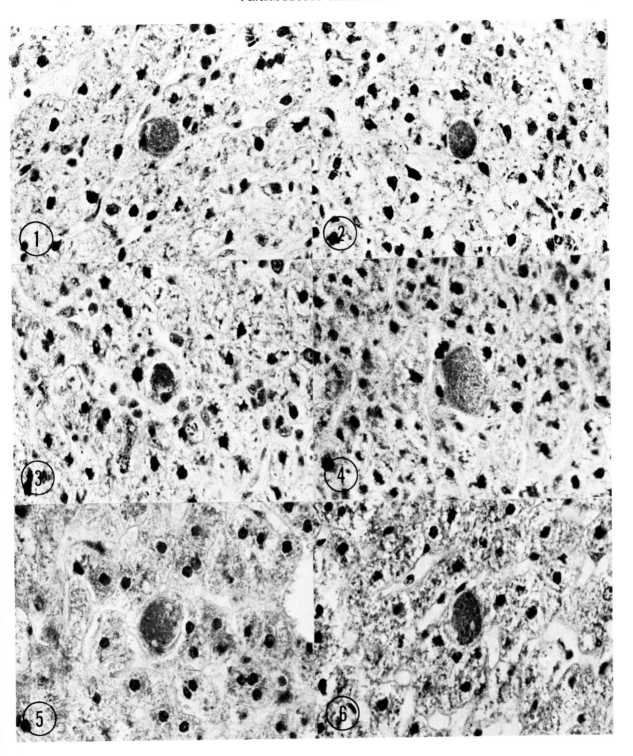

PLATE XIII.—Exoerythrocytic bodies of *Plasmodium hylobati*. X 580.

Figs. 1, 2.   7-day EE body in liver tissue of gibbon, *Hylobates moloch*.

Figs. 3, 4.   14-day EE bodies in gibbon.

Figs 5, 6.   7-day EE bodies in liver tissue of monkey, *Aotus trivirgatus*.

(Sodeman *et al*, 1969), with the 7-day forms of *P. hylobati* one sees considerable difference in the average size which suggests, if there were sufficient comparative measurements, that they might be separated at day 7 on the basis of size. The host animal exhibited a patent infection on day 9 yet EE bodies were found on day 14. We are not able to say, because of their large size, whether these were 'left-over' EE bodies of the initial generation, or, possibly, second generation EE bodies because some were of the same size as 7-day forms; maybe both. This will not be resolved until we have additional information on the tissue stages of this and other ape malarias.

Course of Infection

We know very little about the course of the infection in the normal host except that it does become latent and that it is provoked to exacerbation following splenectomy.

The parasite will infect splenectomized and intact rhesus monkeys. Infection induced by inoculation of parasitized blood in a splenectomized animal is marked by a very high parasitemia (up to 28/100 RBC) which persists at a detectable level for up to four months. Reinoculation has produced infections as high as 8/100 RBC. In intact rhesus, the infection is transient and is eliminated in a few weeks. Infections in *Macaca nemestrina* and *M. fasicularis* monkeys have also been obtained by the inoculation of parasitized blood. The parasitemias were of a low level. Gametocytes were produced, and numerous mosquito feedings were carried out; none of the mosquitoes became infected.

Host Specificity

The natural host of *P. hylobati* is the gibbon; infections have been reported in *H. moloch* from Java and North Borneo. Experimentally, *M. mulatta*, *M. fascicularis*, and *M. nemestrina* have been infected by the inoculation of parasitized blood.

Two human volunteers were exposed to infection through the bites of *A. b. balabacensis* mosquitoes heavily infected with this parasite. No patent infection was produced.

The natural invertebrate host of *P. hylobati* is unknown. On an experimental basis, five species of anopheline mosquitoes have been infected. *Anopheles b. balabacensis* was the most susceptible followed by *A. stephensi*, *A. freeborni*, *A. maculatus* and finally *A. quadrimaculatus*. The intensity of the infections varied from one mosquito species to another (Table 13).

TABLE 13.—Comparative infectivity of *Plasmodium hylobati* in *Anopheles b. balabacensis*, *A. stephensi*, *A. freeborni*, *A. maculatus*, and *A. quadrimaculatus*.

Mosq. species comparison *	Number tests	Number of mosquitoes		Percent infection		GII ** ratios
		Standard	Other	Standard	Other	
Bal						100
Bal : St–1	2	20	15	100	100	49
Bal : F–1	2	20	20	100	90	43
Bal : Mac	2	20	29	100	100	22
Bal : Q–1	2	20	47	100	68	7

   * Bal = *Anopheles b. balabacensis*, St–1 = *A. stephensi*, F–1 = *A. freeborni*, Mac = *A. maculatus*, Q–1 = *A. quadrimaculatus*.
   ** GII = Gut Infection Index = average number of oocysts per 100 guts; the GII ratio is the relationship of the GII of *A. balabacensis* to another species where the GII of *A. balabacensis* = 100.

REFERENCES

GARNHAM, P. C. C., 1966. Malaria parasites and other haemosporidia. Blackwell Scientific Publications, Oxford.

HELD, J. R., CONTACOS, P. G., and COATNEY, G. R., 1967. Studies of the exoerythrocytic stages of simian malaria. I. *Plasmodium fieldi*. J. Parasit. 53 : 225–232.

RODHAIN, J., 1941. Sur un *Plasmodium* du gibbon *Hylobates lensciscus* Geoff. Acta. Biol. Belge *1* : 118–123.

SODEMAN, T. M., CONTACOS, P. G., COATNEY, G. R., and

JUMPER, J. R., 1969. Studies of the exoerythrocytic stages of simian malaria. V. *Plasmodium jefferyi*. J. Parasit. 55 : 1247–1252.

SODEMAN, T. M., CONTACOS, P. G., GARNHAM, P. C. C., JUMPER, J. R., and SMITH, C. S., 1971. Studies of the exoerythrocytic stages of simian malaria VI. *Plasmodium hylobati*. J. Parasit. (in press)

10

Plasmodium jefferyi Warren, Coatney, and Skinner, 1966

IN the case of this malaria, as is true of the early history of many others, there is an interesting side-light. In 1964, Dr. A. A. Sandosham, the Director of the Institute of Medical Research in Kuala Lumpur, Malaysia, and the senior author (GRC) were visting an area in north Malaysia when we chanced to meet a trapper who had, on numerous occasions, obtained animals for us. When queried as to why he had not sent in animals lately, he replied that his traps were in disrepair and that he had no money to pay for wire to fix them. He was given money immediately so his traps could be repaired; and, upon taking our leave, he was told to notify us immediately if he managed to catch a gibbon. The fates were kind. A young female gibbon, G 31, *Hylobates lar*, was brought to the laboratory in July, and when her blood was examined it was found to harbor *Plasmodium youngi* and a low-grade population of another parasite which was morphologically different from any other gibbon malaria. In the hope of obtaining a heavier infection of the then undescribed species, the infection was transferred to a malaria-free gibbon, G 32, by the inoculation of parasitized blood. The original description of the parasite to which Warren, Coatney, and Skinner (1966) gave the name *Plasmodium jefferyi*, in honor of their colleague, Dr. G. M. Jeffery, was based largely on material from that animal.

In reporting on this parasite, the authors were careful to point out the scarcity of young schizonts and the complete lack of mature schizonts in the peripheral blood. They were convinced, however, that they were dealing with a new species and depicted what they saw in a well executed colored plate.

Shortly before the closing of the LPC, NIH laboratory in Kuala Lumpur in 1964, the dual infection, *P. youngi* and the then undescribed species, was passed by inoculation of parasitized blood from G 31 to another gibbon (G 8). Shortly thereafter, both animals were shipped to the Laboratory of Parasite Chemotherapy, Section on Primate Malaria at Chamblee, Georgia. There, it was discovered that G 8 had a high parasite count so blood was withdrawn and deep frozen. Each of the animals died a short time later. The blood was left in the deep freeze until 1968 when a power failure early in that year necessitated immediate action if the specimens were to be saved. The blood was sent to the senior author in New Orleans, Louisiana, and inoculated forthwith into a parasite-free gibbon, *H. lar*, (G 420), at the Delta Regional Primate Research Center, Covington, Louisiana.

The animal (G 420) developed a patent infection 14 days later. However, its infection was quite different from the one in the donor animal (G 8) where *P. youngi* accounted for more than 80 percent of the parasite population at the time blood was drawn for freezing. In G 420, only one species of parasite was present and, although it resembled *P. jefferyi* in many respects, other of its characteristics were quite different. For example, fully mature schizonts, not seen in previous *P. jefferyi* infections, were abundant in the peripheral blood as were distinctive microgametocytes. In addition, the infection appeared to be of a fulminating type.

Our first thought was that maybe the parasite resulted from a latent infection in G 420 triggered by the splenectomy and subsequent manipulations. The splenectomy had been performed some 40 days prior to the transfer of parasitized blood and the prepatent period was within reasonable limits, that is, 14 days. The idea of a latent infection in G 420 therefore seemed remote; the question was *unde venit*, where did it come from? There was only one possible answer. The parasite had come from the blood of G 8.

That animal, as mentioned earlier, had had a dual infection in which the predominant parasite was *P. youngi* and a low-grade infection with the then undescribed new species (= *P. jefferyi*). The infection in G 420 was not *P. youngi*—that parasite apparently failed to survive the freezing episode. Therefore, the parasite in G 420 was *P. jefferyi* but with characteristics not observed and, consequently, not mentioned in the original description. The

situation is understandable when one remembers that the original natural infection exhibited only a low-grade parasitemia with the undescribed species (now carrying the designation *P. jefferyi*) and that that state of affairs was not greatly improved when the infection was transferred to G 32.

The presence of mature schizonts in the peripheral blood of G 420 and a microgametocyte of arresting characteristics had led us away from considering the parasite *P. jefferyi*. Later, the gaps and the inaccuracies in the original description were recognized. Whereupon, Coatney, Orihel, and Warren redescribed the parasite (1969) and included a colored plate to show the complete asexual cycle, the true macrogametocyte, and the distinctive microgametocyte.

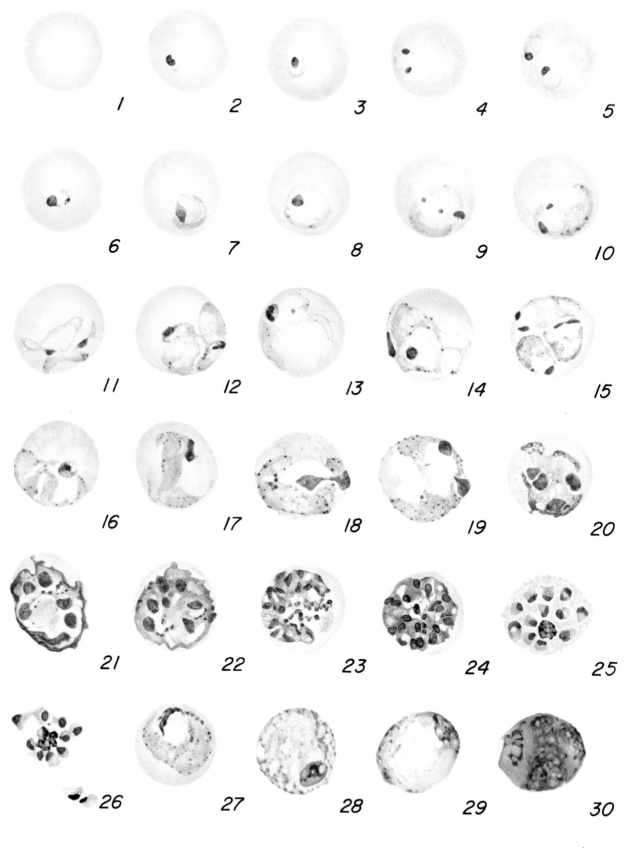

1   *2*   *3*   *4*   *5*

6   *7*   *8*   *9*   *10*

11   *12*   *13*   *14*   *15*

16   *17*   *18*   *19*   *20*

21   *22*   *23*   *24*   *25*

26   *27*   *28*   *29*   *30*

0   10μ

PLASMODIUM JEFFERYI

JWNicholson

Cycle in the Blood
PLATE XIV

The earliest ring forms display a deep red chromatin dot, measuring 1 μ in diameter, sometimes an accessory chromatin dot, and a delicate circle of blue-staining cytoplasm, or there may be two chromatin masses of unequal size. Marginal forms are rare, as are multiple infections in early infections. The host cell is not enlarged (Figs. 2–6). Growth forms may occupy up to one-half or more of the host cell. The nucleus stains a reddish-purple and may lie within a vacuole. The cytoplasm stains a pale blue (Figs. 7–9). The older trophozoites are frequently paisley-shaped with the nucleus, sometimes double, at the broad end and, occasionally, an accessory chromatin dot. The pigment is fine to seed-like and may be arranged along the periphery of the parasite (Figs. 10, 16, 17). Multiple infections of the host cell are common in developed infections (Figs. 5, 12, 14, 15).

Stippling is absent and there is no increase in the size of the host cell. The cytoplasm of the young schizont stains a pale blue and nearly fills the host cell. The pigment is in dust-like granules scattered throughout the cytoplasm. The nuclei stain a deep red (Figs. 18, 19). The older schizonts are more compact and do not fill the host cell. Their nuclei stain a deep red to reddish-purple and number from 4 to 18. The youngest of these forms exhibit a jagged periphery with pale blue cytoplasm confined to the center of the parasite. Light brown pigment granules are distributed unevenly in the cytoplasm (Figs. 20–22). Many of the 6-nucleate forms display an eosinophilic ring reminiscent of *P. fieldi* (Fig. 21). In the older forms, the periphery is smoother, pigment granules are coalesced,

massed toward the center of the parasite, and golden brown in color (Figs. 23, 24).

The mature schizonts have a body size less than that of the host cell (Fig. 25) and exhibit 10 to 18 blue-stained nuclei. The gold-black pigment is clumped. The parasite at this stage often assumes bizarre shapes with the merozoites piled on each other.

The young macrogametocytes, 3 to 4 μ in diameter, display a deeply stained red nucleus, with blue cytoplasm and with, or without, a vacuole. Older forms may have one, sometimes two, large vacuoles and fill or almost fill the host cell. The nucleus is bright pink with a deep reddish-purple bar or skein. The cytoplasm is grayish-blue with evenly distributed dust-like pigment (Fig. 27). The adult forms virtually fill the host cell. Their cytoplasm is without vacuoles and stains a light blue; pigment is in greenish-gold granules scattered evenly. The nucleus is bright red with a deep red bar or strand (Fig. 28).

The young microgametocytes, 3 to 4 μ in diameter, have a deeply stained red nucleus, sometimes two nuclear masses, compact cytoplasm, and only a suggestion of a vacuole next to the nucleus; the cytoplasm appears a very light brown. Older growth forms are roughly ellipsoidal, jug-shaped with one side depressed. The cytoplasm is generally without color and with fine dust-like pigment. The nucleus stains a light pink with a red to purple bar or skein (Fig. 29). Adult forms are predominantly oval, sometimes circular, with a slightly ragged appearance. The nucleus is located at the small end of the parasite and stains dark rosé with a reddish-purple bar, band, or skein. The cytoplasm stains reddish-pink and is overlaid by a golden-brown bead-like pigment sometimes arranged to present a stocking-cap effect to the more bulbous portion of the parasite.

PLATE XIV.—*Plasmodium jefferyi* from the gibbon.

Fig. 1. Normal red blood cell.
Figs. 2–6. Young trophozoites.
Figs. 7–17. Older trophozoites.
Figs. 18, 19. Young schizonts.
Figs. 20–24. Older schizonts.

Figs. 25–26. Mature schizonts.
Figs. 27, 28. Immature and mature macrogametocytes.
Figs. 29, 30. Immature and mature microgametocytes.
(*Plate reprinted, courtesy of the Journal of Parasitology.*)

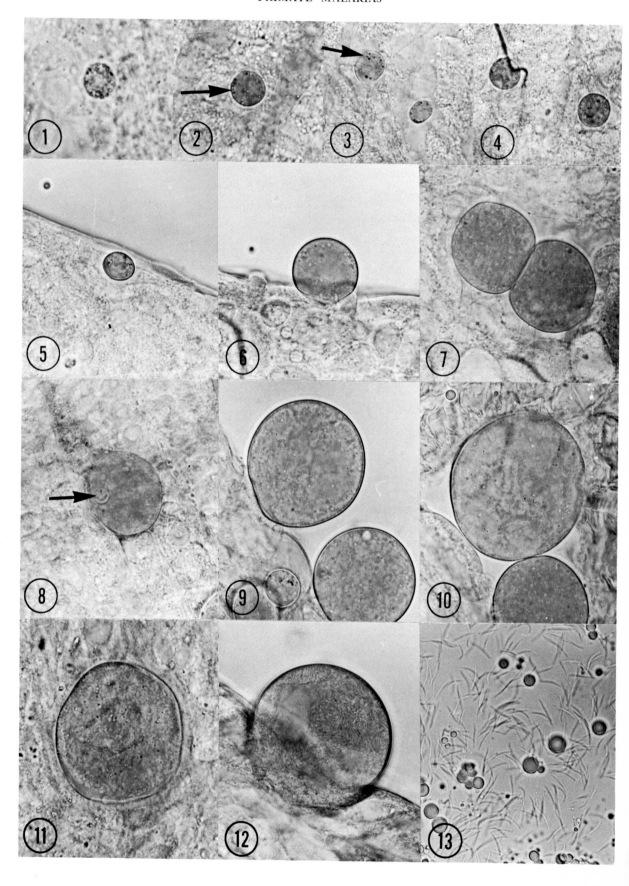

The parasite has a 48-hour periodicity.

Sporogonic Cycle

PLATE XV

During the course of the infection of *P. jefferyi* in gibbon 420, mosquitoes were shipped by air from our laboratory in Chamblee, Georgia, to New Orleans, Louisiana, and carried to the Delta Regional Primate Research Center in Covington, Louisiana, where they were allowed to feed on the animal; after feeding they were returned by air. The total travel time did not exceed 30 hours. Upon return, the mosquitoes were held at 25° C for the remainder of the extrinsic incubation period. Beginning on day 5 and continuing through day 14, sample mosquitoes were examined for the presence of oocysts (Collins and Orihel, 1969).

The oocyst diameters of *P. jefferyi* in four species of *Anopheles* are presented in Table 14. In *A. b. balabacensis*, on day five, the oocysts had a mean diameter of 9 μ with a range of 7 to 11 μ. They continued to grow so that on day 13, the mean diameter was 57 μ with a range of 33 to 77 μ. Sporozoites were present in the salivary glands on day 13.

In *A. freeborni*, the oocysts grew from a mean diameter of 8 μ on day 5 to a mean of 45 μ on day 13. Although differentiation was apparent by day 12, sporozoites were not found in the salivary glands until day 15 and then at a very low level.

In *A. maculatus*, the oocysts grew at a slower pace than in *A. b. balabacensis* and in *A. freeborni*.

The mean diameter on day 13 was 30 μ, versus 57 μ for *A. b. balabacensis*, and some of the oocysts had differentiated. Sporozoites were not seen in the salivary glands until day 17 and then at a low level and, in only one mosquito.

In *A. quadrimaculatus*, the growth rate was difficult to determine because of the limited number of oocysts. Oocyst differentiation was present by day 13 but salivary gland infections were not found through 17 days of observation. It thus appears that of the four test mosquitoes only *A. b. balabacensis* was a favorable host for *P. jefferyi*.

A comparison of the growth curve of *P. jefferyi* with that of *P. cynomolgi* in *A. b. balabacensis* mosquitoes (Fig. 30) shows that *P. cynomolgi* is considerably larger and completes its development approximately 3 days sooner than does *P. jefferyi*. A comparison with another gibbon malaria parasite, *P. hylobati* indicates that *P. jefferyi* is much smaller but takes only one day longer for sporozoites to appear in the salivary glands.

As discussed later, it was not possible to determine if the sporozoites were infective. Even though EE bodies were produced after inoculation of these sporozoites into a clean, splenectomized gibbon, no erythrocytic infection resulted.

Cycle in the Tissue

PLATE XVI

Although four species of gibbon malarias are known, exoerythrocytic parasites of *Plas-*

PLATE XV.—Developing oocysts and sporozoites of *Plasmodium jefferyi* in *Anopheles b. balabacensis* mosquitoes. X 580 (except Figs. 1 and 2).

Fig. 1.   4-day oocyst. X 1300.
Fig. 2.   6-day oocyst showing peripheral pigment. X 1300.
Fig. 3.   7-day oocyst showing prominent pigment.
Fig. 4.   8-day oocyst with pigment becoming less distinct.
Fig. 5.   9-day oocyst.
Fig. 6.   10-day oocyst.
Fig. 7.   10-day oocysts.
Fig. 8.   11-day oocyst showing vacuole containing pigment.

Fig. 9.   12-day oocysts showing two with normal development and one which has failed to develop.
Fig. 10.   12-day oocysts, one of which is showing early differentiation.
Fig. 11.   13-day oocyst showing more advanced differentiation.
Fig. 12.   13-day oocyst showing full differentiation.
Fig. 13.   Sporozoites from salivary gland tissue 14 days after feeding.

TABLE 14.—Oocyst diameters of *Plasmodium jefferyi* in *Anopheles b. balabacensis*, *A. freeborni*, *A. maculatus*, and *A. quadrimaculatus*.

Days Post Infection	A. b. balabacensis			A. freeborni			A. maculatus			A. quadrimaculatus		
	No.	Range*	Mean	No.	Range	Mean	No.	Range	Mean	No.	Range	Mean
5	70	7–11	9	101	5–10	8	20	8–11	9	5	7–11	10
6	57	7–17	12	62	6–13	9	31	7–13	10	4	8–14	8
7	95	8–24	14	100	7–18	12	24	9–19	13	8	8–18	12
8	100	9–26	16	54	8–25	14	27	9–21	12	5	15–26	20
9	38	14–27	19	61	8–20	14	35	9–31	17	38	12–37	18
10	100	9–46	24	100	12–40	19	16	12–50	17	18	14–51	28
11	24	13–36	25	100	15–50	30	34	8–36	21	29	11–40	24
12	100	19–73	40†	29	14–59	31†	23	14–44	27	16	17–54	40
13	41	33–77	57†**	76	14–73	45†	56	19–64	30†	4	28–59	46†
14							80	12–61	35†	2	53–55	54†

*   Measurements expressed in microns; incubation temperature 25° C.
†   Oocyst differentiation.
** Sporozoites present in the salivary glands.

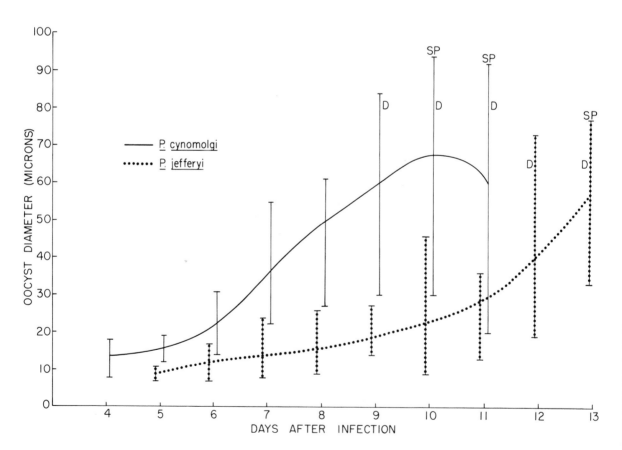

FIGURE 30.—Mean oocyst growth curve and ranges in oocyst diameters of *Plasmodium cynomolgi* and *P. jefferyi* in *Anopheles b. balabacensis* mosquitoes. (D = oocyst differentiation; SP = sporozoites present in the salivary glands).

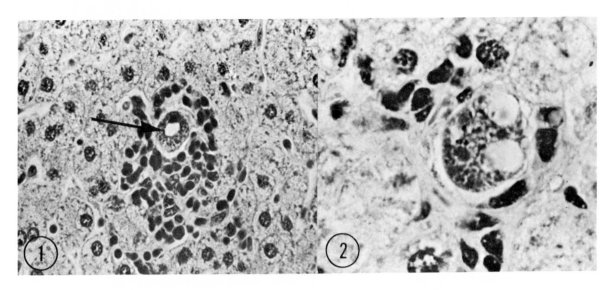

PLATE XVI.—Exoerythrocytic bodies of *Plasmodium jefferyi* in *Hylobates lar*.

Fig. 1.   6-day exoerythrocytic body surrounded by
mononuclear cell infiltration. X 580.

Fig. 2.   6-day exoerythrocytic body containing two
prominent vacuoles. X 930.

modium jefferyi were the first to be described (Sodeman *et al*, 1969). An experimental infection of *P. jefferyi* in a gibbon (*H. lar pileatus*) was induced by inoculating sporozoites directly into the liver at laparotomy, and, by sporozoites introduced intravenously. On day 6, following the inoculations, a biopsy at the site of infection of the liver was taken and the tissue sectioned at 1, 2, 3, 4, and 6 μ. Numerous EE bodies of *P. jefferyi* were found in the sections.

The tissue parasites were round to elliptical. The average dimensions were 16.8 by 19.4 μ with a range of 10.8 to 21.6 by 14.4 to 24.0 μ. The edge of the parasite was smooth and usually enclosed by a distinct thin limiting membrane. The nuclei were usually round but frequently appeared diploid; some had bar and triangular shapes. The nuclei stained magenta, were about 1.0 to 1.5 μ in diameter, and did not display a pattern of distribution.

The cytoplasm was granular in texture and stained a pale blue with irregular-shaped, dark blue, aggregates ("flocculi") scattered through the cytoplasm. The aggregates stained homogeneously but in thin sections small holes were evident. A prominent feature of *P. jefferyi* EE bodies was the presence of 0 to 5 large, round to oval, vacuoles in the body, (Fig. 1, 2). These structures, 4.1 by 4.8 μ, often had pink

or deep-purple stained material in them.

The EE bodies caused enlargement of the liver cell and pushed the normal sized nucleus to one side. Vacuoles were seldom found in unparasitized liver cells. Focal mononuclear cell infiltrates were scattered through the sections; some were associated with portal regions. Infrequently, EE bodies were found within these infiltrates. Mononuclear cell infiltration was not infrequent in areas surrounding the EE bodies, which suggests that the parasite provoked an unfavorable host response (Fig. 1).

The general morphological features of *P. jefferyi* EE bodies are similar to those of other primate malarias as discussed by Held *et al*, (1967). At that time it appeared that the most consistant feature of a given species was the average size of its EE bodies in relation to the day of infection. However, comparison shows that this is hazardous because their measurements present overlapping ranges. If, with the present data, that criterion is not reliable, and there appear to be no other distinguishing features for recognizing the EE stages of *P. jefferyi*, such as nuclear clefts or cytoplasmic patterns different from those in many other simian malaria species; then, species cannot be separated, at the present time, on the basis of the morphology of the fixed tissue schizonts.

Sodeman *et al* in discussing the presence of

11

Plasmodium pitheci Halberstaedter and von Prowazek, 1907

THIS was probably the first true simian plasmodium to be seen and described. Laveran, in 1905, mentions a blood parasite seen in smears taken from an orangutan in Paris. In 1907, Halberstaedter and von Prowazek, working in Borneo, described the parasite they found in the orangutan and named it *Plasmodium pitheci*. Shibayama (1910) saw the parasite in the blood of an orangutan imported to Japan and remarked that Schüffner's dots were not present but, as Wenyon (1926) pointed out, his figures indicate that he used a weak stain which could account for the lack of Schüffner's dots. Dodd (1913) reported the death of an orangutan in the Zoological Gardens of New South Wales as probably due to *Haemoproteus* (= *Plasmodium*) *pitheci*. In 1920, Reichenow put forward the idea, but without conviction, that maybe *P. pitheci* was actually a human parasite although Koch (1900) had failed in an attempt to infect the orangutan and the gibbon with *P. vivax* or with *P. falciparum*. Donovan (1921) carried out a study of blood parasites in simians at the foot of the Nilgiri hills in southern India and reported finding *P. pitheci* in the orangutan. This finding is open to question because, as all authorities agree, these animals occur on Sumatra and Borneo only, although, according to Darlington (1957), they were in India during the Lower Pleistocene era.

The parasite was not seen again until one of us (McWW) visited Borneo in 1966 and while there succeeded in obtaining blood smears from 18 orangutans; ten of the animals harbored *P. pitheci*. The description of the blood stages of the parasite and the color plate is based on that material.

As in any endeavor, success or failure may hang by a slender thread. Such might have been the case in the above instance. In 1966, McWW was given a short-term assignment to study the zoonotic aspects of simian malaria in West Malaysia. During the planning of that work, the desirability of his making a side-trip to Borneo in the vain hope of retrieving the malaria parasite of the orangutan, last seen in 1913, was discussed. It was realized that the Malaysia assignment would be difficult because of the limitation in time and funds, but it was agreed that the trip would be made if at all possible. He went to Malaysia and near the end of his tour he let one of us (GRC) know that it would be difficult for him to complete the original work on schedule and therefore he would probably have to abandon the trip to Borneo. It seemed that to miss this chance of finding *P. pitheci* again would be catastrophic—the effort must be made. A cable was sent to him to the effect: "Go to Borneo or don't come back—letter follows". The letter merely reiterated what we both knew as to the importance of the project and urged him to go to Borneo if at all possible. Upon receipt of the cable, he left immediately for Borneo with excellent results as mentioned earlier. It goes without saying that he finished the original assignment in a highly creditable manner and on schedule. One wonders would he have gone to Borneo sans cable? Who can say—the point is: he did!

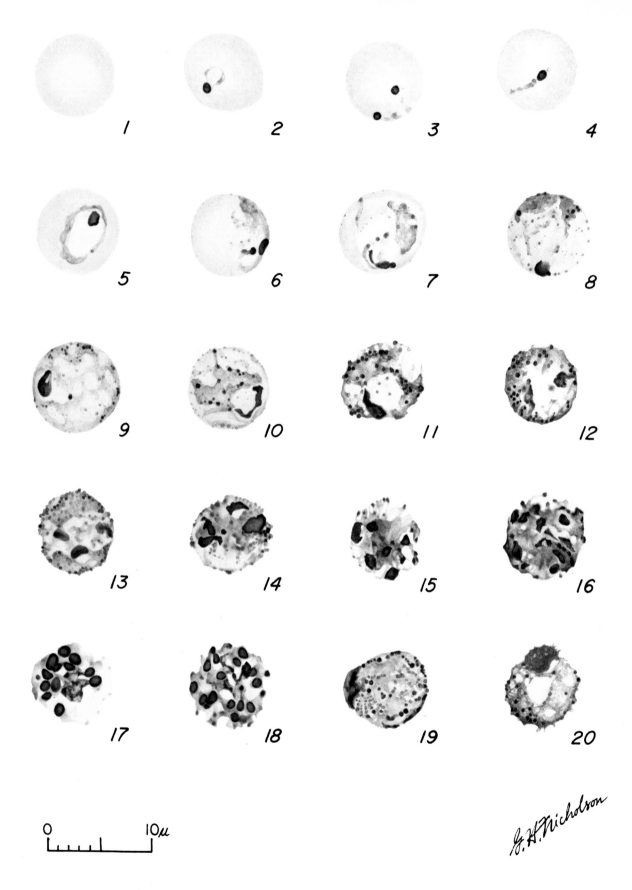

0   10μ

G.H.Nicholson

PLASMODIUM PITHECI

Cycle in the Blood
PLATE XVII

The youngest parasites consist of a small amount of bluish-gray cytoplasm associated with a deep purple-staining nucleus. The cytoplasm may appear as a ring or only as an elongate smudge (Fig. 4). Double invasion of the cell is rare but it may occur (Fig. 3). As growth proceeds, there is an increase in the amount of cytoplasm with the nucleus remaining essentially unchanged. The cytoplasm becomes amoeboid. Very light stippling appears in the red cell as the trophozoite approaches maturity. Pigment first appears as a coarse, greenish-brown granule. As growth continues, the increase in pigment is by the addition of more greenish-brown granules. The nucleus stains wine-red as it increases in size. There is little or no host cell enlargement.

The cytoplasm of the mature trophozoite is amoeboid and frequently assumes a web formation which almost fills the cell. The nucleus may be distorted. The stippling is sparse and granular with little or no host cell enlargement. The pigment is greenish-black and appears as uniform coarse granules.

The nuclear divisions are not out of the ordinary. The color of the nuclei changes from wine-red in the early stages, to deep purple in the mature forms. The cytoplasm gradually changes from light blue to a reddish-purple and virtually disappears in the mature forms. Pigment granules tend to gather in one part of the cell and then the granular bodies coalesce into one or more greenish-yellow masses (Fig. 17). Stippling remains sparse and is sometimes inapparent since the developing schizont usually fills the entire host cell with little or no host cell enlargement or distortion. The mature schizont normally has 12 to 14 merozoites (Fig. 18).

The macrogametocyte fills the host cell completely and without enlargement (Fig. 19). The nucleus is large, usually oval, dark-staining and generally found near the periphery of the parasite. The cytoplasm is uniform and stains grayish-blue. The pigment is abundant, coarsely granular, and evenly distributed. The microgametocyte also fills the host cell without increasing its size (Fig. 20). The nucleus is larger than its counterpart in the macrogametocyte and it takes a lighter stain. It is oval to circular and stains wine-red. The bluish-gray staining cytoplasm is frequently vacuolated and lacks the uniform consistency seen in the macrogametocyte. The pigment is coarse, granular, and generally less abundant than in the macrogametocyte.

Sporogonic Cycle

There are no data on the sporogonic cycle.

Cycle in the Tissue

No exoerythrocytic stages are known.

Course of Infection

The course of the infection, as described by the original investigators, runs a chronic course with little if any pathology. The temperature in infected animals was within the normal range. In contrast, Dodd (1913) was of the opinion that the death of an orangutan kept for some 13 months in the Zoological Gardens in Sydney, NSW, was probably due to an overwhelming infection with *P. pitheci*. It is unfortunate that a thorough post mortem was not done on the animal, or, if it was, that the findings should have been limited to a single note stating that the bone marrow of the femur, humerus, and ribs was decidedly congested. None of the infected animals examined by

PLATE XVII.—*Plasmodium pitheci.*

Fig. 1. Normal red cell.
Figs. 2–4. Young trophozoites.
Figs. 5–9. Growing trophozoites.
Figs. 10–11. Mature trophozoites.

Figs. 12–16. Developing schizonts.
Figs. 17–18. Mature schizonts.
Fig. 19. Mature macrogametocyte.
Fig. 20. Mature microgametocyte.

McWW showed any clinical evidence of infection.

Host Specificity

The normal host of *P. pitheci* is the orangutan, *Pongo pygmaeus*. According to Halberstaedter and Prowazek (1907) the parasite could be transferred successfully by blood inoculation to other orangutans but not to gibbons or to monkeys. In an attempt to augment the above findings regarding host specificity, blood obtained from three infected orangutans in Borneo was shipped to the United States and given intravenously to a young splenectomized chimpanzee (#31) on 11 July 1967. The infection became patent on the 21st of September and remained so, always with a low parasite count, until 17 October 1967. On 2 October 1967 parasitized blood was transferred to three different monkeys: an owl (*Aotus trivirgatus*), a pig-tailed (*Macaca nemestrina*), and a rhesus (*Macaca mulatta*). None of these animals became infected. A similar inoculation into a gibbon was not successful.

Also, during the fall of 1967, parasitized blood was given to a second young splenectomized chimpanzee (#1394), which exhibited a patent infection after 18 days. The parasitemia remained low for ten days whereupon it terminated spontaneously. These limited data tend to show that the parasite does not infect other apes well and does not grow in monkeys. It is hoped that opportunities will be found whereby this parasite, whose host is one of our near relatives evolutionarily, can be given the opportunity to infect man.

The natural invertebrate host is not known and as far as we can learn there have been no attempts to find a mosquito capable of accepting infection with the parasite.

REFERENCES

DARLINGTON, P. J., JR., 1957. Zoogeography: the geographical distribution of animals. John Wiley & Son, Inc., New York.

DODD, S., 1913. Anaplasms or jolly bodies? J. Comp. Path. & Therap. *26* : 97–110.

DONOVAN, C., 1921. Malaria of Monkeys. Ind. J. Med. Res. *7* : 717–720.

HALBERSTAEDTER, L. and VON PROWAZEK, S., 1907. Untersuchungen über die malariaparasiten der affen. Arb. K. Gesundh. -Amte (Berl.) *26* : 37–43.

KOCH, R., 1900. Zweiter bericht über die thätigkeit der malariaexpedition. Deutsche Med. Wochenschr.

26 : 88–90.

LAVERAN, M. A., 1905. Haemocytozoa. Essai de classification. Bull. Inst. Pasteur *3* : 809–817.

REICHENOW, E., 1920. Ueber das vorkommen der malariaparasiten des menschen bei den afrikanischen menschenaffen. Centralbl. f. Bakt. I. Abt. Orig. *85* : 207–216.

SHIBAYAMA, G., 1910. On malaria parasites of the orangoutan. Philippine J. Sci. *5* : 189–191.

WENYON, C. M., 1926. Protozoology. II. William Wood & Co., New York.

12

Plasmodium schwetzi Brumpt, 1939

THE credit for being the first to see parasites of malaria in chimpanzees must go to Ziemann but we are not able to determine with certainty just which species he saw. In 1920 Reichenow, while working in the Cameroons, examined the blood of sixteen apes among which he found human-like tertian, quartan, and falciparum parasites of malaria. The parasite he considered the counterpart of *P. vivax* was found in three of the chimpanzees and in two of the gorillas. He described and illustrated that parasite along with the others. In 1922 Blacklock and Adler, working in Freetown, Sierra Leone, saw each of the three human-like parasites of malaria in the chimpanzee as had Reichenow earlier. Probably because the population of the ovale (vivax)-like parasites was so scanty, they elected not to give it a name; however, they did include it in their plate.

For a little over a decade these interesting parasites appear to have been virtually ignored but in the early thirties, Schwetz began his work in the Belgian Congo (Schwetz, 1933, 1933a). In the blood of two adult gorillas and three young chimpanzees he found *Plasmodium vivax*-forms along with malariae- and falciparum-forms. In the 1933a paper, in discussing the vivax-forms, he mentioned their ovale-like characteristics and his beautifully executed colored plate makes this point doubly clear. In 1934 Schwetz, in describing a double infection in a young chimpanzee, again mentioned the close resemblance of the vivax-like parasites to *P. ovale*. And, here again, in a beautifully painted plate, which emphasizes the heavy stippling so characteristic of *P. ovale*, he figured fourteen of the peripheral blood stages. Because of the close resemblance of these parasites to the human ones, investigators were prompted to attempt cross-infection experiments. The initial results were not altogether convincing which prompted Brumpt (1939) to propose the name *Plasmodium schwetzi* for the ovale-vivax parasite of the chimpanzee under the firm belief that it was enough different, morphologically and biologically, from *P. vivax* or *P. ovale*, to justify the name.

As work continued on these forms the concensus appeared to be that the schwetzi parasite was more like *P. vivax* than it was like *P. ovale* and hence Bray (1958) felt justified in making it a subspecies of *P. vivax*. We are not sympathetic toward subspecies designations, except under very special conditions, and, because our studies have convinced us that *P. schwetzi* is an entity, more closely allied to *P. ovale* than to *P. vivax*, we have elected to consider the parasite *Plasmodium schwetzi* Brumpt.

Plasmodium schwetzi is an African-based parasite with the apes in Sierra Leone and Liberia having the heaviest incidence of infection. The infection continues east and south, almost running out in the eastern Congo. It has been reported as absent in the Lake Kivu area of the Democratic Republic of the Congo by Schwetz and by van den Berghe and, so far, it has not been reported in Uganda. However, we isolated the parasite recently from a chimpanzee taken in the vicinity of Lake Edward, north of Lake Kivu, which places its distribution east to about 29°. *Plasmodium schwetzi* can therefore be said to occur in an area from the Cameroons to 29° E in the lower Congo and thence west into Liberia and Sierra Leone.

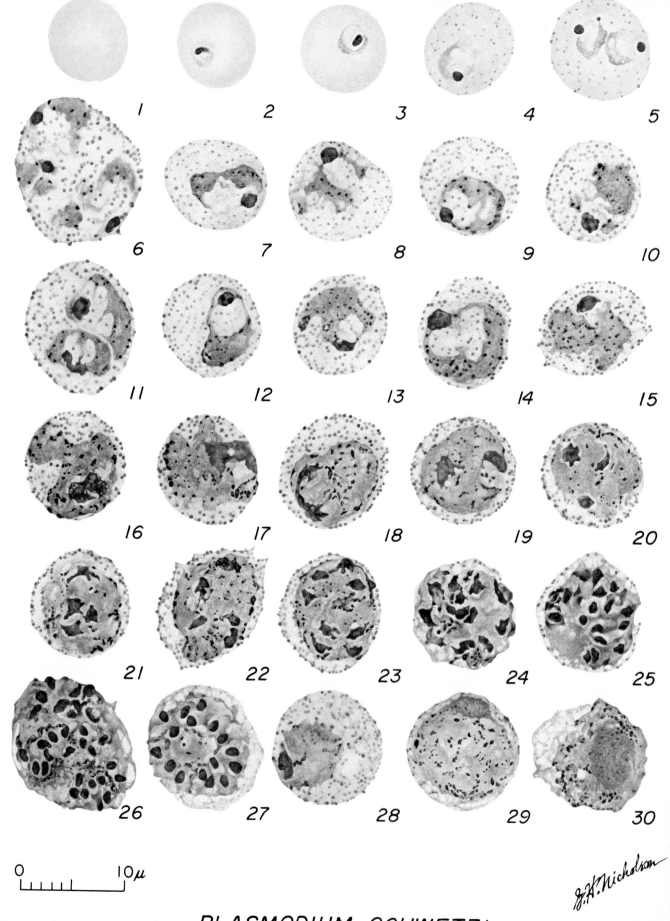

1   2   3   4   5

6   7   8   9   10

11   12   13   14   15

16   17   18   19   20

21   22   23   24   25

26   27   28   29   30

0 |_|_|_|_|_|_|_|_| 10μ

J.H.Nicholson

PLASMODIUM SCHWETZI

Cycle in the Blood
PLATE XVIII

The earliest parasites are relatively compact rings with a round to oval nucleus which stains dark reddish-black with Giemsa. There is practically no cell enlargement, no stippling, and no visible pigment in these early developmental stages (Figs. 2, 3). The first evidence of the parasite's growth is seen in the older ring forms with the expansion of the cytoplasm; the nucleus remains circular to oval, compact, and deep staining. Some enlargement of the invaded red blood cell is seen by the time the parasite occupies one quarter of the host cell (Figs. 4, 5). Light, granular stippling also appears at this time. Multiple infections are not uncommon (Fig. 5). The trophozoite grows with some increase in amoeboidity; the cytoplasm takes a more intense stain indicating that the cytoplasmic density increases as the parasite matures (Figs. 7–10). The host cell is definitely enlarged, the size is stabilized and does not change markedly with the development of the schizonts so long as only one parasite is involved in a single blood cell. The stippling is abundant, evenly distributed, and uniformly coarse. The amount of pigment increases as the parasite matures and appears as greenish-black moderately coarse granules scattered through the cytoplasm. At times this pigment seems to appear in clusters (Fig. 10). The nucleus increases in size as the parasite grows and generally maintains its oval to circular outline although the specific border may be somewhat irregular. With the increase in size the staining of the nucleus lightens considerably from very deep purple to a wine-red with darker inclusions. In the mature trophozoite, the cytoplasm increases in amount but the intensity of the

staining is much the same as that found in the growing trophozoites (Figs. 12–15). The cytoplasmic vacuole, which is quite common in the younger stages, gradually disappears as the parasite matures. Pigment increases in amount and the size of the individual granules seems to become larger and more prominent. There is an increase in the size of the nucleus which is irregular in shape and now displays a lighter staining reaction than that seen in the younger stages (Fig. 15).

During the early stages of nuclear division there is little or no change in the parasite or the host cell except that with continued nuclear division there may be some host cell distortion, reminiscent of *P. ovale*, (Figs. 22, 23) which proceeds as the schizont continues to grow (Figs. 23–25). Following the 6 to 8 nucleate stage, the cytoplasm appears more purple than blue. It is frequently fragmented and irregular in shape although, in some instances, a large segment of the cytoplasm is free of nuclei and these segments retain their initial blue color (Fig. 25). The pigment organizes into one or more distinct masses and these masses take on a yellowish cast (Fig. 25). The stippling becomes difficult to differentiate as the parasite frequently fills most of the red blood cell leaving only a pale eosinophilic web around the border of the parasite (Figs. 25, 27).

The mature schizont usually has from 12 to 16 distinct nuclear masses not infrequently discretely organized around a combination of a blue staining cytoplasmic residual and clusters of pigment (Fig. 27). Mature schizonts are frequently in distinctly oval red blood cells. As the number of nuclei increases, the individual nuclei decrease in size, lose their wine-red color, and assume the dark purple color seen in the young ring stages.

The macrogametocyte is regular in shape

PLATE XVIII.—*Plasmodium schwetzi*.

Fig. 1.   Normal red cell.
Figs. 2, 3.   Young trophozoites.
Figs. 4–14.   Growing trophozoites, showing double and triple host cell infections.
Figs. 15–18.   Older and mature trophozoites.

Figs. 19–24.   Developing schizonts.
Figs. 25–27.   Nearly mature and mature schizonts.
Figs. 28, 29.   Half-grown and mature macrogametocytes.
Fig. 30.   Mature microgametocyte.

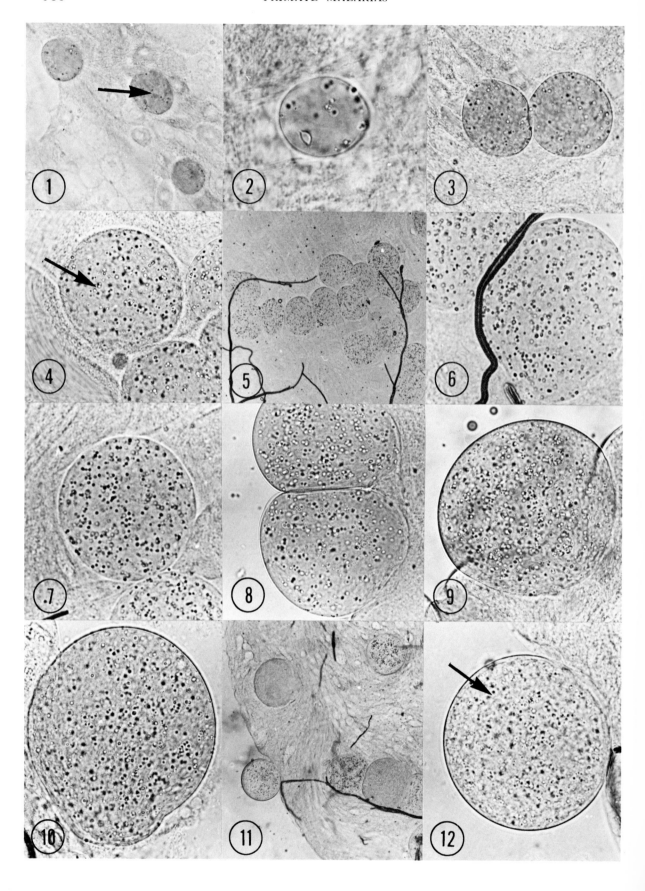

PLATE XIX.—Developing oocysts of *Plasmodium schwetzi* in *Anopheles b. balabacensis* mosquitoes. X 580 (except where indicated).

Fig. 1.   4.5-day oocyst showing scattered pigment.

Fig. 2.   5.5-day oocyst. X 928.

Fig. 3.   6.5-day oocysts showing small vacuoles and pigment.

Fig. 4.   7.5-day oocysts showing numerous small vacuoles.

Fig. 5.   8.5-day oocysts showing prominent vacuolation. X 145.

Fig. 6.   8.5-day oocysts.

Fig. 7.   8.5-day oocysts.

Fig. 8.   9.5-day oocysts showing less prominent vacuolation.

Fig. 9.   10.5-day oocyst.

Fig. 10.   11.5-day oocyst.

Fig. 11.   12.5-day oocysts. X 145.

Fig. 12.   12.5-day oocyst showing first signs of differentiation.

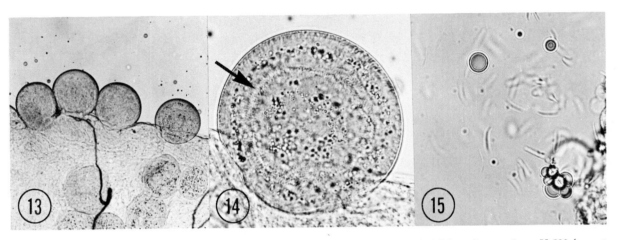

PLATE XX.—Developing oocysts and sporozoites of *Plasmodium schwetzi* in *Anopheles b. balabacensis* mosquitoes. X 580 (except where indicated).

Fig. 13.   13.5-day oocysts. X 145.

Fig. 14.   13.5-day oocyst showing more advanced stage of differentiation.

Fig. 15.   Sporozoites present near salivary gland tissue 15.5 days after feeding.

and stains uniformly blue. The pigment is coarse, black to greenish-black and evenly distributed. The nucleus, usually oval and peripheral, stains a deep wine-red. The mature parasite almost fills the enlarged erythrocyte and is surrounded generally by the eosinophilic web-like border of the host cell (Figs. 28, 29).

The microgametocyte is usually brightly colored with reddish-purple cytoplasm and a large, diffuse wine-red nucleus. The cytoplasmic edge of the parasite is frequently crenated or lace-like and tends to merge with the eosinophilic web of the enlarged host cell. The pigment is coarse, black to greenish-black and evenly distributed (Fig. 30).

The parasite has a 48-hour cycle in the chimpanzee. According to Bray (1963) the cycle may lengthen to a 50- to a 52-hour cycle as the infection progresses; we did not observe this phenomenon.

Sporogonic Cycle
PLATE XIX, XX

The natural vector of this parasite is unknown. The earliest attempt to find a vector was that of Blacklock and Adler (1922) who obtained negative results after feeding 40 *A. costalis* (= *A. gambiae*) on a chimpanzee infected with *P. reichenowi* and *P. schwetzi*. Rodhain and Lassman (1940) successfully infected *Anopheles maculipennis* var. *atroparvus* with *P. schwetzi*. The oocysts were large, measuring up to 88.8 μ; *P. vivax*, in their experience, measured up to 66 μ. Rodhain (1955) obtained a 66 percent infection rate in *A. m. atroparvus*. The oocysts matured in 13 to 14 days; the dimensions were 70 to 74 μ. The sporozoites were in the glands by day 14 to day 15; their chromatin was centrally located.

Bray (1958) was able to study the sexual

development in *A. gambaie*. In that host, the cycle required 10 days at 75-80° F. He did not feel that *A. gambiae* constituted a good vector because the salivary glands were scantily infected. The mature oocysts had an average diameter of 60.6 μ on the 10th day which is larger than *P. vivax* (45 to 55 μ). At the 4- and 5-day level Bray found the *P. schwetzi* oocysts resembled exactly those of *P. vivax*.

Garnham (1966) reported that *P. schwetzi* developed readily in *A. aztecus* at a temperature of 22° C. The oocysts had grown to 18 μ at day 6 and to 68 μ after day 13. In the young oocysts the pigment was found in straight or curved lines. We have been able to infect the Asian anophelines, *A. b. balabacensis* and *A. maculatus*, as well as the California-based anopheline, *A. freeborni* (Collins *et al*, 1969). The mosquitoes were incubated at 25° C beginning 30 hours after exposure. The oocyst diameters are presented in Table 16. In *A. b. balabacensis*, at day 3.5, the mean oocyst diameter was 16 μ with a range of 12 to 21 μ. The oocysts continued to grow so that by day 14.5,

the mean diameter was 81 μ with a range of 47 to 103 μ. The most obvious morphological feature of the oocysts was the presence of numerous small, spherical inclusions which appeared to be vacuoles (Plate XIX). Although such inclusions are found in the oocysts of most of the plasmodia, they are more abundant in *P. schwetzi*. Inclusions were also found abundant in *P. gonderi* and *P. simium* but to a lesser extent. The oocysts are larger than those of most species; their size was comparable to those measured by Rodhain in *A. m. atroparvus*. Sporozoites were present in the salivary glands on day 14.5 and were viable in that *P. schwetzi* infection was transmitted to human volunteers as discussed below.

A comparison of the growth rate of *P. schwetzi* with that of *P. cynomolgi* in *A. b. balabacensis* mosquitoes (Fig. 32) shows that they are approximately of the same size through 10.5 days. However, the oocysts of *P. cynomolgi* have differentiated by that time and sporozoites are present in the salivary glands. In contrast, the oocysts of *P. schwetzi* continue to

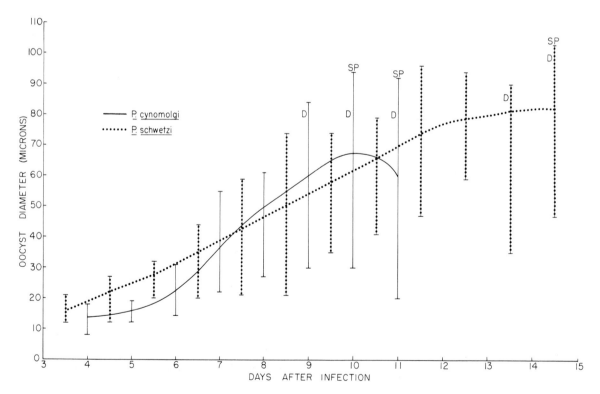

FIGURE 32.—Range in oocyst diameters and the mean oocyst diameter curves of *Plasmodium schwetzi* and *P. cynomolgi* in *Anopheles b. balabacensis* mosquitoes. (D = oocyst differentiation; SP = sporozoites present in the salivary glands).

grow and do not differentiate until day 13.5 with sporozoites in the glands on day 14.5. In other words, *P. schwetzi* requires approximately 4.5 days longer to complete the sporogonic cycle than does *P. cynomolgi*.

Cycle in the Tissue

We regret to say there are no data on the exoerythrocytic cycle of *P. schwetzi*. We were fortunate in obtaining good infections in mosquitoes, discussed above, but unfortunately no chimpanzees were available to us at that time and therefore the opportunity for finding these forms was lost.

Course of Infection

The natural hosts of *Plasmodium schwetzi* are the chimpanzee and the gorilla. It was from these hosts that Reichenow described the parasite originally, having found it in three of eight chimpanzees and in two of eight gorillas. One of the young chimpanzees showed a moderate infection but in the other animals the parasitemia was low. It does not appear to evoke clinical symptoms even in young chimpanzees and we observed no clinical evidence of infection in splenectomized older chimpanzees even though they exhibited high parasitemias.

Plasmodium schwetzi generally occurs as a mixed infection with *P. reichenowi* and *P. rodhaini* and, prior to our studies, begun in 1967, it was assumed that initially one or both of the latter parasites dominated or suppressed the *P. schwetzi* infection. This may be true for intact animals in nature; however, when *P. reichenowi* and *P. schwetzi* are introduced together into a splenectomized and an intact chimpanzee the schwetzi malaria assumes almost complete dominance over *P. reichenowi*.

So far all attempts to infect any of the monkeys with this parasite have failed.

The parasite will grow and produce disease in man as will be detailed below. The early attempts to infect man with *P. schwetzi* resulted in failure. The first was that of Blacklock and Adler (1922) who transferred blood from a chimpanzee infected with *P. schwetzi*, *P. reichenowi*, and *P. rodhaini* to two people. One person received the blood both intravenously and intramuscularly and the other received it subcutaneously. Neither one exhibited evidence of a malarial infection after an observation period of 28 and 17 days, respectively. Rodhain and Muylle (1938) tried to infect three patients requiring malaria therapy. The first patient received the parasitized chimpanzee blood by intramuscular injection, the second and third by the intravenous route. None of the patients contracted the infection.

TABLE 16.—Oocyst diameters of *Plasmodium schwetzi* in *Anopheles b. balabacensis*, *A. maculatus*, and *A. freeborni*.

Days after infection	A. b. balabacensis			A. maculatus			A. freeborni		
	No.	Range	Mean*	No.	Range	Mean	No.	Range	Mean
3.5	100	12–21	16	16	13–15	14	41	9–14	12
4.5	81	12–27	23	12	15–22	19	45	15–21	18
5.5	20	20–32	27	34	13–22	19	75	9–25	20
6.5	65	20–44	35	26	17–26	21	64	19–35	27
7.5	75	21–59	45	64	20–45	32	40	27–53	41
8.5	56	21–74	58	52	26–60	42	60	32–71	55
9.5	60	35–74	53	52	28–59	43	9	51–64	56
10.5	60	41–79	62	60	31–84	55			
11.5	60	47–96	77	15	39–80	63‡			
12.5	15	59–94	79	63	35–83	57‡			
13.5	54	35–90	74†	13	39–76	51†‡			
14.5	41	37–103	81†**	40	28–83	58†‡			

* Measurements expressed in microns; incubation temperature 25° C.

† Oocyst differentiation.

‡ Oocyst degeneration.

** Sporozoites present in the salivary glands.

In the same year (1938) Rodhain, van Hoof and Muylle reported their failures in trying to infect man with the vivax parasite (= *P. schwetzi*) and in 1939 Rodhain again tried to infect man with *P. schwetzi* by the inoculation of infected blood; it failed. He drew the conclusion that *P. schwetzi* was a true parasite of the chimpanzee and not infective to man.

In 1940 Rodhain, concerned with the possible transfer of *P. rodhaini* to man, passaged blood from a chimpanzee infected with *P. rodhaini* and with *P. schwetzi* to two people. The quartan infection appeared in each of the inoculated individuals and with it there appeared a vivax-like parasite too; i.e., *P. schwetzi*. Rodhain expressed some doubt about the latter being *P. schwetzi*, probably because of his previous failures to infect man, and, because the chimpanzee had been inoculated with known *P. vivax* some two years before; that infection had persisted for some weeks. The infection then disappeared and was not seen subsequently during the following two years. In the light of what happened later it is more than probable that the vivax-like parasite in the recipients was actually *P. schwetzi*. For the next fifteen years the question of whether *P. schwetzi* would infect man was allowed to lie fallow.

In 1955 and 1955a Rodhain and Dellaert reported that they had been able to infect man with *P. schwetzi*. They detailed the successful infection of a man and from him to other humans, then back to the chimpanzee, and, again, back to man. In each instance the infection was initiated by the inoculation of parasitized blood. In their first paper, in commenting on the parasite in man they mentioned its close resemblance to *P. ovale*, a fact mentioned as early as 1934 by Schwetz and later by Bray (1958). One wonders, in view of their unqualified success in 1955, why they made no mention of Rodhain's transfer of *P. schwetzi* to man in 1940.

Our own studies of this parasite in man came about through a series of fortuitous circumstances (Contacos et al, 1970). Several chimpanzees at the Delta Regional Primate Research Center in Covington, Louisiana became available for studies in malaria. Blood parasitized with *P. reichenowi* and *P. schwetzi*, obtained from a chimpanzee at the National Communicable Disease Center, Atlanta-Chamblee, Georgia, was inoculated into a chimpanzee in Covington, Louisiana. A patent infection of the two malaria parasites developed in this chimpanzee; but, in a rather short period of time, the *P. schwetzi* parasite became the predominant one. When gametocytes of this species were numerous, mosquitoes (*Anopheles freeborni*, *A. maculatus*, and *A. b. balabacensis*) from our laboratories in Chamblee were shipped by air to New Orleans and carried to Covington, Louisiana, for feeding on the chimpanzee. These were returned to the insectary in Chamblee, Georgia, within 30 hours.

When it was observed that there were sporozoite positive glands in the *A. b. balabacensis* mosquitoes on day 15.5, it was decided to expose three volunteers (2 Caucasians and 1 Negro) to infection. Of the three volunteers exposed to infection by bites of 7 to 9 heavily infected mosquitoes, two (both Caucasians) developed patent infections. One volunteer developed a patent infection at 24 days (day zero being the day of exposure). The other volunteer experienced generalized malaise and headache at irregular intervals beginning on day 14, and on two occasions, day 15 and 17, exhibited temperatures of 100.4 and 99.8° F, respectively. However, this volunteer did not develop a patent infection until day 104. The third volunteer, a Negro, exposed to infection by mosquito bite, did not develop a patent infection through 200 days of observation. Ten other volunteers (9 Caucasians and 1 Negro) were exposed to infection by the inoculation of parasitized human blood. Only the 9 Caucasians developed patent infections.

Patency of infection persisted for up to 145 days. Figure 33 shows the pattern of parasitemia for the above-mentioned infections of *P. schwetzi* in man through 75 days. It can be seen that there is an initial peaking of parasitemia during the first three weeks of patent parasitemia (maximum count of 2,750 parasites per mm^3 of blood). However, it should be noted that parasite counts of 1,000 per mm^3 or higher were frequently observed through the first 65 days of parasitemia.

The fever patterns for infections of *P. schwetzi* in man were variable with a tertian pattern

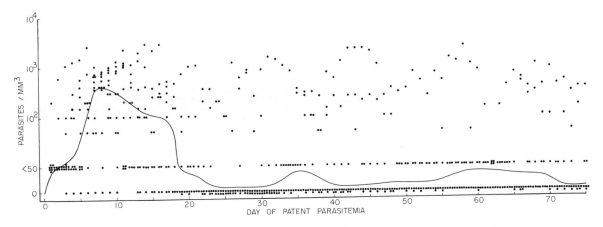

FIGURE 33.—Median parasitemia curve and individual parasite counts in 11 *Plasmodium schwetzi* infections in man (2 sporozoite-induced and 9 blood-induced).

only occasionally evident in most of the volunteers. Paroxysms often occurred daily indicating a two-brood infection. The maximum temperature observed in any volunteer was 105.6° F. Several volunteers had fever free intervals in spite of the presence of patent parasitemia.

Major complaints consisted of headache, generalized malaise, anorexia, and nausea. Vomiting and frank chills were frequently observed. Even though antimalarial therapy was given to several of the volunteers for various reasons, it was not necessary for clinical and/or parasitologic reasons.

An intriguing facet of our human trials was that the two Negro volunteers failed to develop patent infections. This was totally unexpected, especially, in view of the fact that *P. schwetzi* is an African-based parasite. We would not have been too surprised if the sporozoite-induced case had failed to come down but failure in the blood-induced trial left us entirely "at sea".

If one compares the characteristics of our infections with the blood induced infections reported by Rodhain and Dellaert (1955), one finds little difference in maximum parasite counts, maximum temperatures, and in numbers of paroxysms. They observed parasitemias ranging up to 2,060 whereas in our volunteers the range was up to 2,750 parasites per mm³. They reported maximum temperatures of from 104 to 105.8° F and up to 14 paroxysms. In our volunteers, maximum temperatures ranged

from 100.2 to 105.8° F and up to 19 paroxysms were observed. There was, however, one interesting difference. Rodhain and Dellaert made a point of the absence of splenic enlargement in their infections. In our group, 5 of the 11 volunteers had splenic enlargement ranging from tip to 5 centimeters below the left costal margin, with tenderness in 6 of the volunteers.

One of the more interesting observations of the schwetzi infections in man was its close resemblance to human ovale malaria as compared to its appearance in the chimpanzee. The schwetzi parasites as seen in human blood films are illustrated in Plate XXI. On superficial observation the *P. ovale* parasites (Plate XXV) do not resemble the *P. schwetzi* parasites as they appear in man. However when one examines the compact nature of the parasite, the ovaling tendency of many of the parasitized red blood cells and the coarse red stippling, the similarities become apparent.

In addition to what has been discussed above, it is recognized that during the initial phase of an ovale infection the mature schizonts generally show eight merozoites, the half number for *P. schwetzi;* but during relapse (Garnham *et al*, 1955), or following continuous passage (Hauer, 1937), the merozoite number is doubled—the schwetzi number, and the host cell is appreciably enlarged (Garnham loc. cit.), also a schwetzi characteristic. It is also recognized that *Plasmodium ovale* generally exhibits a low parasitemia. The infections in our volunteers and in those reported by Rod-

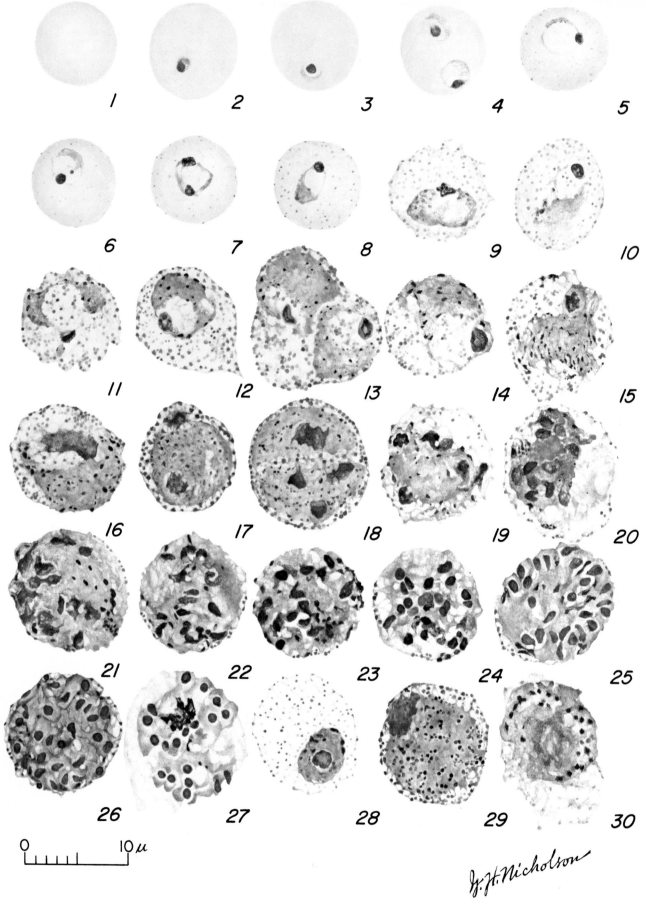

1   2   3   4   5

6   7   8   9   10

11   12   13   14   15

16   17   18   19   20

21   22   23   24   25

26   27   28   29   30

0 ┈┈┈┈┈ 10 μ

G. H. Nicholson

PLASMODIUM SCHWETZI IN MAN

hain and Dellaert followed the same pattern.

The distribution of *P. ovale* in Africa was mentioned earlier and if a map showing the distribution of the chimpanzee (and gorilla) is superimposed over one of *P. ovale* one finds very close agreement. Apropos of that situation, Languillon (1957) working in a forest area of the Cameroons which supported a large chimpanzee population, encountered in a small native village five infants infected with malaria. He determined four of these to be *P. ovale* and one to be *P. schwetzi*. In his comments he suggested that *P. ovale* in man may be an adaptation of *P. schwetzi*. He and Rodhain had alluded to the same relationship two years earlier.

Rodhain had a continuing interest in the parasite specificity of the ape malarias beginning in 1940 and in a paper published shortly before his death (1956) he included a title, with the notation "in preparation", on "The Paradox of *Plasmodium schwetzi* in Humans". As far as we know the manuscript was never completed and we are left to speculate as to what he might have written. In view of the close resemblance of *P. schwetzi* in man to *P. ovale*, one may well wonder how much of the malaria being diagnosed as ovale malaria is truly schwetzi malaria, especially in areas where man and the chimpanzee co-exist.

Host Specificity

Plasmodium schwetzi naturally infects chimpanzees and gorillas (Reichenow, 1920; Schwetz, 1933a). Experimentally, infections have been induced in man by the inoculation of parasitized blood (Rodhain and Dellaert, 1955) and by the bites of infected mosquitoes (Contacos *et al*, 1970). The natural vector is unknown and, in fact, very little information is available on the susceptibility of African anophelines to infection with this parasite. Bray (1958) reported the infection of *Anopheles gambiae* but considered it to be an unsuitable host. Other mosquitoes which have been reported as susceptible to infection are *A. atroparvus* (Rodhain, 1955) and *A. aztecus* (Garnham, 1966). In our own studies (Collins *et al*, 1969), we have obtained infection of *A. b. balabacensis*, *A. freeborni*, and *A. maculatus* mosquitoes; the average number of oocysts per mosquito gut was 82.8, 52.7, and 31.7, respectively. The *A. b. balabacensis* readily transmitted the infection. The latter species is not coindigenous with the parasite and, therefore, cannot serve as its natural vector.

REFERENCES

BLACKLOCK, B., and ADLER, S., 1922. A parasite resembling *Plasmodium falciparum* in a chimpanzee. Ann. Trop. Med. Parasit. *16* : 99–106.

BRAY, R. S., 1958. Studies on malaria in chimpanzees. V. The sporogonous cycle and mosquito transmission of *Plasmodium vivax schwetzi*. J. Parasit. *44* : 46–51.

BRAY, R. S., 1963. The malaria parasites of anthropoid apes. J. Parasit. *49* : 888–891.

BRUMPT, E., 1939. Les parasites due paludisme des chimpanzés. C. R. Soc. Biol. *130* : 837–840.

COLLINS, W. E., ORIHEL, T. C., CONTACOS, P. G., JETER, M. H., and GELL, L. S., 1969. Some observations on the sporogonic cycle of *Plasmodium schwetzi*, *P. vivax* and *P. ovale* in five species of *anopheles*. J. Protozool. *16* : 589–596.

CONTACOS, P. G., COATNEY, G. R., ORIHEL, T. C., COLLINS, W. E., CHIN, W., and JETER, M. H., 1970. Transmission of *Plasmodium schwetzi* from the chimpanzee to man by mosquito bite. Am. J. Trop. Med. & Hyg. *19* : 190–196.

GARNHAM, P. C. C., BRAY, R. S., COOPER, W., LAINSON, R., AWAD, F. I., and WILLIAMSON, J., 1955. The pre-erythrocytic stage of *Plasmodium ovale*. Trans. Roy. Soc. Trop. Med. & Hyg. *49* : 158–167.

GARNHAM, P. C. C., 1966. Malaria parasites and other haemosporidia. Blackwell Scientific Publications. Oxford.

HAUER, A., 1937. Ueber neue beobachtungen an einem

PLATE XXI.—*Plasmodium schwetzi* in man.

Fig. 1.   Normal red cell.
Figs. 2, 3.   Young trophozoites.
Figs. 4–13.   Growing trophozoites.
Figs. 14–16.   Nearly mature and mature trophozoites.

Figs. 17–26.   Developing schizonts.
Fig. 27.   Mature schizont.
Figs. 28, 29.   Developing and mature macrogametocytes.
Fig. 30.   Mature microgametocyte.

REFERENCES—Continued

Plasmodium ovale-Stamm. Arch. f. Schiffs. u. Trop.-Hyg. *41* : 153–157.

LANGUILLON, J., 1957.   Carte epidemiologigue du paludisme au Cameroun. Bull. Soc. Path. Exot. *50* : 585–600.

REICHENOW, E., 1920.   Ueber das vorkommen der malariaparasiten des menschen bei den afrikanischen menschenaffen. Centralbl. f. Bakt. I. Abt. Orig. *85* : 207–216.

RODHAIN, J., 1939.   La réceptivité du chimpanzé *Pan satyrus* au *Plasmodium vivax* humain. C. R. Soc. Biol. *132* : 69–70.

RODHAIN, J., 1940.   Les plasmodiums des anthropoides de l'Afrique Central et leurs relations avec les plasmodiums humains. Ann. Soc. Belge Mèd. Trop. *20* : 489–505.

RODHAIN, J., 1955.   Contribution á l'étude de *Plasmodium schwetzi*, E. Brumpt. Ann. Soc. Belge Méd. Trop. *35* : 69–73.

RODHAIN, J., 1956.   Les formes préérythrocytaires du *Plasmodium vivax* chez le chimpanzé. Ann. Soc. Belge de Méd. Trop. *36* : 99–103.

RODHAIN, J. VAN HOOF, L., and MUYLLE, G., 1938.   Contribution a l'etude des plasmodium des singes africains. Les plasmodium des chimpanzes du Congo Belge. Ann. Soc. Belge Med. Trop. *18* : 237–253.

RODHAIN, J., and MUYLLE, G., 1938.   Sur la spécificité des plasmodium des anthropoides de l'Afrique Centrale. C. R. Soc. Biol. *127* : 1467–1468.

RODHAIN, J., and LASSMAN, P., 1940.   Le cycle schizogonique de *Plasmodium schwetzi* et l'évolution de ce parasite chez *Anopheles maculipennis* var *atroparvous*. Ann. Soc. Belge Méd. Trop. *20* : 179–186.

RODHAIN, J. and DELLAERT, R., 1955.   Contribution a l'étude de *Plasmodium schwetzi* E. Brumpt (2me note). Transmission du *Plasmodium schwetzi* a l'homme. Ann. Soc. Belge Méd. Trop. *35* : 73–76.

RODHAIN, J. and DELLAERT, R., 1955a.   Contribution a l'étude du *Plasmodium schwetzi* E. Brumpt. (3me note). L'infection a *Plasmodium schwetzi* chez l'homme. Ann. Soc. Belge Méd. Trop. *35* : 757–777.

SCHWETZ, J., 1933.   Sur les parasites malariens (*Plasmodium*) des singes supérieurs (Anthropoides) Africains. C. R. Soc. Biol. *112* : 710–711.

SCHWETZ, J., 1933a.   Sur une infection malarienne triple d'un chimpanzé. Zentralb. f. Bakt. I. Abt. Orig. *130* : 105–111.

SCHWETZ, J., 1934.   Contribution á l'étude des parasites malariens des singes supérieurs africains. Riv. Malariol. *13* : 143–147.

13

Plasmodium simium Fonseca, 1951

THERE is an interesting story connected with the discovery of *P. simium* as related by Dr. Deane (Deane *et al*, 1969) who, by his action, actually contributed to its discovery. In 1939 Fonseca was engaged in the study of the yellow fever virus in monkeys from the Itapecerica Forest near São Paulo, Brazil. An unusual temperature curve in the infected howler monkey (*Alouatta fusca*) prompted him to make smears of its blood. When he examined the preparations he came across a plasmodium which he assumed to be *P. brasilianum*. He made a series of smears over the next several days and saved them. Ten years later Deane, anxious to obtain a strain of *P. brasilianum*, asked Fonseca where the howler carrying the brasilianum parasite had been caught. This query prompted Fonseca to reexamine the original smears whereupon, to his surprise, he did not find *P. brasilianum*, as he had recorded in 1939, but a new parasite which he described and named *P. simium* in 1951. Garnham (1966) mentions that he and

Fonseca studied the parasite again in 1955 in another young howler from the Itapecerica Forest.

In recent years Deane and his coworkers (1969) have made extensive studies of the malaria parasites in Brazilian monkeys, concentrating mainly on the southeast and northwest sections of the country. The studies show that *P. simium* occurs only in howlers (*A. fusca*) in the states of Rio Grande Do Sul, Santa Catarina, and São Paulo, but in the state of Esperito Santo it occurs not only in howlers but also in woolly spider monkeys (*Brachyteles arachnoides*). Adult howlers show infection more frequently than immature or very old ones; very young specimens are generally negative. Infections are present throughout the year but there is an increase in incidence during the summer. Why *P. simium* is limited to one small area of Brazil is an interesting question. The answer probably lies with a vector which occupies a very special ecological niche.

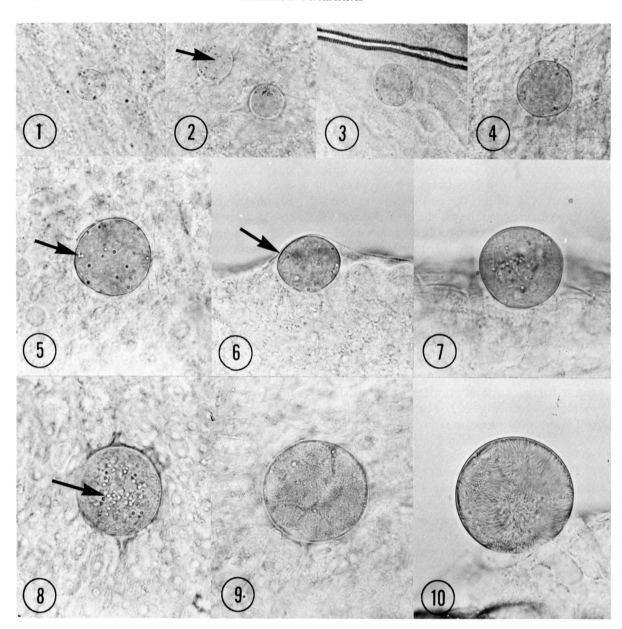

the range for the other test mosquitoes. Sporozoites were found in the salivary glands of *A. b. balabacensis* on day 12.

Plasmodium simium is a smaller parasite than *P. cynomolgi* and it takes about two days longer to complete its sporogonic cycle. This is shown graphically in Figure 34 where its growth curve in *A. freeborni*, the most acceptable test vector, is compared with that of *P. cynomolgi*. Heavy salivary gland infections were present in each of the test species by day 12.

The sporozoites in *A. freeborni* and in *A. maculatus* were fully viable and infective because bites by each of these species transferred sporozoites which initiated infection in splenectomized squirrel monkeys.

Parasites in 9 splenectomized squirrel monkeys were infective to *A. freeborni* mosquitoes when they were allowed to feed as early as 6 and as late as 41 days after onset of patent parasitemia. Oocyst densities of 5 or more per gut occurred in mosquitoes fed 6 to 21 days after onset of parasitemia. Indications are that the best infections result when feedings are carried out during the first 6 to 15 days of patent parasitemia.

Cycle in the Tissue

Fonseca reexamined tissue smears of the spleen, liver, brain, and kidneys of the original monkey whose parasites were seen in 1939 but was unable to find "elements of the exoerythrocytic cycle." We have sought these stages repeatedly, following heavy sporozoite inoculations in owl and squirrel monkeys. Only recently we have found 7-day forms in each of these animals; these forms are similar to *P. vivax* in the owl monkey.

Course of Infection

Until recently it was thought that the only natural host of *P. simium* was the black howler monkey (*Alouatta fusca*); however, Deane *et al* (1968, 1968a) record finding this parasite as a natural infection in the woolly spider monkey (*Brachyteles arachnoides*), also. Deane and his coworkers (1969) were able to observe natural infections in several *A. fusca* for varying periods of time before splenectomy. All of the animals exhibited mild symptoms and moderate to light parasitemias. However, following splenectomy the parasitemia generally increased rapidly up to as high as 225,000 per mm^3 in about 3 weeks (Deane, 1964). He also reported anemia, loss of hair, diarrhea, and fever as high as 41.5° C. It must be kept in mind that howlers are difficult to keep in captivity and consequently some of these manifestations might have been due to their failure to accept food. In this connection Crandall (1964) reported that three howlers lived in captivity between 3 and 5 years. More recently, Malinow *et al* (1968) reported keeping two male howlers in good health, at the Oregon Regional Primate Center, for a period of two years. The latter investigators have since discontinued observations on this species because of the extreme mortality rate in captivity.

So far no one has reported the infection of the rhesus monkey with this parasite.

In the splenectomized squirrel monkey (*Saimiri sciureus*) Deane and Okumura (1965) were able to obtain heavy infections in three out of four animals infected by the inoculation of parasitized blood; in the fourth animal, the parasitemia was low and all evidence of infection had disappeared on the fourth day.

PLATE XXIII.—Developing oocysts of *Plasmodium simium* in *Anopheles freeborni* mosquitoes. X 580 (Except Fig. 2).

Fig. 1. 4-day oocyst.
Fig. 2. 5-day oocysts showing scattered pigment. X 740.
Fig. 3. 6-day oocyst showing pigment and presence of small vacuoles.
Fig. 4. 7-day oocyst.
Fig. 5. 8-day oocyst showing prominent vacuoles.
Fig. 6. 9-day oocyst and mosquito gut membrane.
Fig. 7. 9-day oocyst.
Fig. 8. 10-day oocyst showing numerous small vacuoles.
Fig. 9. 10-day differentiating oocyst.
Fig. 10. 11-day fully differentiated oocyst.

TABLE 17.—Oocyst diameters of *Plasmodium simium* in *Anopheles freeborni, A. stephensi, A. b. balabacensis, A. quadrimaculatus, A. atroparvus,* and *A. maculatus.*

Days after infection	A. freeborni			A. stephensi			A. b. balabacensis			A. quadrimaculatus			A. atroparvus			A. maculatus		
	No.	Range	Mean*	No.	Range	Mean	No.	Range	Mean	No.	Range	Mean	No.	Range	Mean	No.	Range	Mean
3	8	7–11	9															
4	97	9–20	14															
5	200	8–22	14	100	11–17	13	2	14–17	15	6	13–19	17				16	11–13	12
6	201	12–32	19	111	12–26	17	27	13–27	19	25	13–24	18				17	11–18	15
7	136	13–35	23	126	18–39	25				3	24–26	25	12	20–38	28	20	12–35	20
8	132	13–49	26	111	14–53	27	18	20–44	34	28	26–47	35	85	25–53	39	48	15–51	28
9	120	17–54	31	103	19–44	33	8	26–46	36	58	26–59	41	30	20–55	39†	92	14–53	32
10	196	18–55	42†	201	20–61	47†	33	26–48	38	33	31–59	46†	32	24–57	39†	105	18–60	41†
11	110	21–60	47†	200	30–63	49†	20	31–54	43†	34	32–73	47†	13	26–63	49†	66	27–63	49†
12	100	22–63	46†**	194	18–64	46†**	2	40–59	50†**	6	51–63	57†				86	24–71	48†
13				106	24–71	53†**				5	30–65	47†				48	27–67	47†**
Totals	1300	7–63		1252	11–71		110	13–59		198	13–65		172	20–63		498	11–71	

* Measurements expressed in microns; incubation temperature 25° C.

† Oocyst differentiation.

** Sporozoites present in the salivary glands.

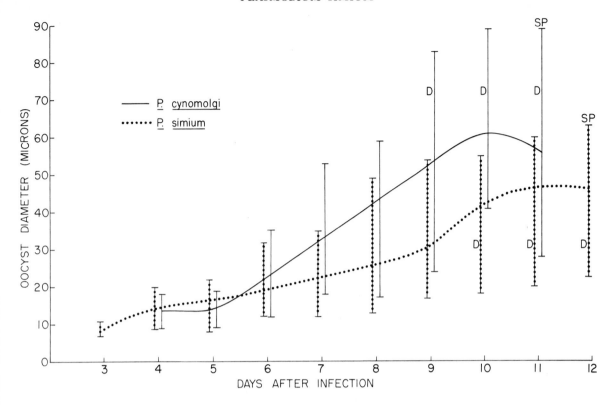

FIGURE 34.—Mean growth curves and ranges in oocyst diameters of *Plasmodium simium* and *P. cynomolgi* in *Anopheles freeborni* mosquitoes. (D = oocyst differentiation; SP = sporozoites present in the salivary glands).

Less severe infections were obtained in *A. paniscus* and in young *A. fusca* (Deane *et al*, 1966a) and mild infections in *Lagothrix lagotricha* (Deane *et al*, 1965a). The marmoset, *Callicebus jacchus*, was found susceptible but the infection was of low order (Deane and Okumura, 1965b). All the animals, as reported by the Brazilian workers, recovered from their infections spontaneously except a single very young specimen of *S. sciureus*.

In our own studies, infection was obtained in 12 splenectomized squirrel monkeys by the inoculation of parasitized blood (Fig. 35). The parasitemia rose rapidly to a median count greater than 10,000 per mm^3 by day 8 and remained at that level or higher for approximately 25 days. The highest parasitemia, approximately 440,000 per mm^3 was obtained in one animal 22 days after inoculation. In another, the parasite count dropped to zero on day 26; 9 of the 12 test animals were negative by day 60. Patent infections persisted in the other three for as long as 112 days.

We were able to transmit the parasite to two splenectomized *S. sciureus* through the bites of *A. maculatus* in one and *A. freeborni* in the other; the prepatent periods were 24 and 38 days, respectively. The maximum parasite counts in these animals ranged from 63,000 to 160,000 per mm^3 of blood. The animal with the highest parasite count died; in the other, parasitemia persisted for 100 days.

In 1966b Deane *et al* reported that one of the members of his research crew, working in the government forest reserve outside São Paulo, had developed fever with a tertian pattern (up to 39.5° C) which lasted about a week. Smears of the man's blood showed scanty parasites of malaria. Some of his blood was given to a splenectomized squirrel monkey which developed a high parasitemia. The authors attributed the human infection to *P. simium* because the parasite was *P. vivax*-like, and, because it grew well in *S. sciureus*. In our opinion it could just as well have been *P. vivax* because in the same year (1966b) Deane *et al*

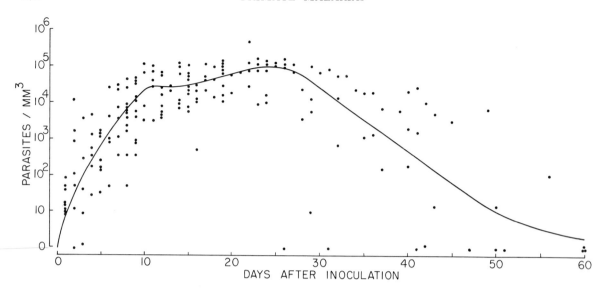

FIGURE 35.—Parasite counts with the median curve of parasitemia for *Plasmodium simium* in 12 splenectomized squirrel monkeys, *Saimiri sciureus*, inoculated with parasitized blood.

showed that *P. vivax* would grow in splenectomized squirrel monkeys. Furthermore, in the following year, using a strain of *P. simium* received from Dr. Deane, we failed in five attempts to infect human volunteers, via mosquito bite, employing *A. stephensi* and *A. freeborni*. In three of these attempts, infectivity of the sporozoites was confirmed by their ability to initiate infection in splenectomized squirrel monkeys. Since these trials, we have learned that by the use of splenectomized Saimiri (squirrel) monkeys sporozoites of *P. simium*, produced by these mosquitoes, are routinely infective. In view of these considerations the acceptance of a *P. simium* infection occurring naturally in man should be held in abeyance until there is more evidence in support of its zoonotic nature.

Host Specificity

The natural vector of *P. simium* is unknown. In 1966a, Deane *et al* incriminated *A. cruzi* as the probable natural vector because it occurs in the area where there are infected howler monkeys and because it feeds in the forest canopy as well as at ground level. In a more recent paper summarizing all his studies through July, 1968 (Deane *et al*, 1969) he contends "one can hardly incriminate another

mosquito . . .". It may well be that *A. cruzi* is the vector and the proof of its ability may come shortly. However, when sporozoites from *A. cruzi* were transferred to three different squirrel monkeys, patent infection did not occur. As mentioned earlier, we were able to infect six species of anophelines with this parasite. The intensity of infections in the mosquitoes varied from one species to another (Table 18). *Anopheles freeborni* was the most acceptable host followed by *A. stephensi*, *A. maculatus*, *A. b. balabacensis*, *A. quadrimaculatus*, and finally *A. atroparvus*. Average oocyst densities greater than one per gut in *A. freeborni* may be expected to yield salivary gland infections of 50 percent or greater after an incubation period of 14 days and a temperature of 25° C.

Antigenic Relationships and Immunity

Two splenectomized *S. sciureus* monkeys were inoculated with sporozoites of *P. simium* but failed to develop a patent infection with that species. One of the animals was splenectomized two days prior to inoculation and the other 18 days after inoculation. Subsequent to the splenectomy, each developed a patent infection with *P. brasilianum* rather than the ex-

TABLE 18.—Comparative infectivity of *Plasmodium simium* to *Anopheles freeborni*, *A. stephensi*, *A. b. balabacensis*, *A. quadrimaculatus*, *A. atroparvus*, and *A. maculatus*.

Mosq. species comparison*	Number tests	Number of mosquitoes		Percent infection		GII** ratios
		Standard	Other	Standard	Other	
F-1						100
F-1 : St-1	20	269	332	38.3	25.3	46.2
F-1 : Bal	9	81	173	60.5	20.2	10.3
F-1 : Q-1	12	89	248	78.7	20.2	10.1
F-1 : Atro	6	43	151	83.7	19.9	8.6
F-1 : Mac	26	286	670	51.7	19.7	8.1

* F-1 = *Anopheles freeborni*, St-1 = *A. stephensi*, Bal = *A. b. balabacensis*, Q-1 = *A. quadrimaculatus*, Atro = *A. atroparvus*, Mac = *A. maculatus*.

** GII = Gut Infection Index = average number of oocysts per 100 guts; the GII ratio is the relationship of the GII of *A. freeborni* to another species where the GII of *A. freeborni* = 100.

pected *P. simium*. It may well be that a latent *P. brasilianum* will prevent the development of a patent *P. simium* infection. Also, in this connection, we have failed to obtain patent *P. simium* infections in intact squirrel monkeys by the inoculation of sporozoites indicating either the necessity for splenectomy or the presence of a latent infection with *P. brasilianum*.

REFERENCES

COLLINS, W. E., CONTACOS, P. G., and GUINN, E., 1969. Observations on the sporogonic cycle and transmission of *Plasmodium simium* da Fonseca. J. Parasit. *55* : 814–816.

CRANDALL, L. S., 1964. The management of wild animals in captivity. Uni. Chicago Press, Chicago.

DEANE, L. M., 1964. Studies on simian malaria in Brazil. Bull. Wld. Hlth. Org. *31* : 752–753.

DEANE, L. M. and OKUMURA, M., 1965. Malária de macacos dos arredores de São Paulo. I. Susceptibilidade do macaco-de-cheiro *Saimiri sciureus* ao *Plasmodium simium* do bugio *Alouatta fusca*. Rev. Paul. Med. *66* : 171–172.

DEANE, L. M., DEANE, M. P., and OKUMURA, M., 1965a. Malária de macacos dos arredores de São Paulo. III. Susceptibilidade do macaco-barrigudo *Lagothrix lagotricha*, a infecçao pelo *Plasmodium simium*. Rev. Paul. Med. *66* : 363.

DEANE, L. M., and OKUMURA, M., 1965b. Malaria de macacos dos arredores de São Paulo. II. Susceptibilidade do sagui *Callithrix jacchus* a infecçao pelo *Plasmodium simium*. Rev. Paul. Med. *66* : 174.

DEANE, L. M., DEANE, M. P., and FERREIRA NETO, J., 1966. A naturally acquired human infection by *Plasmodium simium* of howler monkeys. Trans. Roy. Soc. Trop. Med. & Hyg. *60* : 563–564.

DEANE, L. M., OKUMURA, M., HERTHA, B., and DE SOUZA, W. T., 1966a. Malaria de macacos dos arredores de São Paulo. VI. Infeccao experimental de Macaco coatà *Ateles paniscus* pelo *Plasmodium simium*. Rev. Paul. Med. *68* : 181–182.

DEANE, L. M., DEANE, M. P., and FERREIRA NETO, J., 1966b. Studies on transmission of simian malaria and on a natural infection of man with *Plasmodium simium* in Brazil. Bull. Wld. Hlth. Org. *35* : 805–808.

DEANE, L. M., FERREIRA NETO, J., and SITONIO, J. G., 1968. Novo hospedeiro natural do *Plasmodium simium* e do *Plasmodium brasilianum*: o mono, *Brachyteles arachnoides*. Rev. Inst. Med. Trop. São Paulo, *10* : 287–288.

DEANE, L. M., FERREIRA NETO, J. A. and SITONIO, J. G., 1968a. Estudos sobre malária de macacos no Estado de Espirito Santo. Rev. Brasil. Biol. *28* : 531–538.

DEANE, L. M., FERREIRA NETO, J. A., OKUMURA, M., and FERREIRA, M. O., 1969. Malaria parasites of Brazilian monkeys. Rev. Inst. Med. Trop. São Paulo, *11* : 71–86.

FONSECA, F. DA, 1951. Plasmodio de primata do Brasil. Mem. Inst. Osw. Cruz. *49* : 543–551.

GARNHAM, P. C. C., 1966. Malaria parasites and other haemosporidia. Blackwell Scientific Publications. Oxford. pp. 1114.

MALINOW, M. R., POPE, B. L., DEPAOLI, J. R., and KATZ, S., 1968. Biology of the howler monkey (*Alouatta caroya*). Biblio. Primat. #7 : 224–230.

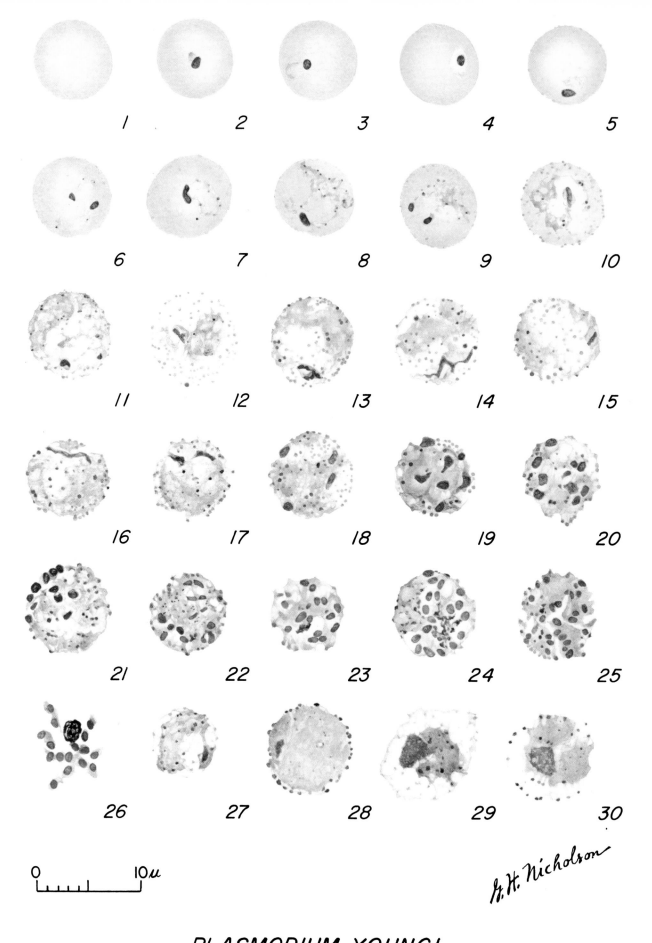

1   2   3   4   5

6   7   8   9   10

11   12   13   14   15

16   17   18   19   20

21   22   23   24   25

26   27   28   29   30

0 ⊢⊢⊢⊢⊣ 10μ

G. H. Nicholson

PLASMODIUM YOUNGI

Cycle in the Blood
PLATE XXIV

The youngest parasites are frequently ring-shaped and measure about 2 μ. The nucleus is generally single but there may be up to four nuclei of unequal size (not shown on plate). Sometimes marginal (appliqué) forms are present, a characteristic of *P. coatneyi* of macaques and of *P. falciparum* of man. Stippling of the Schüffner type appears as the young forms mature and is prominent in cells harboring old trophozoites (Fig. 10). Host cells are not enlarged. The older trophozoites are amoeboid (Figs. 11, 12). The cytoplasm stains a pale blue; pigment becomes heavier and is seen as yellowish-brown granules (Figs. 15, 16). Stippling is fairly prominent and there is no host cell enlargement. The original describers made a point of the latter fact because their figures gave the illusion that the host cell was enlarged.

The cytoplasm of the young schizont takes a slightly darker stain than the earlier forms and may fill the host cell completely. The pigment collects into larger granules and Schüffner's stippling is prominent (Figs. 17–19). The older schizonts appear to have depleted the host cell cytoplasm to the extent that it stains poorly; the cytoplasm of the parasite takes a light blue stain. The merozoites may number from 12 to 20 with an average of about 14. The pigment is concentrated in large yellowish-brown granules and comes together in a single mass during the final stages of schizogony (Figs. 23–26).

The cytoplasm of the young gametocytes takes a deep blue stain and displays a prominent red nucleus. Schüffner's stippling may be prominent. The cytoplasm of the macrogametocyte is compact and stains a pale blue with prominent pigment sometimes located toward the periphery of the parasite. The nucleus is generally eccentric, takes a deep red stain, and encloses a deeper staining, bar-like area. The adult forms fill the host cell (Fig. 28). The cytoplasm of the microgametocyte stains reddish-purple and exhibits a large deep reddish-pink nucleus sometimes with a deeper staining bar-like area. The black pigment is prominent and Schüffner's stippling collects toward the periphery of the host cell. The parasite may not fill the host cell (Figs. 29, 30).

The asexual cycle follows a tertian periodicity.

Sporogonic Cycle

The natural vector of *P. youngi* is unknown but is likely to be a member of the leucosphyrus group of anopheline mosquitoes. Eyles *et al* (1964) found *A. maculatus* partially susceptible in that oocysts developed slowly but failed to produce sporozoites. Warren *et al* (1965) also found only partial development in *A. sundaicus*, *A. balabacensis introlatus*, and *A. maculatus* (see Table 19).

Cycle in the Tissue

The tissue stages of this parasite are unknown.

Course of Infection

According to Eyles *et al* (1964) gibbons (*H. lar*) which received their infection via inoculation of parasitized blood exhibited peak parasitemias of 43,000 to 130,000 per mm³ 12 to 16 days following inoculation. Although the parasitemia declined after the peak, parasites persisted in the circulating blood for up to 192 days. Infections in these animals were more severe than usually seen in malaria infections in lower primates. The maximum temperature

PLATE XXIV.—*Plasmodium youngi*.

Fig. 1.   Normal red cell.
Figs. 2–5.   Young trophozoites.
Figs. 6–15.   Growing trophozoites.
Fig. 16.   Mature trophozoites.

Figs. 17–22.   Developing schizonts.
Figs. 23–26.   Nearly mature and mature schizonts.
Figs. 27–28.   Young adult and mature macrogametocytes.
Figs. 29–30.   Young adult and mature microgametocytes.

encountered was 106.5° F. The animals were clinically ill, anemic, and listless. It is not unlikely that this parasite may actually incapacitate some animals in the wild.

Subsequent to the work of Eyles *et al* (1964) blood-inoculated infections have been studied in 7 additional gibbons and the data pooled. The median parasitemia curve for the 12 animals, during the first 60 days of patent parasitemia (Fig. 36), shows that a peak count of approximately 30,000 per mm³ occurred on day 13. The parasite level then declined to about 100 per mm³ by day 50, followed by a secondary rise.

In instances where blood parasitized with *P. youngi* has been inoculated into rhesus monkeys no infection resulted. No attempts have been made to infect man with this parasite.

Host Specificity

The normal host of *P. youngi* is the white-handed gibbon (*H. lar*). The infection has been transferred by inoculation of parasitized blood to *H. concolor* and another gibbon, possibly *H. agilis*. Neither of these animals developed an intense parasitemia signifying the generally held belief that each of the malarias of gibbons is more or less host specific.

The natural vector is unknown. Experimentally, *Anopheles maculatus*, *A. sundaicus*, and *A. b. introlatus* have been proven susceptible to at least partial development of the parasite (Eyles *et al*, 1964; Warren *et al*, 1965).

Antigenic Relationships and Immunity

No antigen-antibody studies have been carried out. There appears to be little cross-immunity between *P. youngi* and the other malarias of gibbons, according to Warren *et al* (1966). Those investigators were able to obtain a full-blown infection with *P. jefferyi* in a gibbon that had had prior infections with both *P. youngi* and with *P. eylesi*.

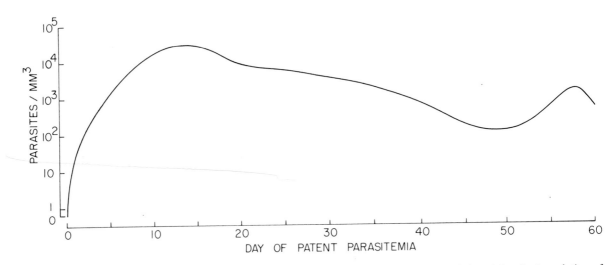

FIGURE 36.—Median curve of *Plasmodium youngi* parasitemia in 12 gibbons, *Hylobates lar*, infected by the inoculation of parasitized blood.

TABLE 19.—Oocyst diameters of *Plasmodium youngi* in *Anopheles b. introlatus*, *A. maculatus*, and *A. sundaicus*.

Days after infection	A. b. introlatus			A. maculatus			A. sundaicus		
	No.	Range	Mean*	No.	Range	Mean	No.	Range	Mean
6.5	13	12–27	18	9	15–22	21			
7.5				10	22–30	27	13	15–30	24
8.5	5	20–27	23						
9.5				1	30	30			
10.5									
11.5				8	30–60	44			

* Measurements expressed in microns.

REFERENCES

CADIGAN, F. C., JR., WARD, R. A., and CHAICUMPA, V., 1969. Further studies on the biology of human malarial parasites in gibbons from Thailand. Milit. Med. *134* : 757–766.

EYLES, D. E., FONG, Y. L., DUNN, F. L., GUINN, E., WARREN, McW. and SANDOSHAM, A. A., 1964. *Plasmodium youngi* n. sp., a malaria parasite of the Malayan gibbon, *Hylobates lar lar*. Am. J. Trop. Med. & Hyg. *13* : 248–255.

FRASER, H., 1909. Annual Report, Institute for Medical Research, Federated Malay States. p. 6.

RODHAIN, J., 1941. Sur un Plasmodium du gibbon *Hylobates lensciscus* Geoff. Acta. Biol. Belge. *1* : 118–123.

SHIROISHI, T., DAVIS, J., and WARREN, McW., 1968. Hepatocystis in the white-cheeked gibbon, *Hylobates concolor*. J. Parasit. *54* : 168.

WARD, R. A., and CADIGAN, F. C., JR., 1966. The development of erythrocytic stages of *Plasmodium falciparum* in the gibbon, *Hylobates lar*. Milit. Med. *131* : 944–951.

WARREN, McW., BENNETT, G. F., SANDOSHAM, A. A., and COATNEY, G. R., 1965. *Plasmodium eylesi* sp. nov., a tertian malaria parasite from the white-handed gibbon, *Hylobates lar*. Ann. Trop. Med. Parasit. *59* : 500–508.

WARREN, McW., COATNEY, G. R., and SKINNER, J. C., 1966. *Plasmodium jefferyi* sp. n. from *Hylobates lar* in Malaya. J. Parasit. *52* : 9–13.

SECTION 3
Ovale-Type Parasites

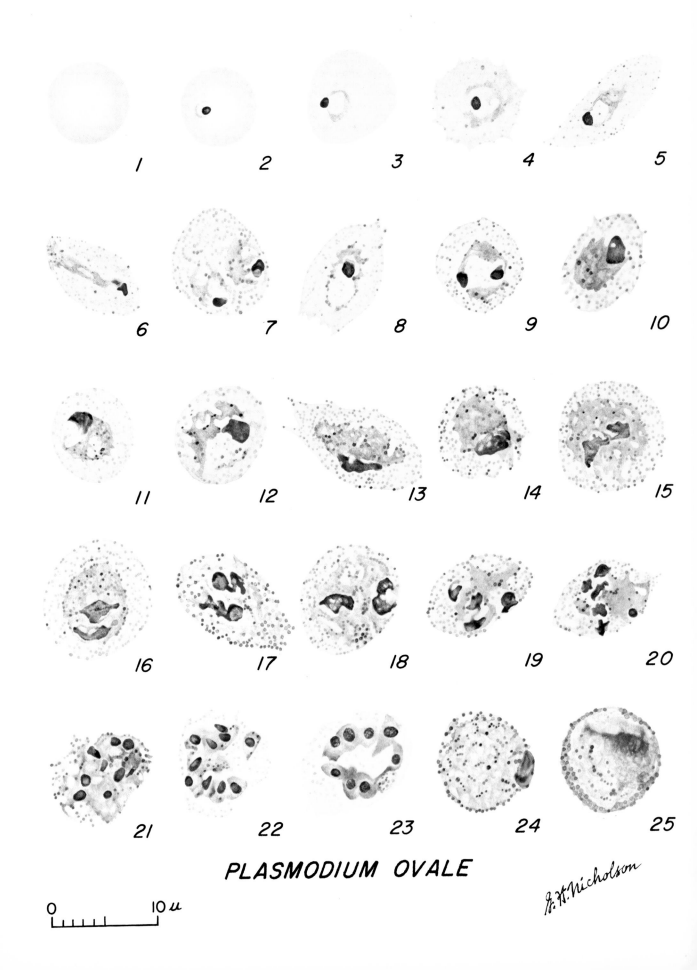

1 2 3 4 5

6 7 8 9 10

11 12 13 14 15

16 17 18 19 20

21 22 23 24 25

PLASMODIUM OVALE

G. H. Nicholson

0 ⊢⊢⊢⊢⊢⊣ 10 μ

Cycle in Blood
PLATE XXV

The young ring forms have a prominent circular nucleus eccentrically placed with a wisp of cytoplasm surrounding a vacuole (Fig. 2). As the parasite grows, the erythrocyte becomes enlarged, the cytoplasm increases in amount, and the vacuole disappears (Fig. 10); older trophozoites come to occupy about half the host erythrocyte (Figs. 10, 11). The cytoplasm may appear pulled out and ragged (Figs. 5, 8) or assume a band-like form, reminiscent of *P. malariae*, (Fig. 6); double infections are not uncommon (Fig. 7). The host cell may appear oval with fimbriated edges (Figs. 8, 13) when the smear is dried in an atmosphere of low humidity; the same feature does not occur in *P. vivax* preparations made under the same conditions. The pigment first appears as fine dust-like grains which later come together to form small greenish-brown beads (Fig. 18) and later mass together in yellowish-brown patches (Fig. 21). The most distinctive characteristic of the circulating ovale parasite is the stippling or Schüffnerization, an apt term probably first applied by Hauer (1937). This stippling appears early in the growth of the parasite (Fig. 4) and becomes intense as the parasite grows (Figs. 15, 17). The host cell cytoplasm becomes pale and transparent and appears as a mass of stippling (Figs. 17, 19). Schüffnerization in *P. ovale* is intense, more pronounced than in *P. vivax* and not too different from *P. schwetzi*.

The cytoplasm of the parasite takes a decided blue stain which fades somewhat during early schizogony (Figs. 16-18) only to appear as purplish-blue during the late stages (Figs. 21-23). The large deep red-staining nuclei of the young forms become larger with deeper red patches as growth proceeds so that just preceding division it is 2 to 4 times its original size (Fig. 14) or about double the size of the same stage nucleus in *P. vivax* but only slightly larger than *P. schwetzi*.

Through the early divisions the nuclei remain large (Figs. 16-19) and at maturity there are ordinarily 8 merozoites although during relapse or following continued passage, the number may be 12 to 16 and located in a much enlarged host cell.

The immature gametocyte is difficult to separate from the compact late trophozoite; but, as growth proceeds, these forms grow to fill the enlarged host erythrocyte.

The cytoplasm of the mature macrogametocyte (Fig. 24) stains a medium blue with an eccentrically placed red-staining prominent nucleus with darker staining areas. The pigment is in granules arranged like a string of beads and these short strands lie scattered in the cytoplasm. The stippling is prominent, takes a red stain, and is arranged in a ring around the parasite.

The mature microgametocyte takes a lighter and more delicate blue stain. The large nucleus occupies about half the parasite. It has a dark red-staining area from which the color fades to a light pink toward the edge. The pigment is in large to medium sized granules scattered throughout the cytoplasm. The parasite is completely enclosed by a prominent circle of eosinophilic stippling (Fig. 25).

The asexual cycle occupies 48 hours.

Sporogonic Cycle
PLATE XXVI

Within the oocyst of *P. ovale*, the pigment granules are arranged in a highly characteristic pattern which differentiates it from the other human malaria parasites (James *et al*, 1932, 1933; Shute and Maryon, 1952). The 50

PLATE **XXV**.—*Plasmodium ovale.*

Fig. 1.   Normal red cell.
Figs. 2-5.   Young trophozoites.
Figs. 6-12.   Growing trophozoites.
Figs. 13-15.   Mature trophozoites.

Figs. 16-22.   Developing schizonts.
Fig. 23.   Mature schizont.
Fig. 24.   Adult macrogametocyte.
Fig. 25.   Adult microgametocyte.

manus mosquitoes (Jeffery *et al*, 1954). Later, Jeffery *et al* (1955) reported 4 transmissions of a Liberian strain of *P. ovale* via the bites of *A. quadrimaculatus* and *A. albimanus* mosquitoes. Bray (1957) using *A. gambiae* mosquitoes, trans-

mitted a local strain of *P. ovale* to a Liberian child and to a chimpanzee. Chin *et al* (1966) reported transmission of a West African strain of this parasite to 5 volunteers using *A. freeborni* and *A. maculatus* mosquitoes.

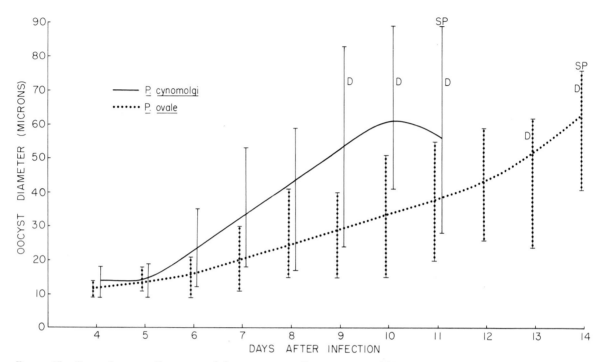

FIGURE 37.—Range in oocyst diameters and the mean oocyst diameter curves of *Plasmodium ovale* and *P. cynomolgi* in *Anopheles freeborni* mosquitoes. (D = oocyst differentiation; SP = sporozoites present in the salivary glands).

TABLE 20.—Oocyst diameters of *Plasmodium ovale* in *Anopheles freeborni*, *A. b. balabacensis*, *A. maculatus*, *A. stephensi*, and *A. quadrimaculatus*.

Days after feeding	A. freeborni			A. b. balabacensis			A. maculatus			A. stephensi			A. quadrimaculatus		
	No.	Range	Mean*	No.	Range	Mean	No.	Range	Mean	No.	Range	Mean	No.	Range	Mean
4	52	9–14	12	38	8–12	11	50	9–14	12	50	8–15	11	53	8–15	12
5	103	11–18	14	100	10–21	14	100	8–19	14	100	10–20	15	100	8–20	15
6	126	9–21	16	100	10–20	16	100	11–24	17	100	10–21	16	100	12–25	19
7	100	11–26	20	98	12–28	20	100	13–34	20	100	13–27	20	100	14–30	24
8	100	15–41	28	100	17–35	26	100	17–35	26	100	15–35	27	100	15–35	30
9	136	15–40	28	109	18–39	29	101	14–35	24	100	15–39	30	100	20–38	35
10	102	15–51	38	100	19–41	32	100	17–43	30	100	14–41	30	100	15–41	29
11	100	20–55	39	55	25–51	36	104	14–50	32	60	25–51	42	108	18–54	39
12	96	24–59	43	89	27–55	40	100	27–53	39	100	12–60	42†	100	19–59	42
13	108	24–65	46†	96	25–65	42	100	20–61	41	100	22–61	45†	30	22–66	44
14	20	41–76	64†**	100	35–71	52†	100	38–71	51†**				108	25–84	54†**
15	50	43–96	68†**	50	35–80	59†**	39	25–55	48†**	8	43–54	48†			
Totals	1093	9–96		1035	8–80		1094	8–71		918	8–61		999	8–84	

* Measurements expressed in microns; incubation temperature 25° C.
† Oocyst differentiation.
**Sporozoites present in salivary glands.

Cycle in the Tissue

The tissue stages of *P. ovale* were first described in liver biopsy material from a human volunteer by Garnham *et al* (1955). The youngest stages described by these authors were considered to be 5-day stages and measured from 28 to 60 μ in length. The smallest of these forms were oval with regular or smooth edges. The larger of these 5-day forms showed small convolutions on the surface. The most striking feature observed in these immature forms was the "relatively" enormous size of the nuclei—approximately 2 μ. The 9-day tissue stage of ovale measured from 70 to 80 μ by 50 μ. The surface was lobated and the nuclei were about half the size found in the 5-day stage, in other words, roughly 1 μ.

The nuclei of the tissue stages had an uneven margin and the cytoplasm was granular. Sometimes the cytoplasm was clumped around each nucleus so that the tissue stage appeared to contain clefts or to be vacuolated. A definite limiting membrane was described for many of the schizonts.

As the EE body of *P. ovale* approaches maturity (on or about the 9th day), it goes through what is described as 3 stages: 1) nuclear multiplication progresses rapidly with no evident merozoite formation; 2) the appearance of merozoites at the edges of the EE bodies, with active nuclear division continuing elsewhere within the parasite; and 3) complete maturation of the schizont with rupture.

The merozoite of the *P. ovale* tissue schizont is described as a remarkable structure. It is large (1.8 μ in diameter), spherical, and consists of 2 portions; a larger portion of cytoplasm and a smaller portion which is the nucleus situated at one side of the parasite. The number of merozoites in one schizont of *P. ovale* has been reported to be as high as 15,000 ±.

In the paper describing the tissue stages of *P. ovale*, the authors noted that *P. ovale* tissue stages differ markedly from those of *P. vivax* and *P. inui*. They were of the opinion, however, that there was a superficial resemblance to those of *P. falciparum*, at least in regard to size and form. Bray (1957) described the development of *P. ovale* tissue stages in the chimpanzee. He reported 7-day stages measured an average of 36.6 x 30.3 μ (range of 45 to 28 μ x 39 to 23 μ). He described 4 different forms of schizonts which occurred regularly in the chimpanzee material. Eighteen day schizonts measured from 91 to 40 μ x 50 to 31 μ. One schizont, found in a 39-day biopsy, measured 31 x 33 μ.

In his paper, Bray (1957) points out that the EE bodies of *P. ovale* display at least 3 characteristics that have not been noted in the tissue stages of *P. vivax* or *P. falciparum*; namely, 1) a definite limiting membrane or periplast; 2) peripheral nuclear bars tangential rather than radial; and 3) a minor but distinct hypertrophy of the host cell nucleus.

Rupture of the mature schizonts of the pre-erythrocytic cycle is believed to occur chiefly on the 9th day after exposure to infection. The positive biopsies of 18 and 39 days suggest the apparent existence of second-generation forms. Bray *et al* (1963) attempted to demonstrate the existence of one or more exoerythrocytic cycles after the initial EE cycle, in the chimpanzee. Biopsy on the 19th day revealed bursting and mature schizonts as had been observed on the 9th day, suggesting the existence of at least a second generation.

Course of Infection

Sinton *et al* (1939) alluded to a mean prepatent period for several strains of *P. ovale* of about 15 days. James *et al* (1949) reported incubation periods (which may, on occasion, be the same as the prepatent period) of 11 to 16 days with a mean of 13.6 days in sporozoite induced infections with 6 different strains of *P. ovale*. They reported one case with a delayed incubation period of 85 days. The Donaldson strain (Jeffery *et al*, 1954) exhibited prepatent periods of 12 to 20 days with a mean of 15.3 days. Employing a Liberian strain, Garnham *et al* (1955), Jeffery *et al* (1955), and Bray (1957) reported prepatent periods of 13.5, 14 to 15 (mean 14.5), and 14 days, respectively. Chin *et al* (1966) working with a West African strain obtained prepatent periods of 14 to 18 days with a mean of 16.8 days.

Generally, *P. ovale* infections are considered to be the least severe of the 4 species of human malaria and are characterized by a mild clinical course. In the mosquito induced infections reported by James *et al* (1949) the onset of the typical primary attack was definitely less severe than that observed with vivax malaria. The characteristic rigor of vivax malaria was a rarity with ovale malaria; only one or two characteristic rigors occurring during the early stages (10 days or so) of the primary attack. Even though the patient may feel chilly, chattering of teeth and the classical shaking with a sensation of being cold from head to foot are seldom or never seen. However, they found the duration of the entire paroxysm to be the same for ovale as it is in vivax malaria (6 to 10 hours). Garnham *et al* (1955) took exception in that the paroxysms in their cases were usually accompanied by chills as well as severe and persistent headache. Temperatures of up to 105° F in one volunteer persisted for 3 weeks. The spleen became palpable after about 10 days.

James *et al* (1949) observed another obvious difference between ovale and vivax malaria; namely, the degree of fever at the peaks of the paroxysms. They reported that only 30 out of 197 patients (15 percent) had 10 or more febrile paroxysms with peak temperatures exceeding 103° F. With the Donaldson strain (Jeffery *et al*, 1954), only 10 percent of the subjects had 10 paroxysms with peak temperatures exceeding 103° F. The first fevers were seen from 14 to 26 days after exposure to

infection, with a mean of 17.7 days or a median of 17 days; maximum mean fever was 105.2° F. The number of paroxysms observed in infections (103 cases) with this strain ranged from 1 to 22 with a mean or median of 8. With the West African strain of ovale malaria, we observed a temperature of only 103.6° F when the parasite count was as high as 32, 450 per mm³.

Using the interval between tertian fever peaks as reference points, the periodicity of Donaldson strain infections was found to range from 34 to 61 hours with a median of 49 hours.

Maximum parasitemia is considered to be generally lower than that observed with vivax malaria. Sinton *et al* (1939) reported variations in maximum parasitemias ranging from 125 to 20,000 per mm³ while James *et al* (1949) reported maximum parasite densities ranging from 500 to 100,000 per mm³. Jeffery *et al*, in studies with the Donaldson strain, reported ranges of maximum counts from 464 to 25,940 parasites per mm³ with a mean of 8,376. With the West African strain of *P. ovale*, we have observed maximum counts ranging up to 32,450 parasites per mm³ in blood-induced infections.

Figure 38 shows the minimum and maximum parasitemia curves for 24 blood-induced infections with the Donaldson strain of *P. ovale* (17 Negro and 7 Caucasian) as well as the

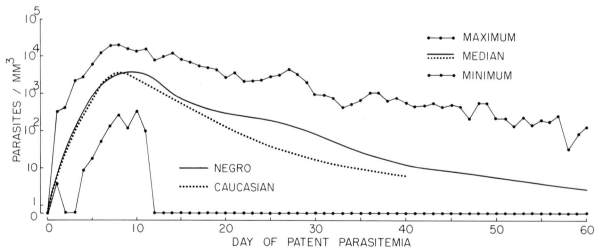

FIGURE 38.—Maximum and minimum parasite counts and median parasitemia curves of 24 blood-induced infections of *Plasmodium ovale* in man (17 Negro and 7 Caucasian).

median parasitemia curves for the two groups. It can be seen that peak parasitemia was reached in the Caucasian and Negro patients on the 8th and 10th days of patent parasitemia with maximum median counts of 4,576 and 3,645 parasites per mm^3, respectively, followed by a steady and slow decline to rather low level parasitemia by day 40. There is no apparent difference between the median parasitemias for the two groups of patients. This is in great contrast with what is generally observed with vivax malaria infections in Negro and Caucasian patients. The differences between the minimum and maximum parasitemia curves on a day to day basis point out the great variability one can observe in infections with most human malarias.

Duration of parasitemia in sporozoite induced infections with the Donaldson strain ranged from 29 to 91 days with a mean of 53.2 days or a median of 51 days. During this period, clinical manifestations lasted for 8 to 26 days with an average of 16.9 days. Primary attacks of ovale malaria characteristically terminate spontaneously without the use of antimalarial drugs even though low level asymptomatic parasitemia may continue intermittently for a time. After cessation of symptoms, in cases of Donaldson strain ovale malaria, parasites continued to be present in the peripheral blood for 11 to 89 days with an average duration of 37.5 days. No more than 2 percent required partial suppression or early termination of the infection as compared to 61 to 87 percent for some strains of vivax malaria.

Ovale malaria, in contrast to most strains of vivax malaria, is equally infective to Negroes and Caucasians. Sinton et al (1939) noted the susceptibility of a Negro patient who had been previously resistant to other human malarias and suggested that the Negro may show lower racial immunity to ovale malaria than to other malarias. Jeffery et al (1954, 1955) found that Negro and Caucasian patients inoculated either with Donaldson strain or the Liberian strain of ovale malaria were equally susceptible to infection. In fact, they observed no obvious differences in prepatent period, incubation period, or clinical activity.

There can be no doubt that ovale malaria is a true relapsing infection; i.e., sporulation

from tissue stages in the liver subsequent to the primary attack. James et al (1949) reported that, in their experience with 36 patients infected by the bites of mosquitoes, no relapses were observed. It is not unlikely that asymptomatic relapses were missed if patients were followed up on a strict clinical basis. Sinton (1939) encountered one relapse in a series of sporozoite induced cases of ovale malaria. Jeffery et al (1954) found that relapses were observed frequently in 38 mosquito induced infections of Donaldson strain ovale malaria. Most of them were asymptomatic relapses. Only 2 of the 38 patients showed symptomatic relapse at 148 and 235 days after termination of the primary attacks with chloroquine. One of these patients subsequently experienced an asymptomatic relapse with low grade parasitemia 152 days later.

Garnham et al (1955) observed relapses in two cases; one relapsed 103 days after chloroquine and again 68 days later and the other relapsed after 98 days, and, again, 101 days later. Chin and Coatney (1971) found that infections with a West African strain of ovale malaria relapsed from 1 to 3 times during a one year period. Relapses occurred as early as 17 days after treatment of the primary attack in one case and as late as 255 days in another case. All of the relapses were symptomatic, except one.

Earlier authors spoke of latent infections (which we recognize as delayed primary attacks), a phenomenon not too uncommon with vivax malaria. As mentioned earlier, James et al (1949) reported such a period of 85 days in one of their mosquito induced infections. Jeffery et al (1954), Trager and Most (1963), and Chin and Contacos (1966) reported delayed primary attacks of 4, 1.8 and 3.5, and 1.3 years, respectively. These delayed primary infections were probably not true latent infections in the classical sense. Rather, they represent late tissue parasite (relapse) activity.

Bray (1957) reported that infection of chimpanzees with ovale malaria, can be obtained either by the inoculation of sporozoites or parasitized blood. In the intact animal, there was evidence of some natural resistance with spontaneous termination of patent parasitemia after 8 days. On the other hand, splenectomized chimpanzees allowed parasitemia to increase for 10 days with a total duration of patent parasitemia of 21 days. In addition, the infection in the chimpanzee differs from that in man by its tendency to produce blood schizonts with more than the usual number of merozoites.

Host Specificity

Man is the natural host of this parasite. Infections have been obtained in intact and splenectomized chimpanzees (*Pan troglodytes versus*) by the inoculation of sporozoites from *A. gambiae* mosquitoes (Bray, 1957). Attempts to infect rhesus monkeys (*M. mulatta*) by the inoculation of parasitized blood have been unsuccessful (Christophers, 1934; Jeffery, 1961). We have made 6 unsuccessful attempts to infect *A. trivirgatus* monkeys with *P. ovale*. However, in view of the ease with which infections with the other human malarias have been adapted to this host, its eventual adaptation is thought likely.

The natural vector of *P. ovale* is unknown. However, since Bray (loc. cit.) was able to obtain infections in *A. gambiae* mosquitoes after they fed on man and on the chimpanzee, this is strongly indicative that it is a vector in Africa. Vectors of this parasite found in the west Pacific have not been determined. Other mosquitoes which have been experimentally infected are shown in the table below:

Species	References
Anopheles albimanus	Jeffery, 1954; Jeffery *et al*, 1954, 1955
A. atroparvus	James *et al*, 1932, 1933; Sinton *et al*, 1939; Shute and Maryon, 1952; Garnham *et al*, 1955
A. freeborni	Chin *et al*, 1966
A. maculatus	Chin *et al*, 1966
A. quadrimaculatus	Jeffery, 1954; Jeffery *et al*, 1954
A. superpictus	Garnham, 1966

In addition, we have infected *A. stephensi* and *A.b.balabacensis* mosquitoes with a West African strain of *P. ovale*. In a comparative study, Jeffery (1954) showed that *A. quadrimaculatus* mosquitoes were more susceptible than strains of *A. albimanus* from Panama and the Florida Keys, to the Donaldson strain of *P. ovale*. The relative susceptibility was *A. quadrimaculatus*, 100; *A. albimanus* (Florida Keys), 77; *A. albimanus* (Panama), 46. In a comparative study with the West African strain, (Table 22), we found that *A. stephensi* mosquitoes were the most susceptible, followed by *A. freeborni*, *A. b. balabacensis*, *A. quadrimaculatus*, *A. maculatus*, and finally, *A. albimanus*. There was a lesser variation in susceptibility to infection than has been found in studies with the other primate malarias.

Immunity and Antigenic Relationships

Sinton *et al* (1939a) showed that a high and almost equal degree of resistance to reinfection

TABLE 22.—Comparative infectivity of *Plasmodium ovale* to *Anopheles freeborni*, *A. stephensi*, *A. b. balabacensis*, *A. quadrimaculatus*, *A. maculatus*, and *A. albimanus*.

Mosq. species comparison*	Number tests	Number of mosquitoes		Percent infection		GII** ratio
		Standard	Other	Standard	Other	
F–1						100
F–1 : St–1	6	169	153	59.8	58.2	121.3
F–1 : Bal	8	206	96	73.8	78.1	83.4
F–1 : Q–1	14	253	452	69.6	41.2	43.7
F–1 : Mac	16	238	302	76.9	61.6	43.4
F–1 : Alb	5	23	23	78.3	30.4	30.7

* F–1 = *Anopheles freeborni*; St–1 = *A. stephensi*; Bal = *A. b. balabacensis*; Q–1 = *A. quadrimaculatus*; Mac = *A. maculatus*; Alb = *A. albimanus*.

**GII = Gut Infection Index = average number of oocysts per 100 guts; the GII ratio is the relationship of the GII of *A. freeborni* to another species where the GII of *A. freeborni* = 100.

developed to homologous and to heterologous strains following a primary infection with *P. ovale*. On the other hand, these investigators found that ovale malaria could be successfully established in persons who were apparently immune to the other species of human malaria.

Jeffery *et al* (1954, 1955) studied the immunologic relationships of several strains of ovale malaria. They observed that one infection with the Donaldson strain of ovale malaria conferred immunity to reinfection with the same strain. Moreover, in comparing a Pacific strain (Donaldson) and a West African strain (Liberian) of *P. ovale*, they found considerable cross-immunity between them, but in no way was the immunity complete. However, the degree of cross-immunity was greater than expected; not only in view of the wide geographic separation in the origin of the two isolates, but also on the basis of their experience with various strains of vivax and falciparum malaria.

These investigators further reported that ovale malaria (Donaldson strain) conferred no effective immunity against the other 3 species of human malaria. The converse was also observed; namely, that previous experience with other species of human malaria did not appreciably effect subsequent susceptibility to infection with the Donaldson strain of *P. ovale*. For

example, a previous Chesson vivax infection did not seem to confer appreciable immunity against a subsequent Donaldson strain infection.

Sinton (1940), on the basis of his studies on the immunity acquired as a result of sporozoite induced infections as compared to the immunity acquired by those infections induced by erythrocytic asexual stages, suggested that immunity in malaria is more complete if the initial infection is induced by sporozoites.

Garnham (1966) stated that the antigenic structure of different strains of *P. ovale* seems to be remarkably homogenous. Sinton (1940), in studying heterologous strain immunity of ovale malaria concluded that the heterologous antigenic element seemed to be so small in the strains studied by him "as to make them almost identical immunologically."

It seems safe to say, that at this writing, no clear-cut statement can be put forth regarding immunity involving *P. ovale*.

Meuwissen (1966) found a high degree of cross-reactivity with *P. fieldi* antigen in sera of patients with *P. ovale* infections using the indirect fluorescent antibody test. In a later study (1968), he found that *P. ovale* antisera would cross-react to the *P. cynomolgi bastianellii* antigen but at a lower level than to the homologous antigen or to the *P. fieldi* antigen.

REFERENCES

BRAY, R. S., 1957. Studies on malaria in chimpanzees. IV. *Plasmodium ovale*. Am. J. Trop. Med. & Hyg. *6* : 638–645.

BRAY, R. S., BURGESS, R. W., and BAKER, J. R., 1963. Studies on malaria in chimpanzees. X. The presumed second generation of the tissue phase of *Plasmodium ovale*. Am. J. Trop. Med. & Hyg. *12* : 1–12.

BRUMPT, E., 1949. The human parasites of the genus *Plasmodium*. In Malariology, Vol. I by Boyd. W. B. Saunders, Philadelphia, Pa. pp. 787.

CHIN, W., CONTACOS, P. G., and BUXBAUM, J. N., 1966. The transmission of a West African strain of *Plasmodium ovale* by Anopheles freeborni and Anopheles maculatus. Am. J. Trop. Med. & Hyg. *15* : 690–693.

CHIN, W. and CONTACOS, P. G., 1966. A recently isolated West African strain of *Plasmodium ovale*. Am. J. Trop. Med. & Hyg. *15* : 1–2.

CHIN, W. and COATNEY, G. R., 1971. Observations on relapse activity of mosquito-induced infections of *Plasmodium ovale* from West Africa. Am. J. Trop. Med. & Hyg. (in press).

CHRISTOPHERS, R., 1934. Malaria from a zoological point

of view. Proc. Royal Soc. Med. *27* : 991–1000.

COATNEY, G. R., 1968. Simian malarias in man: facts, implications, and predictions. Am. J. Trop. Med. & Hyg. *17* : 147–155.

COATNEY, G. R. and YOUNG, M. D., 1941. The taxonomy of the human malaria parasites with notes on the principal American strains. Human malaria. Am. Assoc. Advancement of Science. No. 15.

COLLINS, W. E., ORIHEL, T. C., CONTACOS, P. G., JETER, M. H., and GELL, L. S., 1969. Some observations on the sporogonic cycle of *Plasmodium schwetzi*, *P. vivax* and *P. ovale* in five species of Anopheles. J. Protozool. *16* : 589–596.

CONTACOS, P. G., COATNEY, G. R., ORIHEL, T. C., COLLINS, W. E., CHIN, W., and JETER, M. H., 1970. Transmission of *Plasmodium schwetzi* from the chimpanzee to man by mosquito bite. Am. J. Trop. Med. & Hyg. *19* : 190–196.

CRAIG, C. F., 1900. Report bacteriological Lab., U.S. Army General Hospital, Presidio of San Francisco, Calif. for 1899–1900. Surgeon-General's Rept., U.S. Army.

CRAIG, C. F., 1914. New varieties and species of malaria plasmodia. J. Parasit. *1* : 85–94.

REFERENCES—Continued

CRAIG, C. F., 1933. The nomenclature of *Plasmodium ovale* Stephens 1922. Am. J. Trop. Med. *13* : 539–542.

EMIN, A., 1914. Une variété nouvelle du parasite de Laveran. Séance 7 : 385–387.

EYLES, D. E., COATNEY, G. R., and GETZ, M. E., 1960. Vivax-type malaria parasite of macaques transmissible to man. Science *131* : 1812–1813.

GARNHAM, P. C. C., 1966. Malaria parasites and other haemosporidia. Blackwell Scientific Publications. Oxford. pp. 1114.

GARNHAM, P. C. C., BRAY, R. S., COOPER, W., LAINSON, R., AWAD, F. I., and WILLIAMSON, J., 1955. The pre-erythrocytic stage of *Plasmodium ovale*. Trans. Roy. Soc. Trop. Med. & Hyg. *49* : 158–167.

GIOVANNOLA, A., 1935. *Plasmodium ovale* considered as a modification of *Plasmodium vivax* after a long residence in the human host. Am. J. Trop. Med. *15* : 175–186.

HAUER, A., 1937. Ueber neue Beobachtungen an einem *Plasmodium ovale* -Stamm. Arch. f. Schiffs- u. Trop.-Hyg. *41* : 153–157.

JAMES, S. P., NICOL, W. D., and SHUTE, P. G., 1932. *Plasmodium ovale* Stephens: passage of the parasite through mosquitoes and successful transmission by their bites. Ann. Trop. Med. Parasit. *26* : 139–145.

JAMES, S. P., NICOL, W. D., and SHUTE, P. G., 1933. *Plasmodium ovale* Stephens 1922. Parasitology *25* : 87–95.

JAMES, S. P. NICOL, W. D., and SHUTE, P. G., 1935. The specific status of *Plasmodium ovale* Stephens. Am. J. Trop. Med. *15* : 187–188.

JAMES, S. P., NICOL, W. D., and SHUTE, P. G., 1949. Ovale malaria. In Malariology, Vol. II by Boyd. W. B. Saunders Co. Philadelphia, Pa.

JEFFERY, G. M., 1954. The Donaldson strain of malaria. 3. The infection in the mosquito. Am. J. Trop. Med. & Hyg. *3* : 651–659.

JEFFERY, G. M., 1961. Inoculation of human malaria into a simian host, *Macaca mulatta*. J. Parasit. *47* : 90.

JEFFERY, G. M., YOUNG, M. D., and WILCOX, A., 1954. The Donaldson strain of malaria. 1. History and characteristics of the infection in man. Am. J. Trop. Med. & Hyg. *3* : 628–637.

JEFFERY, G. M., WILCOX, A., and YOUNG, M. D., 1955. A comparison of West African and West Pacific strains of *Plasmodium ovale*. Trans. Roy. Soc. Trop. Med. & Hyg. *49* : 168–175.

LACAN, A., 1962. *Plasmodium ovale* in French-speaking countries of Africa. Mimeographed document: Wld. Hlth. Org. WHO/Mal/363.

LANGUILLON, J., 1957. Carte epidemiologique du palu-

disme au Cameroun. Bull. Soc. Path. Exot. *50* : 585–600.

LYSENKO, A. JA. and BELJAEV, A. E., 1966. Mimeographed document: Wld. Hlth. Org. WHO/Mal/66.577.

MACFIE, J. W. S. and INGRAM, A., 1917. Observations on malaria in the Gold Coast colony, West Africa. Ann. Trop. Med. Parasit. *11* : 1–23.

MEUWISSEN, J. H. E., TH., 1966. Fluorescent antibodies in human malaria, especially in *Plasmodium ovale*. Trop. geogr. Med. *18* : 250–259.

MEUWISSEN, J. H. E. TH., 1968. Antibody responses of patients with natural malaria to human and simian Plasmodium antigens measured by the fluorescent antibody test. Trop. geogr. Med. *20* : 137–140.

ONORI, E., 1967. Distribution of *Plasmodium ovale* in the eastern, western and northern regions of Uganda. Bull. Wld. Hlth. Org. *37* : 665–668.

RODHAIN, J., 1940. Les plasmodiums des anthropoides de l'Afrique centrale et leurs relations avec les plasmodiums humains. Ann. Soc. Belge de Méd. Trop. *20* : 489–505.

SHUTE, P. G. and MARYON, M., 1952. A study of human malaria oocysts as an aid to species diagnosis. Trans. Roy. Soc. Trop. Med. & Hyg. *46* : 275–292.

SINTON, J. A., HUTTON, E. L., and SHUTE, P. G., 1939. Studies of infections with *Plasmodium ovale*. I. Natural resistance to ovale infections. Trans. Roy. Soc. Trop. Med. & Hyg. *32* : 751–762.

SINTON, J. A., HUTTON, E. L., and SHUTE, P. G., 1939a. Studies of infections with *Plasmodium ovale*. II. Acquired resistance to *ovale* infections. Trans. Roy. Soc. Trop. Med. & Hyg. *33* : 47–68.

SINTON, J. A., 1940. Studies of infections with *Plasmodium ovale*. IV. The efficacy and nature of the immunity acquired as a result of infections induced by sporozoite inoculations as compared with those by trophozoite injections. Trans. Roy. Soc. Trop. Med. & Hyg. *33* : 439–446.

STEPHENS, J. W. W., 1918. (See Stephens, 1922.)

STEPHENS, J. W. W., 1922. A new malaria parasite of man. Ann. Trop. Med. Parasit. *16* : 383–388.

STEPHENS, J. W. W. and OWEN, D. U., 1927. *Plasmodium ovale*. Ann. Trop. Med. Parasit. *21* : 293–302.

TRAGER, W. and MOST, H., 1963. A long-delayed primary attack of *ovale* malaria. Am. J. Trop. Med. & Hyg. *12* : 837–839.

YORKE, W. and OWEN, D. U., 1930. *Plasmodium ovale*. Ann. Trop. Med. Parasit. *24* : 593–600.

ZIEMANN, H., 1915. Ueber eigenartige malariaparasitenformen. Zentralbl. Bakt. I. Abt. Orig. *76* : 384–391.

16

Plasmodium fieldi Eyles, Laing, and Fong, 1962

ONLY three species of malaria were known from macaques when Dr. Eyles embarked on his extraordinary series of studies on simian malaria in peninsular Malaysia in mid-August of 1960. In September of that year, he purchased a young pig-tailed macaque (*Macaca nemestrina*) from a trapper who said it had been taken in the district of Kuala Selangor in the state of Selangor, Malayasia. The monkey was carrying a malaria parasite but the parasitemia was too low to allow for species identification. The animal was splenectomized in January, 1961, after which the parasitemia increased permitting more careful study of the parasite which confirmed an earlier assumption that it was a new species. The Eyles group gave it the name *Plasmodium fieldi* in honor of Dr. John W. Field, who has made outstanding contributions to our knowledge of malaria in general and especially in Malayasia.

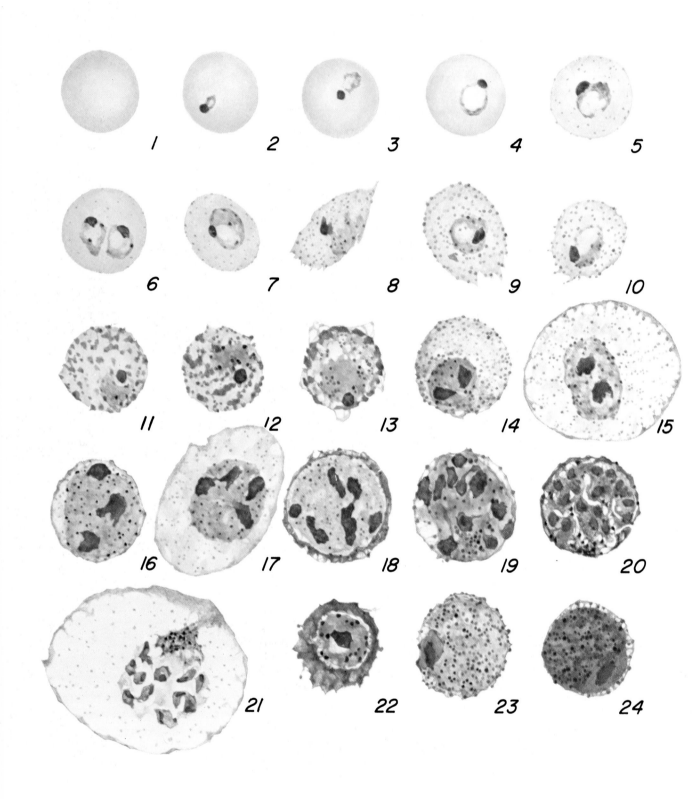

PLASMODIUM FIELDI

G.H.Nicholson

0   10μ

Cycle in the Blood
PLATE XXVII

The youngest parasites are ring-shaped and about 3 μ in diameter. Some have double chromatin bodies. Multiple infections of the erythrocyte are not common; stippling appears when the trophozoite is about half-grown (Fig. 5).

The older trophozoites (Figs. 11–13) are compact, rounded or oval, and display very little amoeboidity. The cytoplasm is compact, stains a deep blue, and the nucleus a deep red; pigment is dark and made up of fine grains; Schüffner-type stippling takes a deep red stain. Some host cells are oval-shaped (Figs. 7–9); older parasites, with the vacuole diminished or lost, occur in cells with aggregates of dark eosinophilic masses sometimes larger than their nuclei (Figs. 11–13). The host cell is slightly enlarged.

Immature schizonts (Figs. 14–20) exhibit dense blue-staining cytoplasm and relatively large deep red nuclei; pigment is granular, well distributed, generally black; stippling is heavy, and, as schizogony proceeds, the eosinophilic masses come together to form a deep red border around the developing schizont (Fig. 18). The host cell may be appreciably enlarged—ballooned-out—, some of them assume an oval shape rather than circular (Figs. 15, 17). The mature schizonts (Figs. 20, 21) produce 4 to 16 large merozoites with a mean number of 12. The golden brown pigment forms a large mass ofttimes in the center of the schizont. The host cell may become greatly distorted (Fig. 21 and earlier); the explanation for this is not known but it appears to be distinctive for this parasite.

The adult macrogametocytes have the nucleus placed off-center; it stains dark red. The cytoplasm stains a deep blue, and supports delicate, dark pigment granules scattered in the cytoplasm. The host cell, which may be slightly enlarged, encloses a red ring of coalesced eosinophilic stippling (Fig. 23).

The mature microgametocytes fill the host cell and exhibit a dark pink cytoplasm. The reddish stained nucleus, with a deep red bar-like mass, is located eccentrically (Fig. 24). The pigment granules are heavy and fairly evenly distributed in the cytoplasm. The host cells show pronounced stippling and some exhibit fimbriated edges.

The asexual cycle is 48 hours.

Sporogonic Cycle
PLATE XXVIII

The sporogonic development of *P. fieldi* has been examined in *A. b. balabacensis*, *A. maculatus*, and *A. freeborni* mosquitoes (Table 23). In *A. b. balabacensis*, at day 5, the mean diameter was 13 μ with a range of 8 to 14 μ. The oocysts continued to grow so that by day 13, the mean size was 68 μ with a range of 32 to 96 μ. Sporozoites were present in the salivary glands by day 14.

Although the oocyst measurements in the *A. maculatus* mosquitoes were limited in number, it appeared that the mean diameters were smaller than in the *A. b. balabacensis* during the period of oocyst differentiation. Sporozoites were present in the salivary glands of these mosquitoes by day 14. The oocyst measurements in the *A. freeborni* were within the ranges of those seen in the other two. Although oocyst differentiation appeared to be normal, sporozoites were found only near the dissected guts of the mosquitoes and there was no evidence that they had invaded the salivary glands.

A comparison of the *P. fieldi* oocyst growth

PLATE XXVII.—*Plasmodium fieldi.*

Fig. 1.   Normal red cell.
Figs. 2–4.   Young trophozoites.
Figs. 5–10. Growing trophozoites.
Figs. 11–13.   Nearly mature and mature trophozoites with pronounced eosinophilic stippling.

Figs. 14–19.   Developing schizonts showing typical host cell distortion.
Figs. 20, 21.   Mature schizonts showing 'ballooned-out' host cell distortion.
Figs. 22, 23.   Developing and mature macrogametocytes.
Fig. 24.   Mature microgametocyte.

from 50,000 to 100,000 per mm³ of blood.

A summary of our studies with *P. fieldi* (Fig. 40) shows that the parasitemias in blood-induced infections, in intact *M. mulatta* monkeys, reached a peak of approximately 9,000 per mm³ by day 7 and declined rapidly to a level of approximately 500 per mm³ by day 15. This level was maintained for the next 30 days, after which, the parasitemia receded slowly to minimal levels. In the splenectomized *M. mulatta* monkeys, the median peak parasitemia was almost 73,000 per mm³. There was considerable variation in the parasitemia curve in these animals with four separate peaks of parasitemia during the 60-day observation period. At 60 days, the median parasite count was less than 500 per mm³. In the monkeys infected by sporozoites, the peak parasitemia was the same as in the blood-induced series, but was delayed by about 3 days. The parasitemia then rapidly declined to a minimal level by day 30. The secondary rise to a peak of approximately 100 per mm³ by day 42, possibly represents relapse activity or the appearance of a new antigenic variant. In the 6 *M. nemestrina* monkeys infected by inoculation of parasitized blood, the peak of the median curve was 475 per mm³ which obtained on day 9. Although there was a secondary rise in the parasitemia at approximately day 25, the levels were generally minimal.

The phenomenon of relapse had intrigued malariologists even before Thayer (1899) published his series of lectures with illuminating references to relapse in *vivax* malaria. Since then, a prodigious literature has accumulated which can not be gone into here except to point out that the phenomenon has received only cursory examination among the simian malarias. True relapses, in contrast to recrudescences, do occur in sporozoite-induced *P. cynomolgi* infections. Our studies with *P. fieldi* lead us to consider it related to *P. ovale*, a 'relapser' in man, and a life-pattern study was set up to test its relapse potential. Each of seven rhesus monkeys with sporozoite-induced infections was allowed to experience an initial parasitemia, which was treated early, as was each succeeding attack, with either quinine sulfate, at a dosage of 300 mg daily for 5 or 7 days, or chloroquine phosphate 150 mg (base) daily for 2 days or 50 mg daily for 3 days (see Fig. 41). These dosages in our hands were known to be curative of blood-induced infections, and would, on that basis, eradicate the blood forms in the sporozoite-induced infections under study. As may be seen by perusal of Figure 41, each infection exhibited two or more relapses at varying intervals. The infection in one animal (T 688) exhibited 14 relapses during a period of 12 months. The relapses did not fall into a distinct pattern, which was not unexpected,

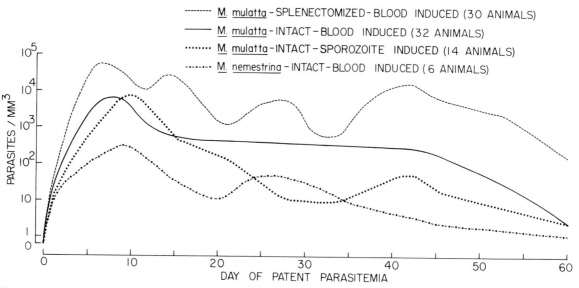

FIGURE 40.—Median parasitemia curves of *Plasmodium fieldi* as seen in 76 *Macaca mulatta* and in 6 *M. nemestrina* monkeys.

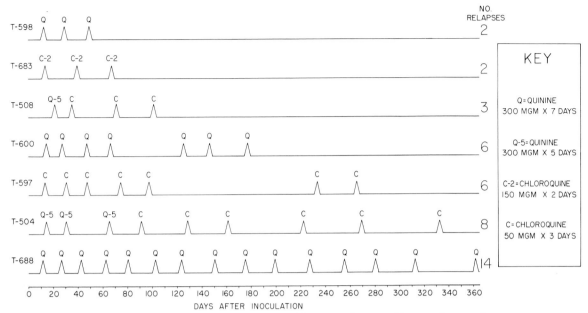

FIGURE 41.—Relapse pattern of *Plasmodium fieldi* as seen in seven *Macaca mulatta* monkeys.

but one may note, that as the time from initial infection increased the tendency for longer intervals between relapses increased also, which *was* expected. The main point was answered, namely, that *P. fieldi* does relapse and that relapse producing infections may last for at least one year.

Host Specificity

The type host of *P. fieldi* is *M. nemestrina*, from which a single isolation was made by Eyles *et al* (1962a). If the parasite was looked for more carefully in this host, it probably would be found, as it was in the kra monkey (*M. irus* (= *fascicularis*)) by Warren and Wharton (1963) in one of twenty of these animals taken in the Kuang forest, north of Kuala Lumpur, Malaysia.

The parasite will also grow in rhesus monkeys (*M. mulatta*) but as Warren *et al* (1964) pointed out the parasite's unique staining characteristics, i.e., large eosinophilic masses and an intense red ring around the parasite, are modified in *M. fascicularis* and in *M. mulatta*. However, these hosts do display the enlarged parasitized host cell. Low level infections have been obtained by us in the baboon (*Papio doguera*) and in *M. radiata*.

Plasmodium fieldi has been isolated from two members of the Leucosphyrus group of mosquitoes, *Anopheles hackeri* and *A. balabacensis introlatus* (Warren and Wharton. 1963). Warren and Wharton (1963) reported that *A. donaldi*, *A. freeborni*, *A. hackeri*, *A. letifer*, *A. maculatus*, and *A. philippinensis* were susceptible to infection, all at a low level. Additionally, *A. b. balabacensis*, *A. kochi*, *A. vagus*, *A. sinensis*, *A. albimanus*, *A. argyropus*, *A. peditaeniatus*, *A. atroparvus*, and *A. quadrimaculatus* were shown to be susceptible, at least to the production of oocysts. *Anopheles freeborni* was the most susceptible (Table 24) followed by *A. b. balabacensis*, *A. kochi*, and *A. vagus*. However, *A. freeborni* did not readily support *P. fieldi* infections to completion and therefore *A. b. balabacensis* is considered the best experimental vector.

Immunity and Antigenic Relationships

Two *M. mulatta* monkeys infected with *P. fieldi* were allowed to have patent parasitemia for 32 and 33 days, respectively, with peak parasitemias of 15,100 and 21,300 per mm^3. They were then given curative treatment with chloroquine. When their blood was parasite-free, one animal was blood-inoculated with *P. fragile* and the other with *P. cynomolgi*.

SECTION 4
Malariae-Type Parasites

18

Plasmodium malariae (Grassi and Feletti, 1890)

SYNONYMS: *Haemamoeba malariae* Feletti and Grassi, 1889; *Plasmodium malariae* M. and C. var. *quartanae* Celli and Sanfelice, 1891; *Plasmodium malariae quartanae* Kruse, 1892; *Haemamoeba laverani* var. *quartanae* Labbé, 1894; *Haemosporidium tertianae* Lewkowicz, 1897; ? *Plasmodium rodhaini* Brumpt, 1939.

There is little doubt that Laveran saw this parasite in fresh blood of patients in Algeria in 1880 because his illustrations show schizonts with 8 merozoites arranged in the typical rosette and a central body of pigment. In his opinion, the human malaria parasites belonged to one species and, possibly for that reason, he did not propose a name. He recognized the phenomenon of periodicity but rejected the idea that it might be a clue toward the taxonomy of the malarias.

Golgi in a short note to the Royal Academy of Medicine in Turin (1885) first recognized the periodic succession of fever attacks and in 1889 he clearly showed how to separate tertian and quartan fevers by linking the development of a particular brood of parasites to the fever episode. He was definite in pointing out that if only young forms are present in the circulating blood there will be 1 or 2 days, depending on the species, free of fever. Golgi was also able to demonstrate quotidian fevers in both tertian and quartan infections and postulated, correctly, that the phenomenon was due to double and triple broods of parasites. This important contribution to the biology of these parasites was more or less ignored at the time and then virtually forgotten until well after the turn of the century.

In attempting to arrive at the correct name and credit for the quartan parasite of man, one runs into considerable difficulties. Coatney and Young (1941) in reviewing the problem arrived at the conclusion that the name *Plasmodium malariae* should be declared valid as the *de facto* name and credited to Grassi and Feletti, 1890. Part of this was accomplished, Opinion 283, under the Plenary Powers of the Commission on Zoological Nomenclature (Hemming, 1954), but credit for the name was given to Grassi and Feletti, 1889. It now appears that the 1889 pamphlet, which is said to have given the authorship in reverse, is no longer extant and therefore the order of authorship cannot be verified. In 1890, Grassi and Feletti gave *malariae* as the specific name for the quartan parasite in the genus *Haemamoeba*, and on the basis of priority, that date is valid. Following this, Grassi and Feletti (1892) described and illustrated the quartan parasite, as seen in the peripheral blood, and separated it from the other blood-inhabiting forms in man and birds under the name *H. malariae* Grassi and Feletti. Garnham (1966) holds that "in view of the authority of this paper, and the disappearance of all traces of the original 1889 pamphlet", the name should be credited to Grassi and Feletti 1892. The tenet that authority is a valid basis for assigning credit is unacceptable, and in view of the loss of the 1889 paper and the fact that the Régles had to be suspended in order to validate the *de facto* name, it appears to us, therefore, that the correct name for the human quartan parasite is *Plasmodium malariae* (Grassi and Feletti, 1890).

Plasmodium malariae is a cosmopolitan parasite which develops where the summer isotherm does not fall below 15° C (59° F). Its distribution is variable and spotty. Why this is true no one has been able to explain although numerous theories have been advanced; it is still, one of the unsolved problems in the biology of human quartan malaria.

One theory to account for its unique distribution was that because the parasite requires an extended sporogonic cycle, its greatest prevalence would be in areas where the vector was able to survive for the longest time. This might obtain in some areas, but it sometimes reaches its highest incidence in parts of the tropics where the vector has only a short life.

Another theory was that quartan malaria demands a special vector. It is true, that experimental infections in mosquitoes are difficult to produce and when obtained, the oocysts fail to develop at a uniform rate which probably accounts for the varied results obtained by such workers as Mayne (1932), Mer (1933), and others. However, the special vector theory hardly seems to cover the problem either because many species transmit the parasite: *A. atroparvus, A. sacharovi, A. stephensi et al.*

The third theory, rested on the presence of an animal reservoir in certain tropical regions. This might be applicable if one is concerned with certain areas in tropical Africa where chimpanzees harbor *P. rodhaini*. In man, that parasite takes on the attributes of *P. malariae* and, in some quarters, is considered to be *P. malariae*. The *inui* parasites of India and the Malaysian area are morphologically distinct from human quartan and so far only one strain has been established in man. The rest of the Old World is without any zoonotic connection to explain the persistence of quartan malaria. In the New World, the situation is altogether different than it is in Africa or the Far East, because it appears relatively clear that the

quartan malaria of monkeys (*P. brasilianum*) came from man, hence an anthroponosis, rather than the other way around.

It may well be that one or more of these factors, along with changes in the environment which might facilitate transmission, play a part in the unique distribution of quartan malaria throughout the world. But whatever the explanation may be, it appears that *P. malariae* is probably the oldest parasite in terms of time, and although Knowles *et al* (1930) considered it a disappearing parasite, it might well be that instead of dying out, it has 'learned' during its long association with man how to cope with adversity and, when conditions permit, to enjoy prosperity.

This is illustrated in the work of Field and Shute (1956) where they cite that in West Malaysia "quartan infections are not commonly found in hospital patients—less than five per cent of the admissions . . .—but there are localized areas where *P. malariae* is the dominant species." In areas of high transmission of all species, *P. falciparum* is dominant for a few months, whereupon, it is succeeded by *P. vivax*, which holds center stage for a time only to be replaced by *P. malariae* which has 'learned' to wait in the wings. Field and Shute call it a "residual infestation" which pretty well sums up the life-cycle of *P. malariae*. It is a highly successful parasite in that it can live in a host longer than any other malaria and without renewed activity from fixed tissue parasites, it causes the host relatively little inconvenience because of its symbiotic nature and, it is always ready, during periods of recrudescence, to gain access to a cooperative vector and, hence, perpetuate the species.

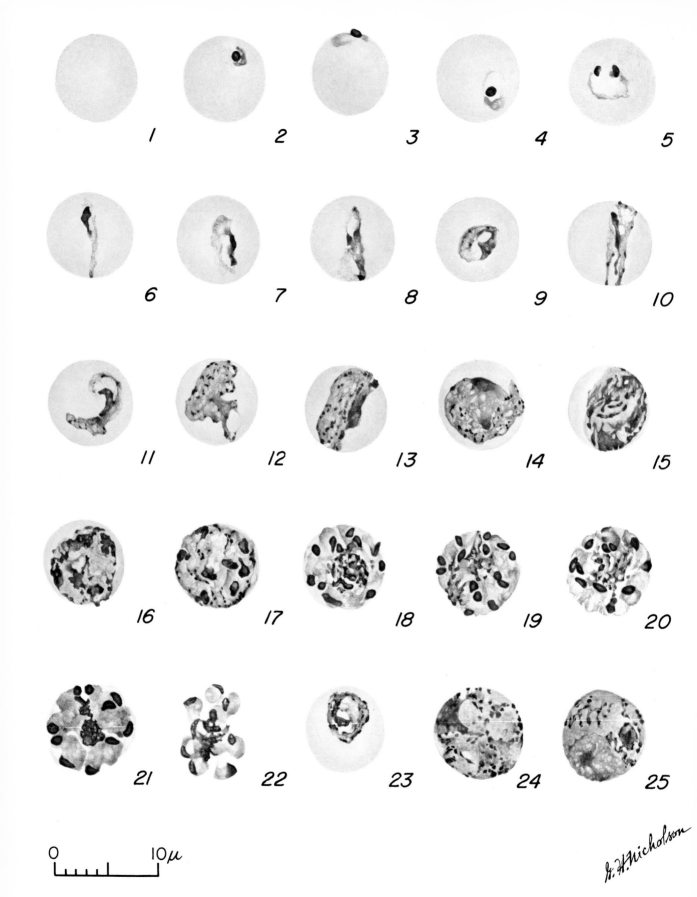

PLASMODIUM MALARIAE

Cycle in the Blood

PLATE XXXIII

The first stage to appear in the peripheral blood is the familiar ring-stage, not shown as a true ring on the plate, a circle of cytoplasm, and a spherical bit of chromatin enclosing a vacuole. It very shortly occupies one-fourth to one-third of the parasitized cell and sometimes exhibits an accessory chromatin dot (Figs. 4,5). Although this parasite generally displays denser cytoplasm and chromatin than *P. vivax*, it is difficult to separate them at this stage because they are about the same size. The parasite grows more slowly than any of the other human malarias. The vacuole disappears after a few hours. In the living condition, the movement is sluggish. Pigment granules appear early in its growth and sometimes a granule may appear in the late ring-stage. The pigment increases rapidly; half grown parasites may exhibit 30 to 50 jet-black granules (Figs. 12,13) in contrast to the rod-like pigment found in *P. vivax*.

As the parasite grows, it assumes various shapes. Some appear stretched out like a ribbon across the host cell and are known as band forms (Figs. 6,10,11). Band forms are found in other species, but are more ferquent in *P. malariae* and hence are considered diagnostic. These forms may be seen at any time until the parasite virtually fills the host cell which is not enlarged or blanched. At about the 54th hour, segmentation begins, and by the 65th hour, the host cell is completely filled, or nearly so, and the parasite contains 5 to 6 chromatin masses; the pigment is scattered (Figs. 14–16). During further growth, the definitive number of nuclei are formed and with the final number, the cytoplasm divides to give each nucleus a small amount of cytoplasm. During this stage, the pigment may appear segregated and then clumped in a loose mass in the center of the cell, surrounded by more or less symmetrically arranged merozoites, to give the "rosette" effect so characteristic of the species. The number of merozoites may be from 6 to 12, sometimes 14; the average is 8 (Figs. 17–22).

The young gametocytes are very similar to the asexual forms which makes it virtually impossible to distinguish them with certainty until about the 54th hour when the asexual forms begin segmentation (Fig. 23). The mature macrogametocyte exhibits a heavy deeply-staining blue cytoplasm with a small, eccentric, well-defined deep red-staining nucleus. The pigment is scattered. The parasite completely fills the host cell (Fig. 24). The cytoplasm of the adult microgametocyte takes a light bluish-pink stain. The pigment is limited to this area of the parasite. The nucleus is diffuse, takes a pinkish-blue stain, and may occupy about half the cell. The parasite fills the entire host cell (Fig. 25). Ordinarily, microgametocytes outnumber the macrogametocytes but this may vary with different strains.

The asexual cycle requires 72 hours.

Sporogonic Cycle

PLATE XXXIV

Observations have been made by a number of workers concerning the sporogonic cycle of *Plasmodium malariae*, but Shute and Maryon (1952) carried out the first definitive studies. These investigators observed its development in *Anopheles atroparvus* mosquitoes incubated at a temperature of 25° C. They found that the pigment, which seldom consisted of more than 30 granules, was very dark brown and variable in size. During the first 7 to 8 days, the granules were distributed over the oocyst, but,

PLATE XXXIII.—*Plasmodium malariae*.

Fig. 1.   Normal red cell.
Figs. 2–5.   Young trophozoites.
Figs. 6–11.   Growing trophozoites.
Figs. 12, 13.   Nearly mature and mature trophozoites.
Figs. 14–20.   Developing schizonts.

Figs. 21, 22.   Mature schizonts.
Fig. 23.   Developing gametocyte.
Fig. 24.   Mature macrogametocyte.
Fig. 25.   Mature microgametocyte.

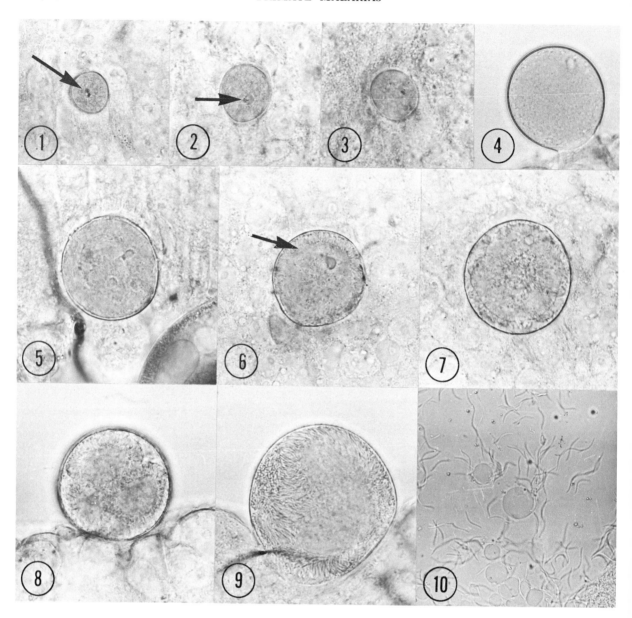

PLATE XXXIV.—Developing oocysts and sporozoites of *Plasmodium malariae* in *Anopheles freeborni* mosquitoes. X 580.

Fig. 1.   10-day oocyst showing small clump of pigment.
Fig. 2.   11-day oocyst showing pigment clumped within small vacuole.
Fig. 3.   12-day oocyst.
Figs. 4, 5.   13-day oocysts.
Fig. 6.   14-day oocyst showing early differentiation.

Fig. 7.   14-day oocyst showing differentiation.
Fig. 8.   15-day oocyst.
Fig. 9.   17-day fully differentiated oocyst.
Fig. 10.   Sporozoites present near salivary gland tissue 19 days after feeding.

from the 9th day onwards, the pigment was clumped in a mass at the periphery. From the 3rd to the 9th day, daily increase in size of the oocyst was less than 2 μ; from the 9th day onward, the daily increase varied from 5 to 8 μ. Oocysts ranged in size from 5 to 44 μ.

The minimum time required for completion of the cycle was 15 days, the maximum, 21 days.

In our studies (Collins and Contacos, 1969), *A. freeborni* was the most suitable mosquito for studying the sporogonic cycle (Table 27). On day 6, at an incubation temperature of 25° C, the mean oocyst diameter was 12 μ with a range of 9 to 14 μ. The oocysts continued to grow so that by day 14, the mean size was 38 μ with a range of 20 to 65 μ. The first signs of oocyst differentiation were apparent by day 14; sporozoites were present in the salivary glands on day 17.

A comparison of the oocyst growth rate of *P. malariae* with that of *P. cynomolgi* (Fig. 45) points-up the marked difference between the 2 parasites. The mean oocyst diameter of *P. cynomolgi* on day 8 is about the same as that of *P. malariae* on day 15. Sporozoites appear in the salivary glands 6 days sooner with *P. cynomolgi* than with *P. malariae*. The comparison of the sporogonic cycle of this parasite with *P. brasilianum* is presented elsewhere (Chapter 19).

Cycle in the Tissue

The first tissue stages of *Plasmodium malariae* were seen and described by Bray (1959, 1960). Liver biopsy specimens (8, 9, 10, 11, 12, and 12.5 days) were taken from 3 different chimpanzees which had received 72 to 110 salivary glands of *Anopheles gambiae;* 33 to 50 percent of them were infected with sporozoites of a Liberian strain of *P. malariae*.

TABLE 27.—Oocyst diameters of *Plasmodium malariae* in *Anopheles freeborni* mosquitoes.

Days post infection	A. freeborni		
	No.	Range	Mean*
6	104	9–14	12
7	105	11–19	14
8	185	12–21	17
9	169	14–27	20
10	146	13–32	21
11	268	13–45	27
12	218	14–51	29
13	195	19–59	37
14	260	20–65	38†
15	260	17–77	50†
16	348	19–88	48†
17	168	15–86	53†**
Totals	2426	9–88	

* Measurements expressed in microns.
† Oocyst differentiation.
**Sporozoites present in the salivary glands.

The 8-day tissue schizont was described as lying in the liver parenchyma cell usually, but not always, in a vacuole. The host cell was enlarged and the cytoplasm pushed aside in a crescent-shape around the parasite. The host cell nucleus was enlarged and pushed to one side. In over 50 percent of the parasitized parenchymal cells, 2 or more enlarged nuclei were present. The tissue schizont usually had

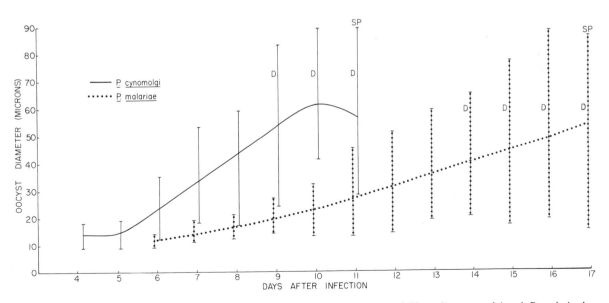

FIGURE 45.—Range in oocyst diameters and the mean oocyst diameter curves of *Plasmodium cynomolgi* and *P. malariae* in *Anopheles freeborni* mosquitoes. (D = oocyst differentiation; SP = sporozoites present in the salivary glands).

a distinct envelope with no clefts. Its cytoplasm was generally homogeneous but was sometimes tenuous or in strands. Occasionally, the periphery showed tiny vacuoles. The nuclei were usually small dots measuring about 0.5 μ or round compact masses of chromatin measuring about 1 μ in diameter. The average size of the 8-day tissue schizont was 12.5 μ (range of 9.5 to 17 μ). The average number of nuclei was 25 (range of 7 to 49).

The 9-day schizonts were generally like the 8-day forms except for the scatter in size, the range was 8.5 to 21 μ (average 12.7 μ). The average number of nuclei was 27 (range of 10 to 83).

The 10-day schizonts were usually within a vacuole in the parenchyma cell. The parasite had pushed the enlarged nucleus, or nuclei, of the enlarged host cell, to one side. The cytoplasm was homogeneous and reasonably dense. In about half of the parasites, the cytoplasm was pulled slightly away from the distinct envelope; in about 40 percent, it had not contracted away from the envelope; in the remaining 10 percent, the cytoplasm was irregularly vacuolated. Some showed, what was described as, 3- or 4-point type nuclei. The size of the 10-day stage averaged 22.1 μ (range of 15 to 29 μ); the average number of nuclei was 100 (range of 33 to 201).

The 11-day schizonts were smaller than the 8- or 9-day stages, the average being 11.7 μ (range of 9.5 to 14 μ); the average number of nuclei was approximately 15 (range of 6 to 30).

The 12-day tissue parasite had a distinct envelope with dense cytoplasm in the central portions of the parasite. The periphery consisted of vacuoles measuring 3 to 6 μ in diameter. The cytoplasm contained a number of small basophilic aggregates. The schizont was sometimes slightly lobulated. The average size was 41 μ (range of 34 to 47 μ). The average number of nuclei was 712 (range of 435 to 1151). The 12.5-day schizonts resembled the 12-day forms except for 2 characteristics; namely, the parasite was markedly lobulated and the peripheral vacuolations were more marked—large peripheral vacuoles measuring 5 to 8 μ were commonly observed.

Bray mentioned several general observations concerning the tissue schizonts at all ages;

namely, the nuclei were always randomly distributed, there were no pseudocytomeres, no evidence of septal formation, or plasmotomy. He saw no mature schizonts or any evidence of sporulation. Bray's studies showed quite distinctly that the tissue stages of *P. malariae* in the chimpanzee differ markedly from the other species of human malaria. It differs from vivax and falciparum malaria in that it causes enlargement of the host cell nucleus, the older forms show considerable vacuolation of the peripheral cytoplasm, it produces fewer merozoites, and the growth rate is considerably slower. It differs from *P. ovale* in that the nuclei of malariae tissue stages are smaller, fewer in number, and its growth rate is slightly slower. The first evidence of parasitemia in the chimpanzees was seen 16 days after the inoculation of sporozoites.

Lupascu *et al* (1967) determined the "exact duration" of the "prepatent period" of the VS (Roumanian) strain of *P. malariae* by the subinoculation of blood into new patients. Only the recipients given blood 15 days or more after inoculation of sporozoites became infected. In other words, with this strain of *P. malariae*, the exoerythrocytic cycle requires exactly 15 days and, therefore, the prepatent period could be as early as day 15.

Lupascu *et al* also described the later tissue stages of *P. malariae*. They inoculated a 3 year-old chimpanzee with a total of 110 salivary glands from *Anopheles labranchiae atroparvus* mosquitoes, 86 to 100 percent infected with the VS strain. Liver biopsy material was obtained at 12, 13, 14, and 15 days. All 4 biopsy specimens contained tissue schizonts. The 12-day stages were usually oval, and, less often, spherical in shape. The contour was usually smooth but occasionally disturbed by the presence of peripheral vacuoles. The parasitized perenchymal cells were greatly enlarged. The host cell nucleus was pushed to one side and much enlarged, somtimes twice its normal size, and frequently pyknotic. The mean diameter of the 12-day schizont was 30 μ. The nuclei were round and interspersed throughout the cytoplasm, being somewhat scantier towards the margin of the parasite. The diameter of the nuclei was approximately 1.5 μ. The cytoplasm tended to accumulate either as individual flocculi or as larger masses. Numerous vacuoles of all sizes were present. The largest vacuoles were 10 μ. The parasite had a definite membrane.

The 13-day forms had an average size of 44 μ, indicating considerable growth in 24 hours. This rapid growth probably accounted for the pronounced lobulation. The internal structure of the parasite was much the same as that of the 12-day schizont except that the nuclei were "less loosely packed." Cytoplasmic clumps and vacuoles persisted and clefts were usually seen.

The 14-day schizonts reached a maximum mean diameter of 47 μ. They were more difficult to measure because of the lobulated surface. The most striking feature was the extensive cleavage of the cytoplasm in some of the schizonts. The cytoplasm was condensed into long strands, studded with nuclei, and sometimes smaller clefts were present throughout the parasite. The nuclei were "tightly packed" and measured about 2 μ in diameter; vacuoles were obvious. The limiting membrane of the parasite was distinct and occasionally thrown into pronounced folds. Only the 14-day schizonts exhibited merozoites.

The 15-day schizonts were considered mature and remnants of ruptured schizonts were readily observed. The mature forms had a mean diameter of about 51 μ. Their shape was mostly oval, although irregular processes (lobulations) were observed. The nuclei, of the near-mature schizonts, lost their spherical shape just prior to the final division, became triangular, and measured as much as 3.3 μ in their greatest dimension. The cytoplasm formed patterns although the nuclei did not enter this material and no cytomeres or any form of aposchizogony was observed. Large vacuoles were present but were less common than in the nearly-mature stage. The authors described curious reddish strands in the cytoplasm of some of the schizonts and considered this feature unique among tissue forms of malaria parasites. The mature schizont, except for the strands and a few vacuoles, consisted, almost entirely, of merozoites within the outer limiting membrane of the parasite. The largest mature schizont measured 41 by 85 μ, the average was 56 μ. The number of merozoites

was directly dependent upon the size of the mature schizont. The largest number of merozoites was estimated to be 18,650 and the smallest 7,500. The merozoite was a sphere measuring 2 μ in diameter, consisting of cytoplasm which indents the nucleus to render it characteristically crescentic in shape.

Lupascu *et al* (1967) in their summary gave the main characteristics of the tissue schizonts of the VS strain of *P. malariae* as: enlargement of the host cell nucleus, many peripheral and internal vacuoles, no cytomeres, large clefts, red-staining strands, and plaques in the mature schizonts.

Course of Infection

As mentioned earlier, the shortest prepatent period for *P. malariae* could be as early as 15 days, on the basis of the findings of Lupascu's subinoculation experiments. However, in actuality, the earliest reported prepatent period has been 16 days in a West African strain (Shute and Maryon, 1951).

Generally, the prepatent periods, with this species, have been longer. Boyd and Stratman-Thomas (1933) transmitted 2 strains in which the prepatent periods were 27, 32, and 37 days. Mer (1933) transmitted a Palestinian strain to 3 patients; prepatent periods were 26, 28, and 31 days. Prepatent periods of 23 to 26 days were reported by de Buck (1935) for 4 patients infected with a Vienna strain. Boyd and Stratman-Thomas (1936) reported a prepatent period of 37 days (thin smear examination); the incubation period was 40 days. This patient had only 5 paroxysms with 4 chills. The paroxysms subsided spontaneously although parasites were found as late as 173 days after exposure to infection. They also reported a prepatent period of 28 days and an incubation period of 30 days in another patient. Marotta and Sandicchi (1939) reported incubation periods of 23 and 29 days in 2 patients.

Boyd (1940) reported on 3 different strains: USPHS, Jones, and Weaver. The prepatent periods ranged from 28 to 37 days (median of 34 days) and the incubation periods from 30 to 49 days (median of 36 days). Siddons (1944) transmitted an Indian strain of *P.*

malariae to a patient who exhibited a prepatent period of 30 days and an incubation period of 36 days. Young and Burgess (1947) observed prepatent periods of 29 and 59 days in 2 patients whose incubation periods were 28 and 69 days. These authors considered the prepatent period of 59 days to be due, possibly, to some immunity on the part of the patient which was substantiated by a short duration of parasitemia and extremely low parasite counts. Mackerras and Ercole (1948) reported a prepatent period of 24 days for a Melanesian strain. Kitchen (1949) reported mean prepatent periods of 32.2 days (range 27 to 37 days) and mean incubation periods of 34.8 days (range 29 to 40 days) for naturally induced infections of American strains of *P. malariae*.

Young and Burgess (1961) transmitted the USPHS strain of *P. malariae* to 2 patients and observed prepatent periods of 33 and 36 days and incubation periods of 28 and 43 days. Ciuca *et al* (1964) reported prepatent periods ranging from 18 to 25 days for a local Roumanian strain, now known as the VS strain. Lupascu *et al* (1968) reported incubation periods of 18 to 19 days with the VS strain of *P. malariae*. As these data show, there is a wide range in the length of the prepatent periods in naturally transmitted *P. malariae* (18 to 59 days) and an equally wide range in the incubation periods (28 to 69 days).

In our transmission studies with a Nigerian strain of *P. malariae*, involving 4 volunteers, we have observed prepatent periods ranging from 24 to 33 days (Contacos and Collins, 1969); with the VS strain, in 4 patients, the prepatent periods ranged from 21 to 30 days.

Malariae malaria infections are considered to be relatively benign when compared to falciparum malaria but more severe than vivax infections. Probably its most peculiar characteristic is its pronounced chronicity, especially the unusually long period of time during which parasites can remain 'dormant' within the host. A less constant characteristic is the tendency to cause renal damage which was dealt with in some detail by Giglioli (1930).

The onset of *P. malariae* attacks is generally more gradual than observed with many vivax and falciparum infections. The initial remittent fever pattern characteristic of vivax infections is seen less frequently in malariae infections. Rather, they exhibit an intermittent pattern (Kitchen, 1949) because the sporulation of this species is highly synchronous.

Young *et al* (1940) studied the periodic phenomenon of the asexual cycle of quartan malaria in Negro paretics. They found that their strain of malariae malaria (USPHS) exhibited a high degree of synchronicity, the asexual erythrocytic cycle repeating itself every 72 hours, but being more exact in some patients than in others. The length of time consumed by the different growth stages was: 54.2 hours for the trophozoites, 10.4 hours for the young schizonts, and 7.4 hours for the segmenters or late schizonts. The process of segmentation required roughly 6 hours. The rise in temperature closely followed the progress of segmentation and reached its height approximately at the end of the process.

Young *et al* (1940a) showed that modifying the external conditions of the host affected the time of sporulation of *P. malariae* in man when patients were placed under reversed conditions of activity; the segmenter-number peaks in one changed from the normal 9:00 a.m. hour to 9:00 p.m. In the other, the cycle was shortened until the segmenters peaked about 22 hours before normally expected. Two other patients were placed under reversed conditions, except lighted continuously. In these, the segmenter-peak time changed from 9:00 a.m. to 9:00 p.m. When one of them was returned to a normal schedule, the segmenter-number peaks returned to the normal time, 9:00 a.m.

Young *et al* (1941) presented data on 420 paroxysms occurring in 15 patients infected with the USPHS strain of *P. malariae*. Chills were observed 102 times (24 percent). Some patients experienced chills more often than others; one had 9 chills in 14 paroxysms (64 percent), while another had only 1 chill in 45 paroxysms (2 percent). Temperatures at the beginning of chills were found to range from 97.6° F to 106.0° F rectally, with an average of 101.8° F. Temperatures at the end of the chills ranged from 97.8° F to 106.0° F, with an average of 103.5° F. The greatest increase in temperature during a chill was observed in a patient whose temperature rose from 98.0° F to 103.0° F during a chill lasting 45 minutes. Two patients experienced the opposite; in other words, a drop in temperature during a chill. One had a temperature of 106.0° F at the beginning and 105.0° F at the end of the chill which lasted 50 minutes. Another patient dropped from 104.2° F at the beginning of the chill to 103.2° F at the end of the chill which lasted 15 minutes. It is interesting that in both these cases, very high temperatures had already been reached by the time the chill began. The durations of all chills ranged from 13 to 195 minutes with an average of 53 minutes (Fig. 46).

According to Kitchen (1949), the malariae paroxysm is less often introduced by chills than are vivax paroxysms. Boyd (1940) found that the initiation of the malariae paroxysm by chills was extremely variable. Indeed, one of 5 naturally induced cases studied by him had no chills at all. In Kitchen's observations, on patients infected with the Trinidad strain, the temperature at the onset of the chill varied between 97.4° F and 104.4° F (mean of 100.3° F). The mean duration of the chills was 55.97 minutes. The mean temperature peak was 104.98° F reached, on an average, 2 hours, 54 minutes after the onset. The interval from peak temperature until the temperature returned to normal was 10 hours, 23 minutes.

The entire paroxysm, therefore, occupied a period of 13 hours and 17 minutes. *Plasmodium malariae* paroxysms are longer in duration than those of *P. vivax*.

In the Young *et al* series, the average fever peak for the 420 paroxysms was 104.1° F rectally, with the highest temperature recorded, 106.4° F. The duration of the fevers ranged from 5 to 32 hours with an average of 10 hours, 58 minutes. The average time for the interval from the beginning of fever to the fever peak was 4 hours, 45 minutes and from the fever peak to the end of the fever was 6 hours, 13 minutes. These authors also observed that some paroxysms were introduced by a chill, while others were devoid of chills. When a chill accompanied the paroxysm, the fever was significantly higher (104.6° F as compared to 104.0° F without a chill) and the duration of the fever was 1 hour, 16 minutes shorter (10 hours duration for the paroxysms with chills as compared to 11 hours, 16 minutes for the paroxysms without chills). In addition, it was obvious that this shortening of the fever period occurred almost entirely in the period between the onset of the paroxysm and the peak of the fever. They believed that the chill exerted a definite influence on the character of the paroxysm. When a chill occurred, the duration of the fever was shorter (1 hour, 16 minutes) which was due, appar-

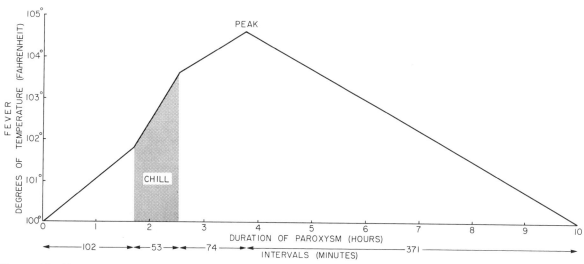

FIGURE 46.—The temperature curve in relation to the chill in 102 paroxysms in *Plasmodium malariae* infections (after Young, Coatney, and McLendon, 1941).

parasitemia was maintained at approximately the same level as that in the primary passages.

Plasmodium malariae grows well in this monkey as indicated by the nearly normal appearance of the parasites in the blood, (Plate XXXV) the long persistence of the infection, and its ready infectivity to mosquitoes (Fig. 49). In one monkey (AO-74), *A freeborni* mosquitoes were allowed to feed beginning day 11 and through day 108 of parasitemia (no feedings were made on days 48 through 56). Infections were obtained on 74 of the 89 feeding days. Although, in general, the percentage of infection was low, there were indications, at least, of an every-third-day peak in the mosquito infection rate during certain periods, such as, on days 16, 19, 25, 28, 34, 37, 40, 43, and 46. Although not as pronounced as with some of the tertian malarias (see Chapters 6 and 23), it suggests that infectivity may be correlated with the schizogonic cycle in the vertebrate host.

Experimental transmission of *P. malariae* by the bites of infected mosquitoes has been demonstrated by a number of workers as listed in Table 28. To that list we can add our experiences in which a Nigerian strain of *P. malariae* has been transmitted to 6 volunteers by the bites of infected *A. freeborni* mosquitoes and, the Roumanian VS strain, to 4 volunteers via the bites of *A. atroparvus*.

Host Specificity

Plasmodium malariae is found naturally in man and, possibly, in chimpanzees. Experimentally, infections have been obtained in owl monkeys, *Aotus trivirgatus*, although, to date, only blood induced infections have been reported.

Mosquitoes which have been reported as susceptible to infection with *P. malariae* are listed in Table 28. In addition, we have obtained infections in *A. b. balabacensis* mosquitoes. A comparative infectivity study with a strain of this parasite from Nigeria (Table 29), indicates that *A. freeborni* was the most susceptible followed by *A. b. balabacensis*, *A. stephensi*, *A. atroparvus*, and finally, *A. maculatus*.

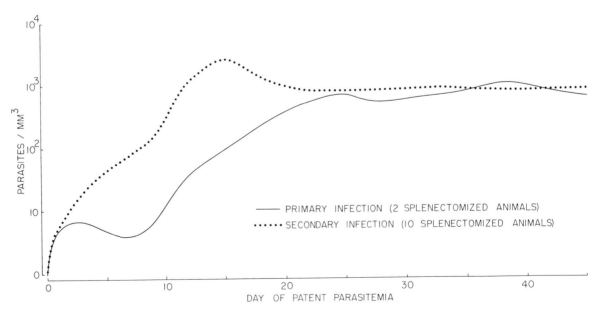

FIGURE 48.—Median parasitemia curves of *Plasmodium malariae* in *Aotus trivirgatus* monkeys after primary inoculation of parasitized blood from man and secondary inoculation into additional monkeys.

TABLE 28.—Anopheline mosquitoes tested for susceptibility to infection with *Plasmodium malariae* and those which effected transmission.—Continued

TABLE 28.—Anopheline mosquitoes tested for susceptibility to infection with *Plasmodium malariae* and those which effected transmission.

Mosquito species	Transmission	References
Anopheles acontius	−	Schuurman and Huinink, 1929
A. annulipes	−	Garnham, 1966*
A. atroparvus	−	Jancsó, 1921
A. atroparvus	−	James, 1931
A. atroparvus	+	de Buck, 1935
A. atroparvus	−	Cambournac, 1942
A. atroparvus	−	Shute, 1951
A. atroparvus	+	Shute and Maryon, 1955
A. atroparvus	+	Ciuca *et al*, 1964
A. atroparvus	−	Constantinescu and Negulici, 1967
A. aztecus	−	Young and Burgess, 1961
A. claviger	−	Grassi *et al*, 1899
A. culicifacies	−	Stephens and Christophers, 1902
A. culicifacies	−	Iyengar, 1933
A. culicifacies	−	Siddons, 1944
A. darlingi	−	Garnham, 1966*
A. fluviatilis	−	Garnham, 1966*
A. freeborni	+	Young and Burgess, 1947
A. freeborni	−	Young and Burgess, 1961
A. freeborni	+	Contacos and Collins, 1969
A. fuliginosus	−	Stephens and Christophers, 1902
A. fuliginosus	−	Anazawa, 1931
A. fuliginosus	−	Sur *et al*, 1932
A. fuliginosus	−	Basu, 1943
A. funestus	−	Garnham, 1966*
A. gambiae	−	Gordon and Davey, 1932
A. gambiae	−	Muirhead-Thompson, 1957
A. hyrcanus sinensis	−	Swellengrebel *et al*, 1919
A. hyrcanus sinensis	−	Anazawa, 1931
A. hyrcanus sinensis	−	Khaw and Kan, 1934
A. jeyporiensis	−	Garnham, 1966*
A. lindesayi	−	Anazawa, 1931
A. maculatus	−	Green, 1929
A. maculatus	−	Anazawa, 1931
A. maculatus	−	Strickland *et al*, 1940
A. melas	−	Garnham, 1966*
A. messeae	+	Marotta and Sandicchi, 1939
A. minimus	−	Anazawa, 1931
A. moucheti	−	Garnham, 1966*
A. plumbeus	−	Gendel'man, 1936
A. punctulatus	+	Mackerras and Roberts, 1947
A. punctulatus	−	Mackerras and Ercole, 1948
A. punctipennis	−	Mayne, 1932
A. punctipennis	−	Young and Burgess, 1961
A. quadrimaculatus	+	Boyd and Stratman-Thomas, 1933
A. quadrimaculatus	−	Boyd and Stratman-Thomas, 1934
A. quadrimaculatus	+	Boyd and Stratman-Thomas, 1936
A. quadrimaculatus	+	Young and Burgess, 1947
A. quadrimaculatus	−	Young *et al*, 1948
A. quadrimaculatus	+	Young and Burgess, 1961
A. sacharovi	−	Khodukin and Lisova, 1930
A. sacharovi	+	Averbouch, 1930
A. sacharovi	+	Mer, 1933
A. splendidus	−	Anazawa, 1931
A. stephensi	−	Sur *et al*, 1932
A. stephensi	−	Iyengar, 1933
A. stephensi	−	Russell and Mohan, 1939
A. stephensi	−	Knowles and Basu, 1943
A. stephensi	+	Shute, 1951; Shute and Maryon, 1951
A. sundaicus	−	Swellengrebel *et al*, 1919
A. sundaicus	−	Hylkema, 1920
A. sundaicus	−	Anazawa, 1931
A. sundaicus	−	Iyengar, 1933
A. sundaicus	+	Brumpt, 1949
A. tessellatus	−	Anazawa, 1931
A. varuna	−	Sur *et al*, 1932
A. varuna	−	Iyengar, 1933

*Listed by Garnham as experimental hosts; reference not given.

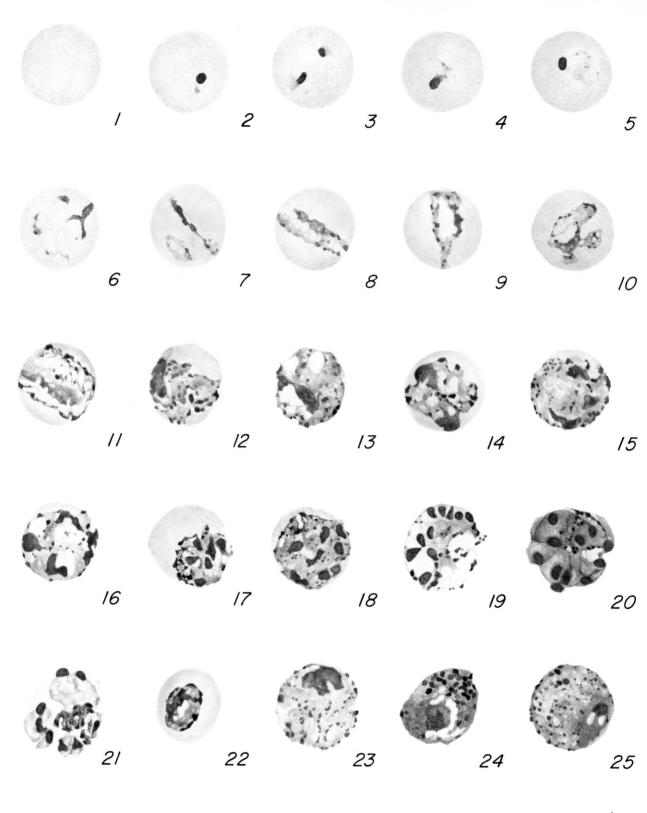

1   2   3   4   5

6   7   8   9   10

11   12   13   14   15

16   17   18   19   20

21   22   23   24   25

0   10μ

G. H. Nicholson

PLASMODIUM MALARIAE IN AOTUS TRIVIRGATUS

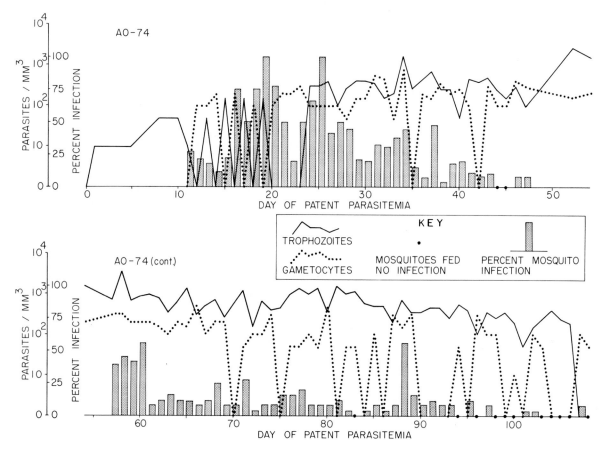

FIGURE 49.—Course of parasitemia and infectivity to *Anopheles freeborni* mosquitoes of an infection of *Plasmodium malariae* in an *Aotus trivirgatus* monkey (AO–74).

Immunity and Antigenic Relationships

Natural infections of *Plasmodium malariae* give rise to a strong immunity but apparently not as strong as those resulting from repeated blood-induced infections. Ciuca *et al* (1934) showed that many patients convalescing from blood-induced quartan malaria acquire a sterile immunity (i.e., large volumes of blood from them were not infective). They also reported, that in patients reinoculated repeatedly with the same strain, the percentage of takes decreased. They showed, also, that homologous immunity was not only clinical but also parasitologic. Reinoculations with the same strain of parasite, after cessation of clinical manifestations, resulted in varying degrees of immunity to clinical symptoms and to parasitemia. By the 5th reinoculation, no patients showed

PLATE XXXV.—*Plasmodium malariae* in the owl monkey, *Aotus trivirgatus.*

Fig. 1.   Normal red cell.

Figs. 2–5.   Young trophozoites.

Figs. 6–10.   Growing trophozoites, note double infection (Fig. 6).

Fig. 11–13.   Nearly mature and mature trophozoites.

Figs. 14–20.   Developing schizonts.

Fig. 21.   Mature schizont.

Figs. 22, 23.   Developing and mature macrogametocytes.

Figs. 24, 25.   Developing and mature microgametocytes.

TABLE 29.—Comparative infectivity of *Plasmodium malariae* to *Anopheles freeborni*, *A. b. balabacensis*, *A. stephensi*, *A. atroparvus*, and *A. maculatus*.

Mosq. species comparison*	Number tests	Number of mosquitoes		Percent infection		GII** ratios
		Standard	Other	Standard	Other	
F–1						100
F–1 : Bal	13	223	116	9.4	17.2	80.4
F–1 : St–1	5	134	65	9.7	4.6	20.3
F–1 : Atro	52	996	238	37.1	12.2	14.9
F–1 : Mac	33	554	865	43.7	11.3	3.5

  * F–1 = *Anopheles freeborni*, Bal = *A. b. balabacensis*, St–1 = *A. stephensi*, Atro = *A. atroparvus*, Mac = *A. maculatus*.

  ** GII = Gut Infection Index = average number of oocysts per 100 guts; the GII ratio is the relationship of the GII of *A. freeborni* to another species where the GII of *A. freeborni* = 100.

fever and parasites. Twenty-three percent had parasites without fever and 77 percent had no fever and no parasites. By the 7th reinoculation, homologous immunity was complete, i.e., 100 percent with no fever and no parasites.

In naturally acquired or induced infections, parasites rarely disappear entirely and/or permanently; rather, there is a tendency for extreme chronicity of infection. Garnham (1966) stated that the assumption by the Roumanian workers that "this 'resistance' is of the nature of premunition" was probably correct. Ciuca *et al* (1955) reported that the forms of immunity acquired as a result of *P. malariae* infection present characteristics enirely different from those for *P. vivax* and *P. falciparum* in the sense that the proportion of residual immunity (immunity without premunition) is superior to that of "concomitante" immunity (immunity with premunition), being, respectively, 72.8 and 27.2 percent.

Plasmodium malariae offers better antigenic quality than the other human malarias for stimulating a more durable immunity which maintains itself even after the disappearance of

parasites. Homologous and heterologous immunity were considered by Ciuca *et al* to develop in parallel. The duration of such immunities was observed to persist from 5 to 14 years.

Antibodies to *P. malariae* were shown to cross-react to *Plasmodium fieldi*, *P. gonderi*, *P. inui*, *P. coatneyi*, *P. knowlesi*, *P. cynomolgi* (B strain), and *P. brasilianum* antigens (Collins *et al* 1966). The highest heterologous reactions were to the *P. brasilianum* antigen and secondarily to *P. fieldi*. Such cross-reactions were also reported by Meuwissen (1968) using *P. falciparum*, *P. vivax*, *P. ovale*, *P. cynomolgi* (B strain), and *P. fieldi* antigens. In a further study, Sulzer *et al* (1969) found that a *P. malariae* antiserum gave a high level of reaction to *P. brasilianum*, followed by lower reactions to *P. vivax*, *P. falciparum*, and, finally, to *P. fieldi* antigens. Dranga *et al* (1969) in testing the cross-reactions between *P. vivax* and *P. malariae* antisera showed that a cross-reaction could always be observed between the 2 antigens but that the homologous responses were higher than the heterologous responses.

REFERENCES

ANAZAWA, K., 1931. Experimental studies on the infectability of anopheline mosquitoes of Formosa. J. Med. Assoc. Formosa *30* : 609–632. (NS).

AVERBOUCH, I., 1930. Expériences sur la transmission á l'homme de la fiévre quarte par les piqûres d'*Anopheles maculipennis* var. *saccharovi*. Rev. Micro. Epid. Parasit. *9* : 379–381. (NS).

BASU, B. C., 1943. Laboratory studies on the infectivity of *Anopheles annularis*. J. Malar. Inst. Ind. *5* : 31–51.

BOYD, M. F., 1940. Observations on naturally and arti-

ficially induced quartan malaria. Am. J. Trop. Med. *20* : 749–798.

BOYD, M. F., 1947. A note on the chronicity of a quartan malaria infection. Ann. Soc. Belge de Méd. Trop., Brussels, December 99–101.

BOYD, M. F. and STRATMAN-THOMAS, W. K., 1933. A note on the transmission of quartan malaria by *Anopheles quadrimaculatus*. Am. J. Trop. Med. *13* : 265–271.

BOYD, M. F. and STRATMAN-THOMAS, W. K., 1934. The comparative susceptibility of *Anopheles quadrimaculatus* Say,

REFERENCES—Continued

and of *Anopheles crucians* Wied. (inland variety) to the parasites of human malaria. Am. J. Hyg. 20 : 247–257.

BOYD, M. F. and STRATMAN-THOMAS, W. K., 1936. The transmission of quartan malaria through two consecutive human-anopheline passages. Am. J. Trop. Med. 16 : 63–65.

BRAY, R. S., 1959. Pre-erythrocytic stages of human malaria parasites: *Plasmodium malariae*. Brit. Med. Jour. 2 : 679–680.

BRAY, R. S., 1960. Studies on malaria in chimpanzees. VIII. The experimental transmission and pre-erythrocytic phase of *Plasmodium malariae*, with a note on the host-range of the parasite. Am. J. Trop. Med. & Hyg. 9 : 455–465.

BRUMPT, E., 1939. Les parasites du paludisme des chimpanzés. C. R. Soc. Biol. 130 : 837–840.

BRUMPT, E., 1949. The human parasites of the genus *Plasmodium*. Malariology, Vol. I, edited by Mark F. Boyd. W. B. Saunders Co., Phila.

CAMBOURNAC, F. J. C., 1942. Sôbre a epidemiologia do sezonismo em Portugal. Soc. Ind. de Tipografia, Lda., Lisbon.

CELLI, A. and SANFELICE, F., 1891. Sui parassiti del globulo rosso nell'uomo et negli animali. Quar. 1st. Igene Sper. Univ. Roma, 1 (N.S.) 33–63 and Ueber die Parasiten des Rothen Blutkorpercheres im Menschen und in Thieren. Fortsch. Med. 9 : 581–586.

CIUCA, M., BALLIF, L., and CHELARESCU-VIERU, M., 1934. Immunity in malaria. Trans. Roy. Soc. Trop. Med. & Hyg. 27 : 619–622.

CIUCA, M., CHELARESCU, M., SOFLETEA, A., CONSTANTINESCU, P., TERITEANU, E., CORTEZ, P., BALANOVSCHI, G., and ILIES, M., 1955. Expérimentale à l'étude de l'immunité dans le paludisme. Editions De L'académie de la Republique Populaire Roumaine (Bucharest), 61–108.

CIUCA, M., RADACOVICI, E., CHELARESCU, M., ATANASIU, M., ISFAN, T., CONSTANTINESCU, P., TERITEANU, E., GIMA, I., SCARLAT, M., CONSTANTINESCU, G., and TAUTU, L., 1956. Cercetari privind durata evolutiei infectiilor cu *Plasmodium vivax*, *Plasmodium falciparum* si *Plasmodium malariae*. Bull. stiint., sect., med. 8 : 549–564.

CIUCA, M., LUPASCU, G., NEGULICI, E., and CONSTANTINESCU, P., 1964. Recherches sur la transmission expérimentale de *P. malariae* à l'homme. Arch. Roum. Path. Exp. Microbiol. 23 : 763–776.

COATNEY, G. R. and YOUNG, M. D., 1941. The taxonomy of the human malaria parasites with notes on the principal American strains. Am. Assoc. Adv. Sci. (No. 15), 19–24.

COLLINS, W. E. and CONTACOS, P. G., 1969. Infectivity of *Plasmodium malariae* in the *Aotus trivirgatus* monkey to *Anopheles freeborni* mosquitoes. J. Parasit. 55 : 1253–1257.

COLLINS, W. E., JEFFERY, G. M., GUINN, E., and SKINNER, J. C., 1966. Fluorescent antibody studies in human malaria. IV. Cross-reactions between human and simian malaria. Am. J. Trop. Med. & Hyg. 15 : 11–15.

CONSTANTINESCU, P. and NEGULICI, E., 1967. The experimental transmission of *Plasmodium malariae* to *Anopheles labranchiae atroparvus*. Trans. Roy. Soc. Trop. Med. &

Hyg. 61 : 182–188.

CONTACOS, P. G. and COLLINS, W. E., 1969. *Plasmodium malariae*: Transmission from monkey to man by mosquito bite. Science, 165 : 918–919.

DE BUCK, A., 1935. Infection experiments with quartan malaria. Ann. Trop. Med. Parasit. 29 : 171–175.

DIAMOND, M. P., 1966. Blood film containing *Plasmodium malariae* from patient who came to this country 12 years ago. Trans. Roy. Soc. Trop. Med. & Hyg. 60 : 425.

DRANGA, A., MARINOV, R., ROMANESCU, C., and TUDOSE, M., 1969. L'evolution des anticorps fluorescents dans le paludisme provogue par inoculation palustre primaire. (Personal communication and WHO/Mal/69.697.)

FELETTI, R. and GRASSI, B., 1889, 1890. Sui parassiti della malaria. Rif. Med. 6 : 62–64. (The 1889 paper was a preprint of the 1890 paper according to Hemming, 1954).

FIELD, J. W. and SHUTE, P. G., 1956. The microscopic diagnosis of human malaria. II. A morphological study of the erythrocytic parasites. Inst. Med. Res., Fed. Malaya, No. 24. pp. 251.

GARNHAM, P. C. C., 1966. Malaria parasites and other haemosporidia. Blackwell Scientific Publications, Oxford. pp. 1114.

GARNHAM, P. C. C., LAINSON, R., and GUNDERS, A. E., 1956. Some observations on malaria parasites in a chimpanzee, with particular reference to the presistence of *Plasmodium reichenowi* and *Plasmodium vivax*. Ann. Soc. Belge de Méd. Trop. 36 : 811–821.

GEIMAN, Q. M. and SIDDIQUI, W. A., 1969. Susceptibility of a new world monkey to *Plasmodium malariae* from man. Am. J. Trop. Med. & Hyg. 18 : 351–354.

GENDLE'MAN, C. A., 1936. Sull'infezione sperimentale dell' *Anopheles nigripes* con plasmodi. Trydii Tropitchkogo Inst. Narkomzdrava Assr. Abhhazii 2 : 70. (NS).

GIGLIOLI, G., 1930. Malarial nephritis. J. & A. Churchill, London. pp. 164.

GOLGI, C., 1885. Sul infezione malarica. J. R. Accad Med. Torino 33 : 734–83.

GOLGI, C., 1889. Sul ciclo evolutive dei parassiti malarici nella febre terzana; diagnosi differenziale tra i parassiti endoglobulari malarici della terzana et quelli della quartana. Arch. Sc. Med. 13 : 173–195.

GORDON, R. M. and DAVEY, T. H., 1932. *P. malariae* in Freetown, Sierra Leone. Ann. Trop. Med. & Parasit. 26 : 65–84.

GRASSI, B. and FELETTI, R., 1890. Parasites malariques chez les oiseaux. Arch. Ital. de Biologie 13 : 297–300.

GRASSI, B. and FELETTI, R., 1892. Contribuzione allo studio die parassiti malarici. Atti Accad. Gioenia. Series 4,5 : 1–81.

GRASSI, B., BIGNAMI, A., and BASTIANELLI, G., 1899. Risoconto degli studi fatti sulla malaria durante il mese di Gennaio. Rend. Atti Accad. Lincei 8 : 100–104.

GREEN, R., 1929. Observations on some factors influencing the infectivity of malarial gamete carriers in Malaya to *Anopheles maculatus*. Bull. Inst. Med. Res. Fed. Malay States 5 : 1–41.

GUAZZI, M. and GRAZI, S., 1963. Considerazioni su un

REFERENCES—Continued

caso di malaria quartana recidivante dopo 53 anni di latenza. Riv. di Malariol. *42* : 55–59.

HEMMING, F., (Ed.), 1954. Opinions and declarations rendered by the International Commission on Zoological Nomenclature. Opinion 283, Vol. 7, London, pp. 225.

HYLKEMA, B., 1920. The development of the parasites of quartan malaria in the *Myzomyia ludlowi* and their transmission to man. Meded. v.d. Burg. Geneesk. d. Nederl.-Indië *6* : 51. (NS).

IYENGAR, M. O. T., 1933. Experimental infection of anopheline mosquitoes. Ind. J. Med. Res. *20* : 841–861.

JAMES, S. P., 1931. Some general results of a study of induced malaria in England. Trans. Roy. Soc. Trop. Med. & Hyg. *24* : 477–525.

JANCSÓ, N., 1921. Experimentelle Untersuchungen über die Malaria-infection des Anopheles und des Menschen beeininflussenden Umstände. Arch. f. Schiffs- u. Trop.-Hyg. *25* : 5. (NS).

KHAW, O. K. and KAN, N. C., 1934. Some observations on the prevalence of malaria in Nanking and its vicinity. Chinese Med. J. *48* : 109–123. (NS).

KHODUKIN, N. I. and LISOVA, A. I., 1930. Zur Frage über die Möglichkeit von Erkrankungen an Malaria im Winter (In Russian). Meditz. Muisl' Uzbekitana *1* : 76. (NS).

KITCHEN, S. F., 1949. Quartan malaria. Malariology, Vol. II, edited by Mark F. Boyd. W. B. Saunders Co., Phila.

KNOWLES, R. and BASU, B. C., 1943. Laboratory studies on the infectivity of *Anopheles stephensi*. J. Malar. Inst. Ind. *5* : 1–29. (NS).

KNOWLES, R., SENIOR-WHITE, R., and DAS GUPTA, B. M., 1930. Studies in the parasitology of malaria. Ind. J. Med. Res. Memoir 18 : 1–436.

KRUSE, W., 1892. Der Gegenwartige Stand Unserer Kenntnisse von den Parasiten Protozoen. Hyg. Rdschr. *2* : 357–380 and 453–500.

LABBÉ, A., 1894. Récherches zoologiques et biologiques sur les parasites endoglobulaires du sang des vertebrates. Arch. Zool. exp. *2* : 55–258.

LAVERAN, A., 1880. Note sur un nouveau parasite trouvé dans le sang de plusieurs malades atteints de fièvre palustre. Bull. Acad. Med. *9* : 1235–1236.

LENTINI, D. and TECCE, T., 1955. Recidiva a lunga scadenza di infezione malarica quartana. Riv. di Malariol. *34* : 259–265.

LEWKOWICZ, X., 1897. Ueber den Entwickelungsgang und die Einteilung der Malariaparasiten. Zentralbl. Bakt. 1 Abt. Orig. *21* : 130–133.

LUPASCU, G., CONSTANTINESCU, P., NEGULICI, E., GARNHAM, P. C. C., BRAY, R. S., KILLICK-KENDRICK, R., SHUTE, P. G., and MARYON, M., 1967. The late primary exo-erythrocytic stages of *Plasmodium malariae*. Trans. Roy. Soc. Trop. Med. & Hyg. *61* : 482–489.

LUPASCU, G., CONSTANTINESCU, P., NEGULICI, E., SHUTE, P. G., and MARYON. M. E., 1968. Parasitological and clinical investigations on infections with the VS Romanian strain of *Plasmodium malariae* transmitted by *Anopheles labranchiae atroparvus*. Bull. Wld. Hlth. Org. *38* : 61–67.

MACKERRAS, M. J. and ERCOLE, Q. N., 1948. Observations on the life-cycle of *Plasmodium malariae*. Australian J. Exper. Biol. & Med. Sci. *26* : 515–519.

MACKERRAS, M. J. and ROBERTS, F. H. S., 1947. Experimental malarial infections in Australasian anophelines. Ann. Trop. Med. Parasit. *41* : 329–356.

MAROTTA, G. and SANDICCHI, G., 1939. Contributo all'infezione sperimentale di anofeli con *Plasmodium malariae* c inoculazione della malattia all'uomo. Riv. di Malariol. *18* : 89–94. (NS).

MAYNE, B., 1932. Note on experimental infection of *Anopheles punctipennis* with quartan malaria. Pub. Hlth. Rep. *47* : 1771–1773.

MER, G., 1933. Observations on the development of *Plasmodium malariae* Lav. in *Anopheles elutus* Edw. Ann. Trop. Med. Parasit. *27* : 483–488.

MEUWISSEN, J. H. E. TH., 1968. Antibody responses of patients with natural malaria to human and simian Plasmodium antigens measured by the fluorescent antibody test. Trop. geogr. Med. *20* : 137–140.

MUIRHEAD-THOMSON, R. C., 1957. Notes on the characters of *P. malariae* oocysts of possible value in mixed infections. Am. J. Trop. Med. & Hyg. *6* : 980–986.

RODHAIN, J., 1948. Contribution a l'etude des Plasmodiums des anthropoides Africains. Ann. Soc. Belge de Méd. Trop. *28* : 39–49.

RUSSELL, P. F. and MOHAN, B. N., 1939. On experimental malaria infections in certain Anopheles of south-eastern Madras. J. Mal. Inst. Ind. *2* : 425–431.

SCHUURMAN, C. J. and HUININK, A. S. B., 1929. A malaria-problem in Java's South-coast. Meded. Dienst d. Volksgezondh. in Mederl.-Indië *18* : 120–142. (NS).

SHUTE, P. G., 1951. Mosquito infection in artificially induced malaria. Brit. Med. Bull. *8* : 56–63.

SHUTE, P. G. and MARYON, M., 1951. Studies in the transmission of *Plasmodium malariae* by Anopheles mosquitoes. Parasitology *41* : 292–300.

SHUTE, P. G. and MARYON, M., 1952. A study of human malaria oocysts as an aid to species diagnosis. Trans. Roy. Soc. Trop. Med. & Hyg. *46* : 275–292.

SHUTE, P. G. and MARYON, M., 1955. Transmission of *Plasmodium malariae* by laboratory-bred *Anopheles maculipennis* var. *atroparvus* Meigen. Ann. Trop. Med. Parasit. *49* : 451–454.

SIDDONS, L. B., 1944. The experimental transmission of quartan malaria by *Anopheles culicifacies* Giles. J. Malar. Inst. Ind. *5* : 361–373.

STEPHENS, J. W. W. and CHRISTOPHERS, S. R., 1902. The relation of species of anopheles to malarial endemicity. Rep. Malar. Comm. Roy. Soc. 7th series, p. 20.

STRICKLAND, C., ROY, D. N., and SEN GUPTA, S. C., 1940. *Anopheles maculatus* and malaria. Trans. Roy. Soc. Trop. Med. & Hyg. *33* : 639–652.

SULZER, A. J., WILSON, M., and HALL, E. C., 1969. Indirect fluorescent-antibody tests for parasitic diseases. V. An evaluation of a thick-smear antigen in the IFA test for malaria antibodies. Am. J. Trop. Med. & Hyg. *18* : 199–205.

SUR, S. N., SARKAR, H. P., and BANERJI, K. M., 1932. Plasmochin as a malarial gametocide. Ind. Med. Gaz.

REFERENCES—Continued

67 : 490–493.

SWELLENGREBEL, N. H., SCHÜFFNER, W., and SWELLEN-
GREBEL-DE GRAAF, J. M. H., 1919. The susceptibility
of anophelines to malarial-infections in Netherlands
India. Meded. Burgerlijk. Geneesk. Dienst. Ned. Indië.
3 : 1–64. (NS).

YOUNG, M. D. and BURGESS, R. W., 1947. The transmission of Plasmodium malariae by Anopheles maculipennis
freeborni. Am. J. Trop. Med. 27 : 39–40.

YOUNG, M. D. and BURGESS, R. W., 1961. The infectivity
to mosquitoes of Plasmodium malariae. Am. J. Hyg.
73 : 182–192.

YOUNG, M. D., COATNEY, G. R., and McLENDON, S. B.,
1941. Studies on induced quartan malaria in Negro
paretics. III. Measurements of the paroxysmal phases.

Southern Med. Jour. 34 : 709–712.

YOUNG, M. D., STUBBS, T. H., and COATNEY, G. R., 1940.
Studies on induced quartan malaria in Negro paretics.
1. Periodic phenomena of the asexual cycle. Am. J. Hyg.
31 : 51–59.

YOUNG, M. D., COATNEY, G. R., and STUBBS, T. H., 1940a.
Studies on induced quartan malaria in Negro paretics.
II. The effect of modifying the external conditions. Am.
J. Hyg. 32 : 63–70.

YOUNG, M. D., HARDMAN, N. F., BURGESS, R. W., FROHNE,
W. C., and SABROSKY, C. W., 1948. The infectivity of
native malarias in South Carolina to Anopheles quadrimaculatus. Am. J. Trop. Med. 28 : 303–311.

(NS) = Not seen.

19

Plasmodium brasilianum Gonder and von Berenberg-Gossler, 1908

IN 1908, Gonder and von Berenberg-Gossler had the opportunity to examine the blood of a Cacajao monkey, *Brachyurus calvus* (= *Cacajao calvus*) imported to Hamburg, Germany, from the Amazon region of Brazil. In it, they encountered a quartan-like malaria parasite to which they gave the name *Plasmodium brasilianum*. The following year (1909), von Berenberg-Gossler made a careful study of the parasite and compared it with *P. malariae*, which it closely resembles, and other malarias then known from monkeys.

Seidelin (1912) had kept a spider monkey (*Ateles* sp.) in his laboratory in Mérida, Yucatan for some time and in its blood, he found delicate rings which some authors, including Wenyon (1926), considered to be a plasmodium. Repeated examination of the blood showed only rings with one or two chromatin masses which is emphasized on his colored plate, and, therefore, as suggested by Garnham (1966), it was probably a piroplasm.

Plasmodium brasilianum is relatively common in the monkeys of Panama where Clark (1930, 1931) first encountered it. Then, the Taliaferros (1934, a, b, and 1944) carried out an exhaustive experimental study of the parasite. Porter, *et al*, (1966) summarized the records involving 1994 primates from Panama, collected from 1931 through 1957, among which 4 species in 3 genera exhibited the parasite.

The parasite is fairly common in northwestern Brazil. In 1969, Deane and Ferreira Neto reported *P. brasilianum* from the territory of Amapa, also known as Brazilian Guyana, in eastern Amazonia. There is only one report of a natural infection in Venezuela (Serrano, 1967) but numerous surveys in Colombia, the most recent was that of Marinkelle and Grose (1968), have shown the parasite to be widespread. The work of Dunn and Lambrecht (1963) extended the distribution of this parasite into the lowland forests of Colombia and Peru.

Following the work of the Taliaferros in Panama, little attention was given to the malarias of the New World monkeys until after the National Institute of Allergy and Infectious Disease's group launched an extensive program following accidental and purposeful infections in man with *P. cynomolgi* in 1960. Beginning in 1964, Deane and his co-workers entered upon an overall study of the simian malarias of Brazil which has been extremely fruitful.

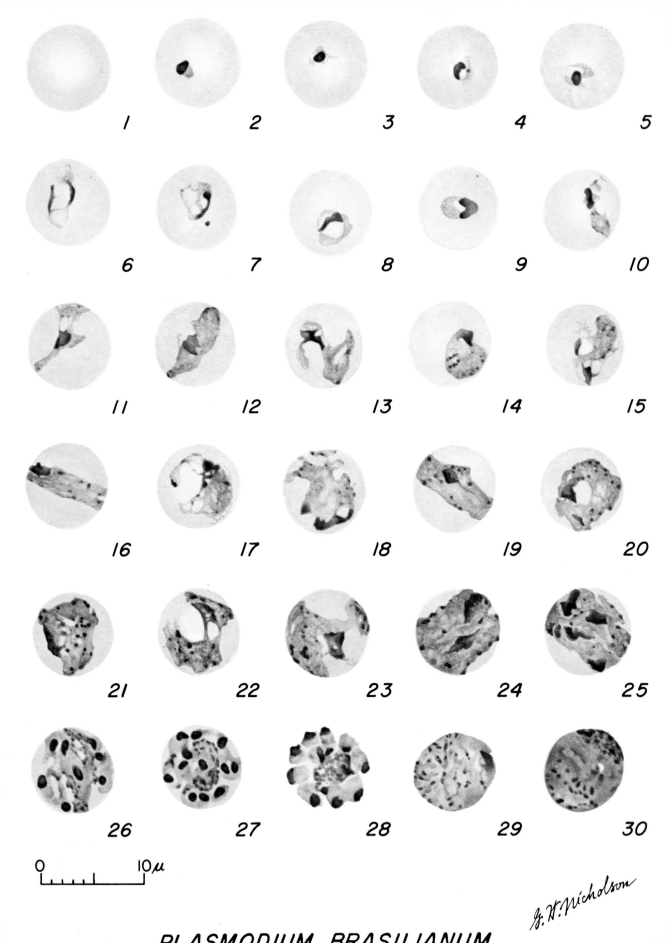

1   2   3   4   5

6   7   8   9   10

11   12   13   14   15

16   17   18   19   20

21   22   23   24   25

26   27   28   29   30

0   10 μ

G. W. Nicholson

PLASMODIUM BRASILIANUM

Cycle in the Blood

PLATE XXXVI

The initial forms in the peripheral blood are small rings with a prominent dark-staining nucleus. As growth proceeds, a small vacuole is formed which eventually disappears in the older forms. The rings often exhibit accessory dots. The nucleus may elongate to form a part of the periphery of the older rings (Figs. 6, 7). With the disappearance of the vacuole, the compact parasite displays irregular protrusions (Figs. 10, 11). These loitering amoeboid forms are not unlike similar ones seen in *P. malariae*. At about this time black granular pigment appears scattered in the blue-staining cytoplasm. Band forms appear during the late trophozoite stage (Figs. 16, 19) and although these forms are found in the blood of all simian species susceptible to the infection, they occur with greater frequency in *Alouatta*. The host cell is not enlarged and does not appear inconvenienced by the parasite. At about 50 hours, the parasite occupies a large part of the erythrocyte, at which time, it begins to divide. The process of schizogony moves toward completion generally with decided synchronicity. At maturity, each schizont harbors 8 to 12 merozoites but there may be only 4 or up to 16 arranged more or less as a rosette or, what is sometimes described, as a "daisy-head" (Fig. 28). The mature schizont may produce a slight increase in the size of the host cell; a condition not found with *P. inui*. With appropriate staining, Ziemann's stippling can be demonstrated during the late ring stage.

The young gametocytes are difficult to recognize and, as is common in all quartan infections, sexual forms are scarce at best. The mature forms fill the host cell and cause some enlargement of it. The macrogametocyte, which stains a median blue, harbors a compact pink-staining nucleus with a darker reddish area and occupies an eccentric position. The dark pigment, in the form of short rods, is scattered in the cytoplasm (Fig. 29). The microgametocyte exhibits a large diffuse nucleus which stains dark pink. The cytoplasm takes a very pale blue to purplish stain, with the pigment in large granules more or less scattered in the matrix.

The asexual cycle requires 72 hours which the Taliaferros described and illustrated in precise detail. They went on to show (1934) that the decidedly synchronous cycle could be reversed in a short time if the infected animals were subjected to a reversal of night and day conditions. Under normal conditions sporulation took place around 8 a.m. but after the conditions were reversed the cycle slowly became modified so that it occurred at 8 p.m. Some years later (1940) Young, Coatney and Stubbs produced the same results with *P. malariae* in man.

Sporogonic Cycle

PLATE XXXVII

Clark and Dunn (1931) reported development of *P. brasilianum* to the sporozoite level in *Anopheles tarsimaculatus* (= *aguasalis*), and *A. albimanus*. Garnham *et al* (1963) infected *A. aztecus*, *A. atroparvus*, and *A. albimanus*. At an incubation temperature of 26 to 28° C, the oocysts grew slowly and were characterized by a fragile cyst wall. On the 8th day oocysts measured 20 to 24 μ and contained pigment arranged along irregular threads, in circles, or in clusters. By the 12th day, the oocysts approached maturity with diameters of 38 to 45 μ. Sporozoites were present in the salivary glands on day 13. The sporozoites were reported to be sickle-shaped with a central

PLATE XXXVI.—*Plasmodium brasilianum.*

Fig. 1.   Normal red cell.
Figs. 2–5.   Young trophozoites.
Figs. 6–13.   Growing trophozoites.
Figs. 14–23.   Nearly mature and mature trophozoites
(Note band-forms Figs. 16, 19).

Figs. 24–26.   Developing schizonts.
Figs. 27–28.   Mature schizonts.
Fig. 29.   Mature macrogametocyte.
Fig. 30.   Mature microgametocyte.

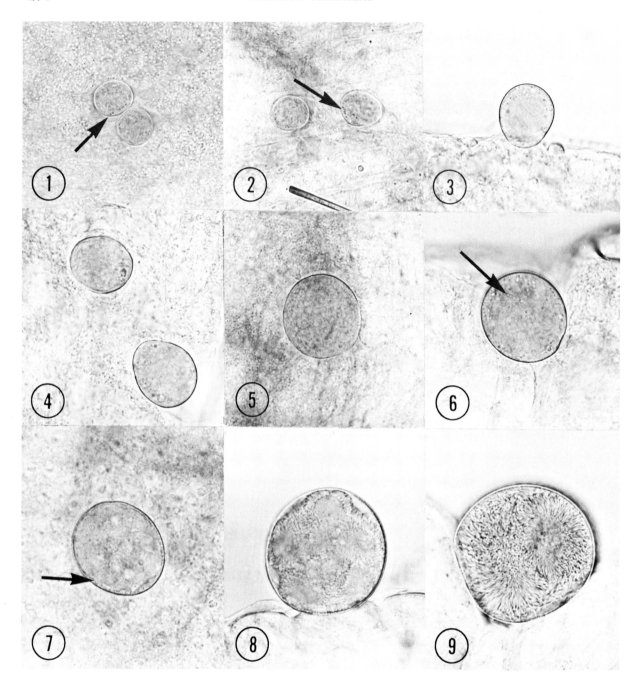

PLATE XXXVII.—Developing oocysts of *Plasmodium brasilianum* in *Anopheles freeborni* mosquitoes. X 580.

Fig. 1. 8-day oocysts with small grains of pigment.
Fig. 2. 9-day oocysts showing pigment near periphery.
Fig. 3. 10-day oocyst.
Fig. 4. 11-day oocysts.
Fig. 5. 12-day oocyst.

Fig. 6. 13-day oocyst showing small number of vacuoles.
Fig. 7. 14-day oocyst showing earliest stage of differentiation.
Fig. 8. 15-day differentiating oocyst.
Fig. 9. 18-day fully differentiated oocyst.

nucleus. In the fresh state, they measured about 14 to 16 μ in length.

Garnham *et al* (1963) studied the fine structure of the sporozoites of *P. brasilianum*. Their material was not of the best quality and therefore they were unable to give a complete and precise description. They found that the pellicle was about 30 Mμ in width and appeared as two layers separated by a less dense area. An apical cup was not demonstrated but a well-defined micropyle was seen. Peripheral fibers were hollow, but their exact number could not be determined. The "paired organelle" was an obvious structure suggesting a secretory function.

In our studies, *A. freeborni* has proved to be the most suitable mosquito for observing the sporogonic cycle of *P. brasilianum* (Table 29). At an incubation temperature of 25° C, on day 6, the mean oocyst diameter was 11 μ with a range of 9 to 13 μ. The oocysts continued to grow so that by day 14, the mean size was 40 μ with a range of 17 to 60 μ. At this time, the first signs of differentiation were apparent. The development was slow, however, and sporozoites were not present in the

TABLE 29.—Oocyst diameters of *Plasmodium brasilianum* in *Anopheles freeborni* and *A. stephensi*.

Days after infection	A. freeborni			A. stephensi		
	No.	Range	Mean*	No.	Range	Mean
6	43	9–13	11			
7	176	8–18	13			
8	148	11–20	15			
9	181	12–25	18	24	14–24	19
10	181	12–32	21	23	15–28	23
11	183	14–39	25	13	28–37	30
12	123	14–42	30			
13	142	17–53	34			
14	196	17–60	40†	16	28–51	38†
15	175	20–63	41†			
16	150	17–70	46†			
17	112	26–70	53†**			
Totals	1810	9–70		76	14–51	

* Measurements expressed in microns; incubation temperature of 25° C.
† Oocyst differentiation.
** Sporozoites present in the salivary glands.

salivary glands until 17 days after feeding.

A few measurements of oocysts developing in *A. stephensi* mosquitoes gave values well within the range of the diameters seen in the

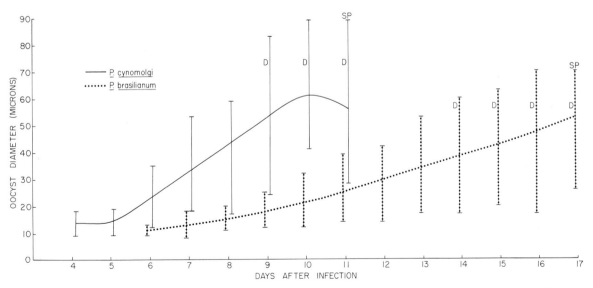

FIGURE 50.—Range in oocyst diameters and the mean oocyst diameter curves of *Plasmodium cynomolgi* and *P. brasilianum* in *Anopheles freeborni* mosquitoes. (D = oocyst differentiation; SP = sporozoites present in the salivary glands).

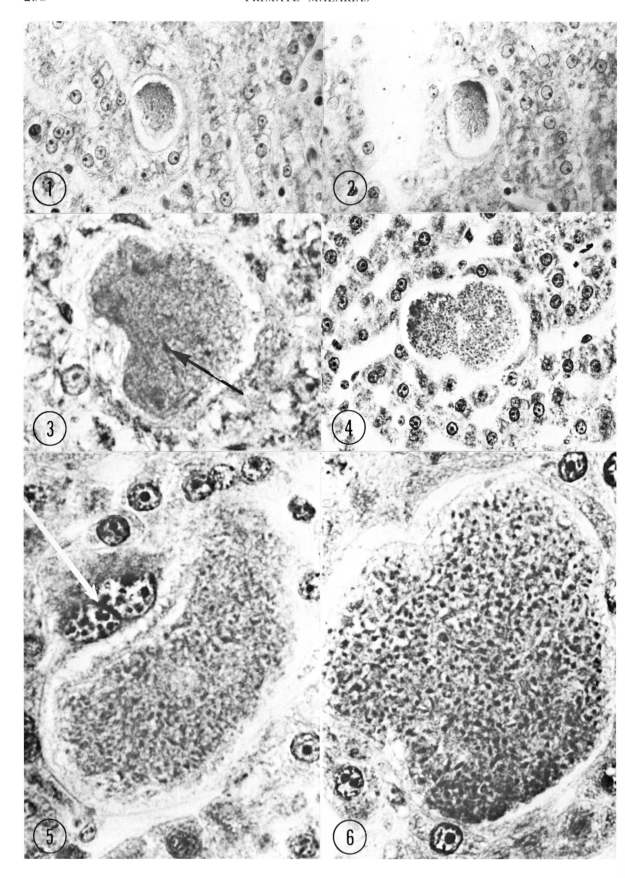

Course of Infection

Taliaferro and Taliaferro (1934) showed that blood-induced infections with *P. brasilianum* were characterized by an initial rise in the number of parasites, a marked dimunition in numbers, a low grade blood infection, and finally, short periods of subpatent parasitemia interspersed with spontaneous recrudescences. The height to which the parasitemia rose varied among individuals of the same species, but showed a tendency to be more acute among the white-throated (*Cebus capucinus*) and spider monkeys (*Ateles geoffroyi*) than among the howlers (*Alouatta palliata* (= *villosa*). Sharp peaks in temperature occurred at sporulation, particularly in the spider, howler, and night monkeys (*Aotus zonalis* (= *trivirgatus*) and in the marmoset (*Leontocebus* (=

Saguinus) *geoffroyi*), provided parasites were in sufficient numbers.

In our studies, infections have been obtained in *Saimiri sciureus*, *Ateles paniscus*, and *Aotus trivirgatus* monkeys both by blood inoculation and by the introduction of sporozoites. In intact *A. paniscus* monkeys (Fig. 52), the parasitemia rose slowly to a peak of approximately 10,000 per mm³ by day 16, followed by a fall, and then a secondary rise to a level almost equal to the initial peak by day 60. In the intact *S. sciureus* monkeys, the parasitemia curve exhibited a saddle-back effect with two peaks, on days 8 and 20, followed by a slow decline in the parasitemia. In *A. paniscus*, the median parasitemia by day 60 was 10,000 per mm³, whereas in the *S. sciureus*, the median parasitemia, on day 60, was approximately 100. In splenectomized *S. sciureus* monkeys, the

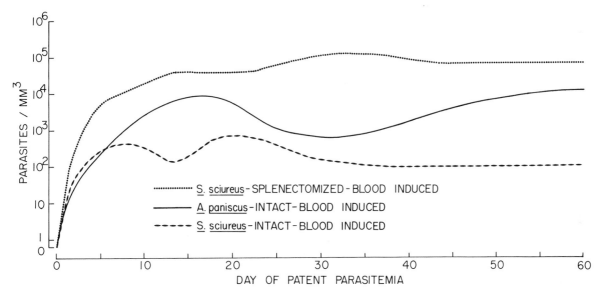

FIGURE 52.—Median parasitemia curves of *Plasmodium brasilianum* in 13 intact *Ateles paniscus*, 7 intact *Saimiri sciureus*, and 12 splenectomized *S. sciureus* monkeys inoculated with parasitized blood.

PLATE XXXVIII.—Exoerythrocytic bodies of *Plasmodium brasilianum* in liver tissue of the squirrel monkey, *Saimiri sciureus*.

Fig. 1. 14-day body showing elliptical shape. X 580.

Fig. 2. 14-day body. X 580.

Fig. 3. 18-day body showing dark, irregular-shaped, aggregated flocculi. X 1450.

Fig. 4. 21-day body. X 580.

Fig. 5. 21-day body showing two enlarged host cell nuclei. X 1450.

Fig. 6. 21-day body showing irregular-shaped parasite nuclei. X 1450.

peak parasitemia was reached after about 35 days. At 60 days, the median count was approximately 70,000 per mm^3. None of the animals, whether intact or splenectomized, died or required chemotherapy for survival. One splenectomized *A. trivirgatus* monkey, infected by the inoculation of sporozoites, had a peak parasitemia of 35,600 per mm^3 on day 35 after which, the parasitemia slowly declined to a subpatent level by day 90. No further parasites were seen in the blood of the animal during the next 57 days, when it died.

In our experience, infections with *P. brasilianum* in *Ateles* and *Saimiri* monkeys usually persist for an extended period of time, during which the presence of gametocytes allows for the infection of mosquitoes, and such infectivity can continue for at least 249 days. On the other hand, daily feedings on an *A. trivirgatus* monkey, infected with *P. brasilianum*, resulted in no infections; an unexpected occurrance in view of our other successes.

During the course of an infection, the parasitemia may rise and fall in what, at times, appears to be a predetermined pattern. This was observed in an *A. paniscus* monkey (AT–36) inoculated with parasitized blood. The animal had a low-grade infection for approximately 7 weeks at which time it was splenectomized. The parasitemia rose to a maximum of 120,500 per mm^3 one month later and then slowly dropped to a near negative level after six weeks. This was followed by a subsequent rise to a maximum count of 52,000 per mm^3 followed by a subsequent drop to zero. Following the initial parasitemia, 6 additional periods of high parasitemia occurred, followed by drops to negative or near negative levels. The intervals between these peaks were 3.5, 3, 4, 5, 4, and 4 months, respectively, after which the animal failed to exhibit parasites during an observation period of 18 months. Because the animal was blood-inoculated, the appearance of pronounced waves of parasitemia following periods of latency were true recrudescences. The observations in this animal suggest an almost set time interval for the development of new antigenic variants—about four months. It would appear that the animal had then been able to produce an immunity to all the variants

which the infection could produce thereby preventing any visible reoccurrence of the infection.

The first investigators to carry out experiments toward infecting man with *P. brasilianum* were Clark and Dunn (1931, 1931a). These investigators selected 8 volunteers who had recently arrived in Panama from their home states in the U. S. where malaria was not endemic. Five of the volunteers and a control monkey were given parasitized blood intravenously from a black spider monkey. Two other volunteers plus each of the original five and a control animal received parasitized blood subcutaneously also from a black spider monkey. The control monkeys developed the infection but only one of the volunteers gave any evidence of infection which was recorded as a few doubtful intracorpuscular bodies on an occasional blood film. After two weeks of observation the authors considered the trial a failure.

At that juncture, they decided to attempt infection by mosquito bite. They were able to infect *A. albimanus*, and *A. tarsimaculatus* which were allowed to bite seven volunteers. The men were observed for varying lengths of time, but again, only one exhibited any evidence of infection which consisted of several elevations of temperature at or near 100° F. and, on two occasions, "one or two forms which we consider to be malarial parasites but there was nothing satisfactory to report." It is unlikely, but possible, that a *P. brasilianum* infection was initiated in any of the volunteers.

Our own studies toward infecting man with *P. brasilianum* actually began in London. The senior author (GRC) had stopped there in 1962 to visit Professor P. C. C. Garnham at the London School of Hygiene and Tropical Medicine. In the course of the conversations, he mentioned our good fortune in getting *P. cynomolgi* to grow in man and offered the prediction that it probably would be extremely difficult, if not impossible, to get other species to infect man. I thought otherwise, and offered a wager that we could infect man with *P. brasilianum* in a matter of weeks. Upon my return to Washington, the problem was—where to obtain *P. brasilianum*? Dr. Carl Johnson, then Director of the Gorgas Memorial Laboratory in Panama, had some 8 months before agreed to be on the lookout for a brasilianum infected monkey, but we had had no word from him. Knowing Dr. Carl's penchant for not writing letters, a young staff member was dispatched to Panama with instructions to remain there until he had obtained a monkey infected with *P. brasilianum*. He departed for Panama and four days later called one of us (PGC) from Miami, Florida, with the query "what do I do with the infected monkey". The secret of the young man's phenomenal success in obtaining an infected monkey so readily was that Dr. Johnson had been holding the animal for some time and welcomed the opportunity to get it to us. Once the monkey, a spider (*A. paniscus**) was ensconced in the laboratory in Chamblee, Georgia, *A. freeborni* mosquitoes were allowed to feed on it; they became infected and were allowed to bite 9 volunteers. Five of the nine became infected (3 Caucasians and 2 Negroes) with prepatent periods of 29 to 64 days (Contacos *et al*, 1963). Later, two additional men were infected via mosquito bites with this same isolate of *P. brasilianum*. In another experiment, *A. freeborni* mosquitoes were also

* Originally reported incorrectly as *A. geoffroyi*.

infected after feeding on a squirrel monkey (*S. sciureus*) naturally infected with *P. brasilianum*. This strain or isolate was subsequently transmitted by their bites to one of 3 volunteers whose prepatent period was 63 days. All together, we have been able to study brasilianum infections in 25 volunteers, of which 18 were induced by the intravenous inoculation of parasitized homologous blood. Because there was little difference between the parasitologic and clinical picture in these infections, their parasite counts and median parasitemia curve have been combined and are shown graphically in figure 53. The parasite counts rarely exceeded 50 per mm^3. The maximum count was 200 per mm^3. The duration of parasitemia did not exceed 27 days. The clinical manifestations were generally milder than seen in *P. cynomolgi* or *P. knowlesi* infections; symptoms consisted mainly of headache and loss of appetite. Fevers were present, the maximum being 103.8° F. The quartan fever pattern was hardly the rule, but appeared more consistently in the sporozoite induced infections than in those induced by blood inoculation. It did not appear, in this small number of cases, that the parasitologic or clinical picture was enhanced by blood pas-

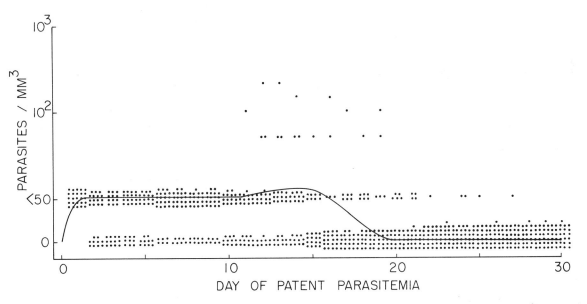

FIGURE 53.—Parasite counts and median parasitemia curve of 25 infections of *Plasmodium brasilianum* in man (7 sporozoite- and 18 blood-induced).

sage from volunteer to volunteer. When the parasite was blood-passaged back to the monkey, typical infections resulted.

This was the second simian malaria, in point of time, experimentally transmitted to man by mosquito bite and the ease with which human infections were obtained points up its zoonotic and/or anthroponotic potential when man introduces himself into a simian environment. Also, there is another point which bears discussion and that is the true identity of the brasilianum parasite. In the preceeding sections we have called attention to the close parallelism between *P. malariae* and *P. brasilianum* to the point where only an expert might presume to tell the difference either in the blood, fixed tissue, or the sporogonic cycle. This being the case, one wonders if *P. brasilianum* isn't actually a strain of *P. malariae* which became adapted to New World monkeys sometime after the early sixteen hundreds.

Host Specificity

As mentioned earlier, *P. brasilianum* has been found in Panama, Venezuela, Colombia, Peru, and Brazil. A list of the animals found infected in nature through 1969, is given in Table 30.

Although marmosets have not been found infected in nature Deane and his coworkers (1969) were able to infect *Callithrix jacchus* by transfer of parasitized blood from *Ateles paniscus*. They also transferred the infection from *A. fusca* to *Lagothrix lagotricha* and to *Saimiri sciureus*. The Taliaferros (1934) transferred the infection from *Aotus zonalis* (= *trivirgatus*), the night monkey, to *Leontocebus* (= *Saguinus*) *geoffroyi*, a marmoset, as well as from *Ateles darisensis* (= *paniscus*), the black spider monkey, to *Alouatta p. palliata* (= *villosa*), the mantled howler.

Clark and Dunn (1931) showed that *Anopheles tarsimaculatus* (= *aguasalis*) and, *A. albimanus* were susceptible to infection with *P. brasilianum*. Garnham *et al* (1963) were able to infect *A. aztecus* and *A. atroparvus*. In our studies, *A. freeborni*, *A. stephensi*, *A. sundaicus*, *A. quadrimaculatus*, *A. b. balabacensis*, and *A. maculatus* have been found infectible. The relative susceptibility to infection varied from one

TABLE 30.—Natural infections of *Plasmodium brasilianum* reported in Neotropical Primates from Panama, Colombia, Venezuela, Peru, and Brazil.

HOST SPECIES	REFERENCE
Alouatta fusca	Deane *et al*, 1969
Alouatta palliata	Clark, 1931
Alouatta seniculus straminea	Serrano, 1967
	Deane *et al*, 1969
Alouatta villosa	Porter *et al*, 1966
	Galindo*
Ateles fusciceps	Clark, 1931
	Porter *et al*, 1966
Ateles geoffroyi	Clark, 1931
	Porter *et al*, 1966
	Marinkelle and Grose, 1968
Ateles g. geoffroyi	Galindo*
Ateles g. grisescens	Galindo*
Ateles paniscus (includes "*A variegatus*")	Dunn and Lambrecht, 1963
Ateles p. paniscus	Deane *et al*, 1969
Ateles p. chamek	Deane *et al*, 1969
Brachyteles arachnoides	Deane *et al*, 1969
Callicebus moloch ornatus	Renjifo and Peidrahita, 1949**
Callicebus torquatus	Deane *et al*, 1969
Cebus albifrons	Dunn and Lambrecht, 1963
	Marinkelle and Grose, 1968
Cebus apella (probable infection)	Dunn and Lambrecht, 1963
Cebus apella	Marinkelle and Grose, 1968
	Deane *et al*, 1969
Cebus capucinus	Porter *et al*, 1966
	Marinkelle and Grose, 1968
Cebus c. capucinus	Clark, 1931
Cebus c. imitator	Clark, 1931
	Galindo*
Chiropotes chiropotes	Deane *et al*, 1969
Lagothrix cana	Deane *et al*, 1969
Lagothrix infumata	Dunn and Lambrecht, 1963
Lagothrix lagotricha	Deane *et al*, 1969
	Garnham *et al*, 1963
	Marinkelle and Grose, 1968
Saimiri boliviense	Dunn and Lambrecht, 1963
Saimiri sciureus	Renjifo *et al*, 1952
	Garnham *et al*, 1963
	Dunn and Lambrecht, 1963
	Roca-Garcia (not published)
	Marinkelle and Grose, 1968
	Deane *et al*, 1969
	Groot†

* According to Dunn and Lambrecht, 1963
** According to Marinkelle and Grose, 1968
† According to Garnham, 1966

species to another (Table 31). By far, the most susceptible species was *A. freeborni*. No infections were obtained with *A. albimanus*.

of the EE bodies of *P. osmaniae* stressed their size, they were larger than *P. inui*, as an argument for species status and Garnham (1967) supported that view. If that criterion were accepted, then each of the strains studied by the Held group would represent separate species. We hold that this is untenable, for the present at least, because all other essential characters of these strains are so similar. And, too, observations on a few EE bodies which lack consistent specific morphologic differences, with the possible exception of size at a given time after infection, can hardly supplant the results of prolonged study of the blood stages by competent investigators over many years.

Course of Infection

Although *P. inui* infects many species of monkeys, most of the studies have been confined to the rhesus monkey, *M. mulatta*. Eyles (1963) stated that infections produced in this animal were moderate when compared to *P. cynomolgi* and remarkably long lasting. In our own experience, many animals have maintained infections for many years.

A perusal of the median parasitemia curve for 66 intact *M. mulatta* monkeys infected with *P. inui* by the inoculation of parasitized blood will show (Fig. 55) a peak parasitemia of approximately 35,000 per mm³ on the 14th day of patent parasitemia. The parasitemia then dropped and fluctuated between 4,000 and 6,000 per mm³ for the remainder of the 60-day observation period. Such levels were commonly maintained for months and even years. In some individual monkeys, parasite levels of 100,000 per mm³ or greater were maintained for many months. Sporozoite induced infections (20 monkeys) rose to a peak of approximately 15,000 per mm³ by day 14 and thereafter dropped to a level of approximately 2,500 per mm³ after 60 days. In splenectomized monkeys (27 animals), the peak parasitemia of approximately 500,000 per mm³ was obtained after 16 days. This dropped rapidly to a level of 70,000 per mm³ after 30 days of patent parasitemia. Some of the animals continued to maintain a high level of parasitemia for many months. Garnham (1966) reports that *M. mulatta* monkeys which have severe infections are apt to develop a sterilizing immunity and throw off the infection entirely. He also reported a similar occurrence of splenectomized monkeys. We have not had this experience. Some of our animals have maintained fairly high parasitemias for 3 to 4 years after splenectomy.

There is no evidence that *P. inui* possesses

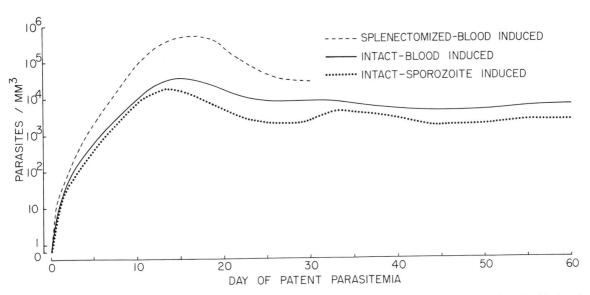

FIGURE 55.—Median parasitemia curves for 113 infections of *Plasmodium inui* in *Macaca mulatta* monkeys (66 blood-induced and 20 sporozoite-induced infections in intact animals, and 27 blood-induced infections in splenectomized animals).

the mechanism for true relapse. Several of our monkeys, infected by sporozoite inoculation, had their blood infection cured by the administration of schizontocidal drugs. They failed to develop secondary infections during a 6-month observation period. Later, they were shown to be susceptible to reinfection when inoculated with parasitized blood of the same strain.

Infections in the *M. fascicularis* and *M. radiata* monkeys are usually less severe than those in the rhesus monkey (Garnham, 1966).

Plasmodium inui is infectious to man as shown by Das Gupta (1938). The volunteer was given blood directly from an infected *S. irus* (= *M. fascicularis*) monkey by intramuscular injection. Twenty-three days later the patient developed a patent parasitemia and febrile symptoms on the 28th day, which continued for a total of 3 days. The maximum temperature observed was 102° F. The strain of *P. inui* employed by Das Gupta was obtained directly from Col. Sinton which leaves little doubt as to the identity of the parasite.

Our own studies in man (Coatney *et al*, 1966) were carried out with the OS strain of *P. inui*. The name originally suggested for the parasite (Shortt *et al*, 1961) was *P. osmaniae*. Because that name was only a suggested one, Bray (1963) proposed the name *P. shortti*. Eyles obtained the parasite through the courtesy of Professor Garnham and after carefully comparing it with the original strain of *P. inui* was unable, on morphological grounds, to separate it from the original strain. Nevertheless, he elected to consider it a subspecies, *P. inui shortti*. The parasite was sent to us from our installation in Kuala Lumpur, Malaysia, and after careful study, we agreed with Eyles that it was an inui-type parasite; until further studies convince us of its taxonomic status, we prefer to designate the osmaniae-shortti parasite as the OS strain of *P. inui*.

Two Caucasian male volunteers were exposed to the bites of infected mosquitoes and 5 other volunteers, including one Negro, received their infections by the intravenous inoculation of parasitized blood from one of the previously infected volunteers.

One volunteer was bitten by 5 *Anopheles*

maculatus and by 7 *A. stephensi*. The other, received bites from 19 *A. maculatus*. Infection of the mosquitoes was proved by postprandial dissection. Each man became infected. The prepatent periods were 31 and 56 days; and parasitemia continued for 21 days in one and for 24 days in the other. The maximum parasite count was 2,520 per mm³ of blood. Each of the 5 volunteers who received parasitized blood developed infections which were patent for 10 to 26 days with a maximum parasite count of 450 per mm³ (Fig. 56).

The quartan pattern was well marked in two of the volunteers with maximum fever of 103.2° F. The others exhibited low-grade, remittent-type fever or, in the case of the Negro patient, no fever at all. No morphological changes were observed in the parasites as a result of their sojourn in man. Blood from 4 of the volunteers was inoculated into clean rhesus monkeys which produced typical *P. inui* infections.

The major complaints voiced by the volunteers were headache, malaise, muscular and joint pains, and loss of appetite. When chills occurred, they were mild and of short duration. In no case was anti-malarial therapy necessary.

Some interesting biological facts emerged as a result of this study. Blood was drawn from one volunteer on day 16, following his exposure to infection by mosquito bite, and given to another, who developed a patent infection 47 days later. At the time blood was drawn, the donor had mild symptomatic complaints although parasites could not be demonstrated in his blood until day 56. The fact that the recipient became infected shows that tissue schizogony had taken place by day 16 and, further, that only a small number of parasites is needed to establish a patent infection in man.

It is well known that Negroes are universally susceptible to *P. malariae*, the human quartan parasite, and we had shown that the quartan parasite of New World monkeys, *P. brasilianum* (see Chapter 19) and *P. inui* of Old World monkeys are infective to Negroes. In contrast to these successes, we have not been able to infect Negroes with tertian parasites, *P. cyno-*

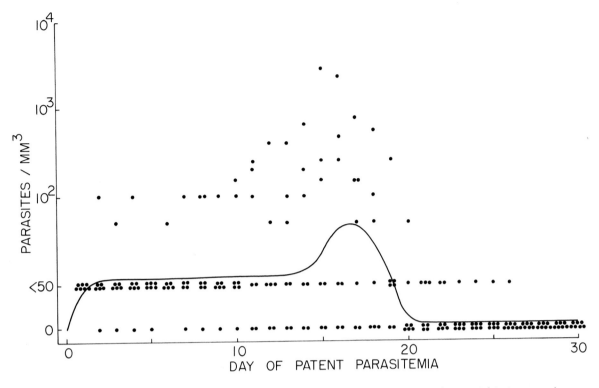

FIGURE 56.—Parasitemias and median parasitemia curve for 7 infections of *Plasmodium inui* (OS strain) in human volunteers.

molgi (see Chapter 6) and *P. schwetzi* (see Chapter 12). Likewise, it is sometimes dicffiult to infect Negroes with the human tertian parasite, *P. vivax* (see Chapter 5). So far we cannot account for this resistance phenomenon.

It probably should be mentioned, too, that prior to, and subsequent to, our successful transmission of this strain of *P. inui* to man, by mosquito bite, we had made several attempts, using other strains, each time without success. To some this might indicate that true *P. inui* would not grow in man. Since the osmaniae-shortti parasite did infect man, some might consider that reason enough for accepting it as an entity outside the inui group. However, as mentioned earlier, Das Gupta was able to infect man with the original strain of *P. inui* following inoculation of parasitized blood. Why our earlier attempts failed and this one succeeded, we are not prepared to say.

Host Specificity

Plasmodium inui naturally infects many monkeys as listed below:

SPECIES	REFERENCES
Cercopithecus mitis (Experimentally)	Garnham, 1966
Cynopithecus niger	Eyles and Warren, 1962
Macaca cyclopis	Hsieh, 1960
M. fascicularis	Many references
M. mulatta	Schmidt *et al*, 1961; Notananda *et al*, 1961
M. nemestrina	Halberstaedter and von Prowazek, 1907
M. radiata	Mulligan and Swaminath, 1940
Presbytis cristatus	Collins *et al*, 1970
P. obscurus	Eyles *et al*, 1962

Plasmodium inui has been isolated from *Anopheles leucosphyrus* (Wharton *et al*, 1962) and *A. b. introlatus* (Warren and Wharton, 1963), in Malaya. Experimentally, *P. inui* is infectious to a large number of mosquitoes as listed below:

SPECIES	REFERENCES
Anopheles albimanus	Eyles, 1960a
A. atroparvus	Weyer, 1937; Garnham, 1951; Mohiuddin, 1957; Shortt *et al*, 1963
A. aztecus	Mohiuddin, 1957; Bano, 1959; Shortt *et al*, 1963; Garnham, 1966
A. b. balabacensis	Collins *et al*, 1968
A. freeborni	Eyles, 1960
A. gambiae	Garnham, 1951
A. letifer	Warren and Wharton, 1963
A. maculatus	Warren and Wharton, 1963; Collins *et al*, 1966, 1968
A. philippinensis	Warren and Wharton, 1963
A. quadrimaculatus	Eyles, 1960
A. stephensi	Garnham, 1951; Shortt *et al*, 1963; Collins *et al*, 1966, 1968

In addition to the above, we have obtained infections in *A. kochi*, *A. vagus*, *A. sinensis*, and *A. riparis*. Thirteen species of mosquitoes are listed (Table 33) for comparison as to their susceptibility to infection with *P. inui*. The most readily infected was *A. b. balabacensis* and the least was *A. letifer*.

Immunity and Antigenic Relationships

Singh and Singh (1940) observed that homologous superinfection with *P. inui* resulted in a very mild and transient parasitemia. Chronic infections with *P. inui* afforded no protection against either *P. cynomolgi* or *P. knowlesi*. Monkeys with chronic infections of *P. cynomolgi* or *P. knowlesi* showed no resistance to typical infections with *P. inui*.

In contrast, Voller *et al*. (1966) found that monkeys immune to infection with *P. knowlesi* or *P. shortti* (= *P. inui*) developed low parasitemias of *P. inui* upon challenge. Voller and Rossan (1969) confirmed this observation by finding that in monkeys with chronic infections of *P. knowlesi*, infections with *P. inui* developed more slowly and had lower peak parasitemias than did animals infected with *P. inui* alone.

Antisera to *P. inui* gave a fluorescent antibody cross-reaction at a very high level to *P. fieldi* and *P. shortti* (= OS strain *P. inui*) (mean reciprocal titer ratios of 100:107 and 100:88) and reacted at somewhat lower levels to *P. brasilianum*, *P. coatneyi*, and *P. cynomolgi* (mean reciprocal titer ratios of 100:57, 100:57, and 100:46, respectively). In the reverse procedure, *P. inui* antigen cross-reacted to none of the heterologous antisera at a high level, the highest response was to the OS strain with a mean reciprocal titer ratio of 100:35 (Collins *et al*, 1966). Antigen to the OS strain gave fluorescent antibody cross-reactions of a much lower magnitude with *P. fieldi* and *P. inui* giving the highest levels of response (mean reciprocal titer ratios of 100:47 and 100:35, respectively). In the reverse procedure, the OS strain antigen gave a high level cross-reaction to the *P. inui* antigen only (mean reciprocal titer ratio of 100:88).

In a further study of antigenic relationships (Collins *et al*, 1970), antisera from monkeys each infected with one of 15 different isolates of *P. inui* from different geographical and ecological areas of South Central and Southeast Asia were allowed to react with their homologous and heterologous antigens using the fluorescent antibody technique. It was shown, using the test of relatedness statistic, that there were significant antigenic differences between each pair of isolates of *P. inui* included in the study. The OS strain parasite was, on the average, more distantly related to the remainder of the strains than was any other strain. The next most distantly related was a parasite from the Celebes.

El-Nahal (1967) reported that antisera to *P. inui* and *P. shortti* (= OS strain *P. inui*) failed to respond to exoerythrocytic antigens of *P. cynomolgi* and *P. malariae* using a fluorescent antibody procedure.

TABLE 33.—Comparative infectivity of *Plasmodium inui* to thirteen species of *Anopheles*.

Mosq. species comparison	Number tests	Number of mosquitoes		Percent infection		GII** ratio
		Standard	Other	Standard	Other	
Bal						100
Bal : F–1	63	492	629	83.9	65.5	59.9
Bal : Kochi	5	131	88	93.9	87.5	52.1
Bal : St–1	109	991	759	66.1	69.2	44.9
Bal : Mac	23	123	208	80.5	68.3	41.4
Bal : Q–1	83	1223	1176	47.9	38.6	17.8
Bal : Vagus	6	74	29	83.8	62.1	9.6
Bal : Sin	2	31	17	83.9	17.6	9.2
Bal : Atro	29	583	570	34.6	15.3	7.1
Bal : Phil	1	16	2	87.5	100	4.2
Bal : Rip	2	61	3	88.5	100	3.8
Bal : Alb	46	696	835	39.4	5.1	1.5
Bal : Let	5	66	50	80.3	10.0	1.3

* Bal = *Anopheles b. balabacensis;* F–1 = *A. freeborni;* Kochi = *A. kochi;* St–1 = *A. stephensi;* Mac = *A. maculatus;* Q–1 = *A. quadrimaculatus;* Vagus = *A. vagus;* Sin = *A. sinensis;* Atro = *A. atroparvus;* Phil = *A. philippinensis;* Rip = *A. riparis;* Alb = *A. albimanus;* Let = *A. letifer.*

** GII = Gut Infection Index = average number of oocysts per 100 guts; the GII ratio is the relationship of the GII of *A. b. balabacensis* to another species where the GII of *A. b. balabacensis* = 100.

REFERENCES

BANO, L., 1959. A cytological study of the early oocysts of seven species of *Plasmodium* and the occurrence of postzygotic meiosis. Parasitology *49* : 559–585.

BOUILLIEZ, M., 1913. Nouvelles récherches expérimentales sur un *Plasmodium* des singes. C. R. Soc. Biol. (Paris) *74* : 1070–1072.

BRAY, R. S., 1963. Malaria infections in primates and their importance to man. Ergeb. Mikrob. Immunit. Experim. Therap. *36* : 168–213.

COATNEY, G. R., CHIN, W., CONTACOS, P. G., and KING, H. K., 1966. *Plasmodium inui*, a quartan-type malaria parasite of Old World monkeys transmissible to man. J. Parasit. *52* : 660–663.

COLLINS, W. E., CONTACOS, P. G., GUINN, E. G., and HELD, J. R., 1966. Studies on the transmission of simian malarias. I. Transmission of two strains of *Plasmodium inui* by *Anopheles maculatus* and *A. stephensi*. J. Parasit. *52* : 664–668.

COLLINS, W. E., CONTACOS, P. G., GUINN, E. G., and HELD, J. R., 1968. Some observations on the transmission of *Plasmodium inui*. J. Parasit. *54* : 846–847.

COLLINS, W. E., SKINNER, J. C., and GUINN, E. G., 1966. Antigenic variations in the plasmodia of certain primates as detected by immuno-fluorescence. Am. J. Trop. Med. & Hyg. *15* : 483–485.

COLLINS, W. E., WARREN, McW., SKINNER, J. C., and ALLING, D. W., 1970. *Plasmodium inui*: Serologic relationships of Asian isolates. Exp. Parasit. *27* : 507–515.

DAS GUPTA, B. M., 1938. Transmission of *P. inui* to man. Proc. Natl. Inst. Sci. India *4* : 241–244.

EL-NAHAL, H. M. S., 1967. Study of serological cross-reactions of exo-erythrocytic schizonts of avian, rodent and primate malaria parasites by the fluorescent antibody technique. Bull. Wld. Hlth. Org. *37* : 154–158.

EYLES, D. E., 1960. *Anopheles freeborni* and *A. quadrimaculatus* as experimental vectors of *Plasmodium cynomolgi* and *P. inui*. J. Parasit. *46* : 540.

EYLES, D. E., 1960a. Susceptibility of *Anopheles albimanus* to primate and avian malarias. Mosq. News *20* : 368–371.

EYLES, D. E., LAING, A. B. G., WARREN, McW. and SANDOSHAM, A. A., 1962. Malaria parasites of Malayan leaf monkeys of the genus *Presbytis*. Med. J. Malaya *17* : 85–86.

EYLES, D. E. and WARREN, McW., 1962. *Plasmodium inui* in Sulawesi. J. Parasit. *48* : 739.

EYLES, D. E., 1963. The species of simian malaria: taxonomy, morphology, life cycle, and geographical distribution of the monkey species. J. Parasit. *49* : 866–887.

GARNHAM, P. C. C., 1951. The mosquito transmission of *Plasmodium inui* Halberstaedter and von Prowazek, and its pre-erythrocytic development in the liver of the rhesus monkey. Trans. Roy. Soc. Trop. Med. & Hyg. *45* : 45–52.

GARNHAM, P. C. C., 1966. Malaria parasites and other haemosporidia. Blackwell Scientific Publications. Oxford. pp. 1114.

GARNHAM, P. C. C., 1967. Abstract of a paper by Coatney *et al*, 1969. Trop. Dis. Bull. *64* : 464.

GREEN, R., 1932. A malarial parasite of Malayan monkeys and its development in anopheline mosquitoes. Trans. Roy. Soc. Trop. Med. & Hyg. *25* : 455–477.

HALBERSTAEDTER, L. and VON PROWAZEK, S., 1907. Untersuchunger über die malariaparasiten der affen. Arb. K. Gesundh.-Amte (Berl.) *26* : 37–43.

HELD, J. R., CONTACOS, P. G., JUMPER, J. R., and SMITH, C. S., 1968. Studies of the exoerythrocytic stages of simian malaria. III. *Plasmodium inui*. J. Parasit.

54 : 249–254.

HSIEH, H. C., 1960. Malaria parasites of the Tiawan monkey. Formosan Science. *14* : 477–487.

LAMBRECHT, F. L., DUNN, F. L., and EYLES, D. E., 1961. Isolation of *Plasmodium knowlesi* from Philippine macaques. Nature. *191* : 1117–1118.

LEGER, M. and BOUILLIEZ, M., 1912. Sur un *Plasmodium* des singes. Passages par espéces variées. Action pathogéne. C. R. Soc. Biol. *73* : 310–313.

LEGER, M. and BOUILLIEZ, M., 1913. Recherches experimentales sur "Plasmodium inui" Halberstadter et Prowazek d'un "Macacus cynomolgus". Ann. Inst. Pasteur. *27* : 955–985.

MATHIS, C. and LEGER, M., 1911. Plasmodium des macaques du tonkin. Ann. Inst. Pasteur. *25* : 593–601.

MAYER, M., 1907. Ueber malaria beim affen. Med. Klin. *3* : 579–580.

MOHIUDDIN, A., 1957. Notes on a new strain of "Plasmodium inui". Riv. di. Malariol. *36* : 203–208.

MULLIGAN, H. W. and SWAMINATH, C. S., 1940. Natural infection with *Plasmodium inui* in *Silenus sinicus* from South India. J. Malar. Inst. Ind. *3* : 603–604.

NOGUCHI, H., 1928. Etiology of oroya fever. XII. Influence of malarial infection (*Plasmodium inui*), splenectomy, or both, upon experimental carrion's disease in monkeys. J. Exp. Med. *47* : 812–827.

NOTANANDA, V., NILUBOL, S., and SWASDIWONGHORN, P., 1961. A preliminary note on the discovery of simian malaria in Chingmai. Minuten Nadeln. *1* : 27.

SCHMIDT, L. H., GREENLAND, R., ROSSAN, R. and GENTHER, C., 1961. The occurrence of malaria in wild-caught rhesus monkeys. Science *133* : 753.

SEZEN, N., 1956. Studies on the life-cycle of two strains of *Plasmodium inui* and the development of immunity. Türk. Ij. tecr. Biyol. Dreg. *16* : 240–242. (NS).

SHORTT, H. E., RAO, G., OADRI, S. S., and ABRAHAM, R., 1961. *Plasmodium osmaniae*, a malaria parasite of an Indian monkey *Macaca radiata*. Jour. Trop. Med. & Hyg.

64 : 140–143.

SHORTT, H. E., BAKER, J. R. and NESBITT, P. E., 1963. The pre-erythrocytic stage of *Plasmodium osmaniae*. Jour. Trop. Med. & Hyg. *66* : 127–129.

SINGH, J. and SINGH, H., 1940. Observations on immunity in monkey malaria as evidenced by the results of super-infection. J. Malaria Inst. India *3* : 99–114.

SINGH, J., RAY, A. P., NAIR, C. P., and BASU, P. C., 1951. Isolation of a strain of *P. inui* from mixed infection in Malayan monkey. Ind. Jour. Malariol. *5* : 433–445.

SINTON, J. A. and MULLIGAN, H. W., 1933. A critical review of the literature relating to the identification of the malarial parasites recorded from monkeys of the families Cercopithecidae and Colobidae. Rec. Mal. Surv. India *III* : 381–443.

SINTON, J. A., 1934. A quartan malaria parasite of the lower oriental monkey, *Silenus irus* (*Macacus cynomolgus*). Rec. Mal. Surv. India *4* : 379–410.

VOLLER, A., GARNHAM, P. C. C. and TARGETT, G. A. T., 1966. Cross immunity in monkey malaria. Jour. Trop. Med. & Hyg. *69* : 121–123.

VOLLER, A. and ROSSAN, R. N., 1969. Immunological studies on simian malaria parasites. IV. Heterologous superinfection of monkeys with chronic *Plasmodium knowlesi* infections. Trans. Roy. Soc. Trop. Med. & Hyg. *63* : 837–845.

WARREN, McW., and WHARTON, R. H., 1963. The vectors of simian malaria: identity, biology, and geographical distribution. J. Parasit. *49* : 892–904.

WHARTON, R. H., EYLES, D. E., WARREN, McW. and MOORHOUSE, D. E., 1962. *Anopheles leucosphyrus* identified as a vector of monkey malaria in Malaya. Science *137* : 758.

WEYER, F., 1937. Versuche zur übertragung der affenmalaria durch stechmücken. Arch. Schiff. f. Tropenhyg *41* : 167–172.

(NS) = not seen

21

Plasmodium rodhaini Brumpt, 1939

IN 1920, Reichenow studied the malarias of chimpanzees and gorillas in the Cameroons and found three species which he considered identical to *P. vivax*, *P. falciparum*, and *P. malariae* in man. Blacklock and Adler (1922) in Sierra Leone and Schwetz (1933, 1933a, 1934) in the Belgian Congo saw the same three forms. The first authors did not accept the Reichenow view of their being human malaria counterparts because they proposed a new name *P. reichenowi* for the falciparum-like parasite. Schwetz, on the other hand, considered them identical to those of man. Rodhain and Muylle (1938) did not accept the Schwetz opinion because they were unable to infect human subjects with falciparum- and vivax-type parasites from the chimpanzee. Brumpt (1939), after considering the morphological similiarity between the ape and human forms, the failures in cross infection experiments, and the lack of success in infecting known human vectors with the chimpanzee parasites, decided that the forms were different. In that paper, he named the vivax-like parasite *Plasmodium schwetzi* (see chapter 12); to the quartan parasite he gave the name *Plasmodium rodhaini* in honor of the Belgian investigator Dr. Jerome Rodhain. At that point, each of the three human-like malarias of apes had received names.

Rodhain was not satisfied. His interest was more biological than taxonomic and, to that end, he entered upon a susceptibility study which continued intermittently during the rest of his life. In 1940, he succeeded in transferring *P. malariae* from man to the chimpanzee by the inoculation of parasitized blood and *P. rodhaini* from a chimpanzee to each of two people by the same route (1940, 1940a, 1941). Other human infections resulted under similar circumstances, as detailed in the above papers, with moderate to low parasitemias and fever up to 40° C. The above results convinced him that the *P. rodhaini* parasite of Brumpt was in fact *P. malariae*. In 1943, Rodhain and Dellaert reported the transfer of *P. rodhaini* from a chimpanzee to a paretic in the Hospital Stuyvenberg. The patient became infected and from him twenty-three other patients were given the infection in tandem.

It was clear that *P. rodhaini* of the chimpanzee when blood passaged to man would grow and produce disease. However, there was no evidence that the reciprocal would be equally true. This was answered by Rodhain in 1948 when he reported the successful transfer of *P. malariae* to each of three young chimpanzees. Following this experiment, he again declared that the quartan parasite in man and the chimpanzee was *P. malariae*.

In 1956, Garnham *et al* transferred *P. malariae* to an intact chimpanzee which exhibited a light infection. When the spleen was removed, the parasitemia increased to a peak of 160,000 per mm³. They were not able to infect mosquitoes. Bray (1960) was able to infect *Anopheles gambiae* mosquitoes when fed on man with *P. malariae*, and on chimpanzees carrying *P. rodhaini*. *Plasmodium malariae* infections were obtained in the chimpanzees by mosquito bites, but he was not able to carry out the reverse procedure. Nevertheless, he was willing to accept the name *P. malariae* for the quartan parasite of man and the higher apes. Garnham (1966) concurred in that opinion, which is accepted generally, when, in speaking of Rodhain's work of 1940 (loc. cit.) he wrote "This was the first step in the sinking of *P. rodhaini* into synonomy with *P. malariae*." At present, we cannot take issue with the view that the quartan parasite of man and the chimpanzee are the same parasite.

Granted that *P. rodhaini* is synonomous with *P. malariae*, then, one must conclude that the human parasite became adapted to the chimpanzee, or that it was a simian parasite originally which became adapted to early man. It seems likely, in the light of recent work involving other simian malarias (Coatney, 1968), that in relatively recent times it went from man to the apes, and, therefore, qualifies as an anthroponosis. If that is not the case, then it is a zoonosis of long standing.

For reasons stated above, plus the fact that we were unable to obtain an infected animal from which we might obtain material, we elected not to include a plate depicting the blood forms of the parasite; reference should be made to our plate of *P. malariae*.

Plasmodium rodhaini is a quartan malaria of the chimpanzee (*Pan stayrus verus*). The infection extends along the coast of West Africa from Sierra Leone to Angola and thence east to some point deep in the Congolese Republic. The infection rate appears to be low. Reichenow (1920) found it in only two of eight chimpanzees, Rodhain and Dellaert (loc. cit.) reported finding it in some of the young chimpanzees available to them, and Bray, according to Garnham (1966) examined seventy-eight chimpanzees in Liberia and found it in only eight percent of them.

REFERENCES

BLACKLOCK, B., and ADLER, S., 1922. A parasite resembling *Plasmodium falciparum* in a chimpanzee. Ann. Trop. Med. & Parasit. *16* : 99–106.

BRAY, R. S., 1960. Studies on malaria in chimpanzees. VIII. The experimental transmission and pre-erythrocytic phase of *Plasmodium malariae*, with a note on the host-range of the parasite. Am. J. Trop. Med. & Hyg. *9* : 455–465.

BRUMPT, E., 1939. Les parasites du paludisme des chimpanzés. C. R. Soc. Biol. *130* : 837–840.

COATNEY, G. R., 1968. Simian malarias in man: facts, implications, and predictions. Am. J. Trop. Med. & Hyg. *17* : 147–155.

GARNHAM, P. C. C., LAINSON, R., and GUNDERS, A. E., 1956. Some observations on malaria parasites in a chimpanzee, with particular reference to the persistence of *Plasmodium reichenowi* and *Plasmodium vivax*. Ann. Soc. Belge Med. Trop. *36* : 811–821.

GARNHAM, P. C. C., 1966. Malaria parasites and other haemosporidia. Blackwell Scientific Publications, Oxford.

REICHENOW, E., 1920. Ueber das vorkommen der malariaparasiten des menschen bei den afrikanischen menschenaffen. Centralbl. f. Bakt. I. Abt. Orig. *85* : 207–216.

RODHAIN, J., 1940. Les plasmodiums des anthropoides de l'Afrique centrale et leurs relations avec les plasmodiums humains. Ann. Soc. Belge Med. Trop. *20* : 489–505.

RODHAIN, J., 1940a. Les Plasmodiums des anthropoides de l'Afrique centrale et leurs relations avec les plasmodiums humains. Réceptivité de l'homme au *Plasmodium malariae*. (*Plasmodium rodhaini* Brumpt) du chimpanzé. C. R. Soc. Biol. *133* : 276–277.

RODHAIN, J., 1941. Les plasmodiums des anthropoides de l'Afrique centrale et leurs relations avec les plasmodiums humains. Bull. Acad. Roy. Med. Belgique *6* : 21–60.

RODHAIN, J., 1948. Susceptibility of the chimpanzee to *P. malariae* of human origin. Am. J. Trop. Med. & Hyg. *28* : 629–631.

RODHAIN, J., and DELLAERT, R., 1943. L'infection á *Plasmodium malariae* du chimpanzé chez l'homme. Etude d'une premiére souche isolée de l'anthropoide *Pan satyrus verus*. Ann. Soc. Belge Med. Trop. *23* : 19–46.

RODHAIN, J., and MUYLLE, G., 1938. Sur la spécificité des plasmodium des anthropoides de l'Afrique centrale. C. R. Soc. Biol. *127* : 1467–1468.

SCHWETZ, J., 1933. Sur les parasites malariens (*Plasmodium*) des singes supérieurs (Anthropoides) africains. C. R. Soc. Biol. *112* : 710–711.

SCHWETZ, J., 1933a. Sur une infection malarienne triple d'un chimpanzé. Zentrabl. f. Bakt. Parasit. Infektionskrankheiten I. Abt. Orig. *130* : 105–110.

SCHWETZ, J., 1934. Sur le paludisme des pygmées. C. R. Soc. Biol. *115* : 1228–1229.

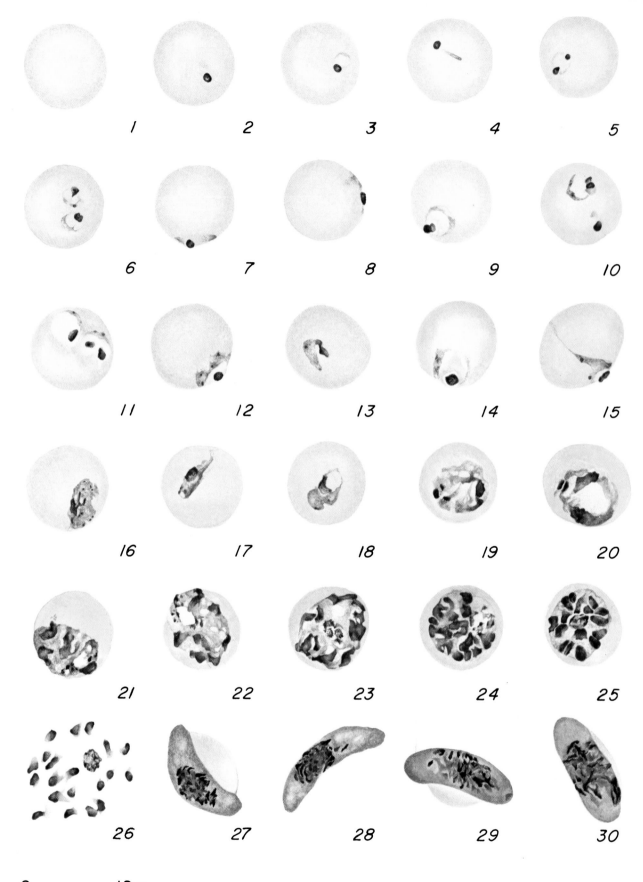

1   *2*   *3*   *4*   *5*

6   *7*   *8*   *9*   *10*

11   *12*   *13*   *14*   *15*

16   *17*   *18*   *19*   *20*

21   *22*   *23*   *24*   *25*

26   *27*   *28*   *29*   *30*

0   10 μ

PLASMODIUM FALCIPARUM

G. W. Nicholson

Cycle in the Blood
PLATE XLII

The youngest ring forms of *Plasmodium falciparum* are smaller than those of other human malarias and are commonly referred to as tiny, hair-like rings, with a vacuole, and a prominent nucleus. Sometimes, there is an accessory chromatin dot (Fig. 2–5). Multiple invasion of the host cell by equal-aged parasites is more common in this species than in the other human malarias (Figs. 6, 10, 11). Field and Shute (1956) illustrate 7 ring-stage parasites in a single cell and state that "eight rings in a cell has been recorded." Appliqué or accollé forms are common and, hence, have some diagnostic value. As development proceeds, the overall size of the parasite is increased, the vacuole and the nucleus of the parasite become more prominent (Fig. 14), and tenue forms (Fig. 15) may appear; aside from these abnormal forms (see Field and Shute, 1956), there is no appreciable amoeboidity. The parasite now becomes smaller and more compact, the cytoplasm stains a deep blue, it loses its vacuole, the nucleus ceases to be circular, and dark pigment grains appear in the cytoplasm (Figs. 16–19).

At this juncture, the number of parasites in the peripheral blood decreases due to their penchant for retreating into the deeper circulation—a practice common to *P. coatneyi*, too —so that in cases of high synchronicity, it is sometimes difficult to find late developing forms. In general, however, the phenomenon of asynchronicity produces enough tardy forms to permit following the remainder of the cycle. As a rule, the presence of appreciable numbers of segmenters in the peripheral blood is an indicator of grave consequences, but this is not always the case. In our own experience, we have seen a case in which the patient was not particularly ill, was ambulatory, and had a parasite count of about 5,000 per mm³, yet he continued to show a high proportion of segmenters for several days.

During schizognoy, the nucleus divides repeatedly, the parasite increases in size until it may occupy a large part of the host cell. At first the pigment comes together in small aggregates, but, as the parasite nears maturity, it collects in a single yellowish-brown mass. The mature schizont is less symmetrical than those of other human malarias and its merozoites number 8 to 20; the usual number is about 16 (Figs. 20–25).

One of the striking features of erythrocytes infected with the asexual parasites is the early development of Maurer's dots, or clefts, which make their appearance shortly after the hair-like ring stage. As the development of the parasite proceeds, these abnormalities become more pronounced. They are demonstrable in the parasitized red cells only under certain staining procedures, not ordinarily applied, and therefore are not shown in our plate.

The mature gametocytes are unique among human malarias because of their sickle or crescent shape, a feature well appreciated by Laveran. In most malarias, the gametocytes appear about the same time as the asexual forms, but in falciparum malaria, it is about 10 days after the first appearance of the asexual forms that they appear as a wave of full grown parasites. Preceding their appearance, the young gametocytes have been growing in the blood spaces of the spleen and bone marrow.

The macrogametocyte is relatively slender, has pointed ends, and is generally longer than the microgametocyte. The cytoplasm stains a decided blue. The nucleus is compact and may be masked by pigment granules which appear to cover it. The red cell may be seen as stretching across the curvature of the gametocyte

PLATE XLII.—*Plasmodium falciparum.*

Fig. 1.   Normal red cell.
Figs. 2–11.   Young trophozoites.
Figs. 12–15.   Growing trophozoites.
Figs. 16–18.   Mature trophozoites.
Figs. 19–22.   Developing schizonts.
Figs. 23–26.   Nearly mature and mature schizonts.
Figs. 27, 28.   Mature macrogametocytes.
Figs. 29, 30.   Mature microgametocytes.

268 PRIMATE MALARIAS

(Figs. 27, 28). The microgametocyte is sausage-shaped with blunt-rounded ends. The cytoplasm stains light blue to purplish-blue. The nucleus occupies about half the total length of the parasite. It is diffuse, and generally shows some dark red dots scattered in a pale pink area. Lying well within the periphery of the nuclear area are clustered dark brown to black pigment granules. The host cell generally hugs the body of the parasite, but may show as a bulb-like area in the slight curvature of the gametocyte (Figs. 29, 30).

The asexual cycle is 48 hours.

Sporogonic Cycle

PLATE XLIII

There have been many studies on the sporogonic cycle of *P. falciparum* since Ross (1897) described finding oocysts on the gut of a mosquito which had fed on a gametocyte carrier. Bastianelli *et al* (1898) observed pigmented oocysts in anopheline mosquitoes which had fed on an individual infected with *P. falciparum*, and, in the same year, Grassi *et al* (1898) observed complete development of *P. falciparum* in *Anopheles claviger* (= *A. maculipennis*). In 1899, Bastianelli and Bignami not only described the development of the parasite in mosquitoes, but, also, demonstrated its transmission to man.

Shute and Maryon (1952) observed the development of oocysts of *P. falciparum* in *A. atroparvus* mosquitoes incubated at a temperature of 25° C. The black pigment granules (between 10 and 20 in number) were usually arranged (between days 3 and 7) in a double semicircle around the periphery of the oocyst. By the 8th day, the pigment was obscure; the oocysts measured from 8 to 60 μ in diameter. The sporogonic cycle was completed in 11 to 12 days. From the 3rd to the 5th day, the daily increase in oocyst diameter was approximately 4 μ. From the 6th to the 10th day, the daily increase was about 10 μ.

Our studies of the sporogonic cycle of this

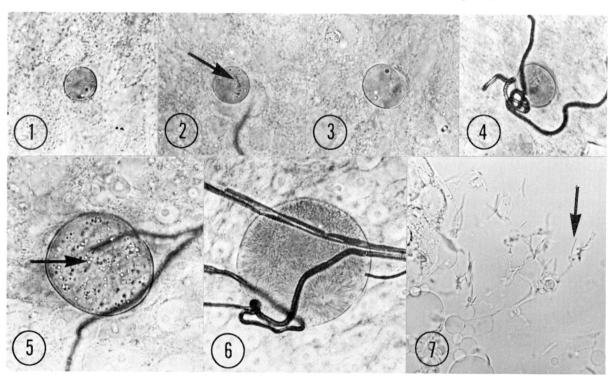

PLATE XLIII.—Developing oocysts and sporozoites of *Plasmodium falciparum* in *Anopheles freeborni* mosquitoes. X 580.

Fig. 1. 7-day oocyst.
Fig. 2. 7-day oocyst showing line of pigment.
Fig. 3. 8-day oocyst.
Fig. 4. 10-day oocyst.
Fig. 5. 14-day oocyst showing numerous small vacuoles.
Fig. 6. 14-day differentiated oocyst.
Fig. 7. Sporozoites present near salivary gland tissue 14 days after feeding.

parasite have been limited, but we have followed its development in *A. freeborni* infected with the Malayan IV and the McLendon strains of *P. falciparum*, and in *A. quadrimaculatus* infected with the McLendon strain only (Table 34). In *A. freeborni*, with the Malayan IV strain, on day 5, oocysts had mean diameters of 12 μ, with a range of 8 to 15 μ; on day 12, the mean size was 50 μ, with a range of 21 to 78 μ. There are some differences in the development of the 2 strains in *A. freeborni*. The Malayan IV had slightly larger mean oocyst diameters, but, more significantly, sporozoites were present in the salivary glands on day 12 whereas the McLendon strain required 14 days. The development in the *A. quadrimaculatus* was similar to that seen in *A. freeborni* infected with the McLendon strain. Sporozoites were present in the salivary glands on day 14.

A comparison of the oocyst growth rate of the Malayan IV strain of *P. falciparum* with that of *P. cynomolgi* (Fig. 57) shows a marked difference between the 2 parasites. The *P. cynomolgi* was much larger both with regard to mean and maximum oocyst diameters. Sporozoites were present in the salivary glands of the mosquitoes infected with *P. cynomolgi* one day sooner than in those infected with *P. falciparum*.

Experimentally, *P. falciparum* has been transmitted to man via the bites of many species of mosquitoes on numerous occasions. In that connection, Garnham (1966) lists 66 species of anophelines which will serve as hosts of *P. falciparum*.

Cycle in the Tissue

The tissue stages of *Plasmodium falciparum* have been demonstrated in experimental infections of man as well as chimpanzees. This species of human malaria differs from *P. vivax* and *P. ovale* in that the exoerythrocytic cycle is restricted to a single generation; in other words, there is no secondary exoerythrocytic or other continuing fixed tissue stage.

The tissue cycle of *Plasmodium falciparum* was first demonstrated by Shortt *et al* (1949, 1951) in liver biopsy material from a human volunteer who had been bitten by 770 Anopheles mosquitoes (93 percent infection rate) over a period of 3 days. The strain of falciparum malaria used by these authors was of Roumanian origin. The liver biopsy was taken 5¾ days after mosquitoes had first bitten the volunteer. The exoerythrocytic schizonts described by these authors were considered to be 4-, 5-, and 6-day stages. The 4-day schizonts

TABLE 34.—Oocyst diameters of *Plasmodium falciparum* (Malayan IV and McLendon strains) in *Anopheles freeborni* and *A. quadrimaculatus* mosquitoes.

Days after infection	Malayan IV strain			McLendon strain					
	A. freeborni			A. freeborni			A. quadrimaculatus		
	No.	Range	Mean*	No.	Range	Mean	No.	Range	Mean
4				118	5–11	10			
5	106	8–15	12	193	7–14	10	5	8–14	11
6	122	9–21	15	115	11–20	15	116	8–20	14
7	163	9–28	19	152	8–20	15	134	12–23	18
8	255	12–38	23	120	11–31	20	187	11–32	19
9	199	14–45	32	169	12–41	24	101	18–38	28
10	111	26–64	41	150	17–53	35	168	18–50	33
11	112	20–73	45†	132	19–61	40	126	20–58	40
12	154	21–78	50†**	150	20–72	47†	110	18–60	42
13	36	31–71	56†**	139	19–70	49†	132	27–68	48†
14				164	20–67	45†**	109	30–68	54†**
Totals	1258	8–78		1602	5–72		1188	8–68	

* Measurements expressed in microns.
† Oocyst differentiation.
** Sporozoites present in salivary glands.

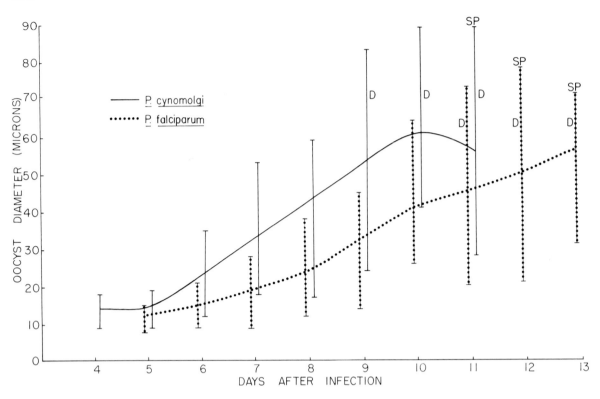

FIGURE 57.—Mean oocyst diameter curves and ranges in oocyst diameters of *Plasmodium cynomolgi* and *P. falciparum* (Malayan IV strain) in *Anopheles freeborni* mosquitoes. (D = oocyst differentiation; SP = sporozoites present in the salivary glands).

were described as ovoid or spherical in shape, with some tendency toward the production of lobose projections. They measured about 30 μ in diameter and were surrounded by a thin membrane. The cytoplasm was faily dense and there were no vacuoles. Nuclei were rather sparsely distributed, slightly irregular masses measuring approximately 1.5 μ in diameter. Cytoplasm tended to condense around each nucleus; and, according to the authors, this possibly represented the first step in the formation of the so-called pesudocytomeres.

Five-day old schizonts measured roughly 50 μ in their longest dimension. The tendency to produce the lobose character was more pronounced. There was no local tissue reaction. There was a tendency for the cytoplasm to separate into areas resembling cytomeres. These pseudocytomeres varied in shape from spherical to elongate; each contained a large number of nuclei. The size of the individual nuclei, in active division, was roughly 0.8 μ. The membrane surrounding the parasites was

less apparent.

The 6-day stages showed the parasite had undergone very rapid growth, expanding in an irregular fashion in many directions. Six-day forms measured 50 to 60 μ in length and were described as being more "mis-shapen" than *P. vivax* because of the pronounced tendency to lobosity. The number of nuclei had increased tremendously, the cytoplasm being thickly strewn with them. Near maturity, the parasite appeared to break up into small islands of cytoplasm, measuring approximately 2 μ in diameter, each island contained two very small nuclei.

With a final division of the nuclei, one has a mature schizont, measuring 60 μ or more in its greatest dimension, containing an enormous number of merozoites. Each merozoite, about 0.7 μ in diameter, consists of a nucleus with a trace of cytoplasm. The number of merozoites in a large mature schizont was estimated as roughly 40,000.

Jeffery *et al.* (1952) carried out a study, involving 14 patients, designed to demonstrate the exoerythrocytic stages of *Plasmodium falciparum* in the human liver. Inoculation was either by the bites of heavily infected mosquitoes, the intravenous inoculation of dissected salivary glands, or both. Each volunteer received from 2 to 6 inoculations. Biopsies were performed 3 to 8 days after the first inoculation. Material from 13 of the 14 patients was negative. The 14th patient, who received a total of 8,516 mosquito bites along with the intravenous inoculation of 1,403 pairs of salivary glands, yielded material positive for falciparum tissue schizonts. The authors found 125 parasites; 100 were complete.

The smallest parasites were 15 μ in their greatest diameter. However, the authors stated that due to shrinkage, the living parasites were undoubtedly larger than 15 μ. The biopsy was done on day 6 and inoculations occurred on day 0, 1, 2, and 3, and consequently, the tissue stages could have been anything from 3 to 6 days old. The cytoplasm was described as being granular, sometimes containing small vacuoles. The outline of the parasite appeared to be wavy which was probably due to shrinkage. The smallest number of nuclei observed was about 40.

Parasites approximately 25 μ in their greatest diameter were also observed. The cytoplasm was homogeneous, contained a few vacuoles, and a larger number of nuclei. The largest parasite, about 40 μ, was considered to be nearly mature. The cytoplasm was vacuolated, the outline of the parasite was smooth, and, occasionally, small lobes were observed. The stage considered nearest maturity was described as having an increase in the complexity of the vacuoles and an apparent formation of cords and islands of cytoplasm (pseudocytomeres) from which the merozoites arise. Most parasites at this stage were 55 to 60 μ in their greatest diameter.

The parasites were found in the parenchymal tissue of the liver lying within the liver cords. The host cells were enlarged but no changes were observed in the host cell nuclei. There were no detectable morphologic reactions to the presence of the parasite. In addition, there was no leukocytic infiltration into areas around the parasite.

The parasites described by Jeffery *et al* (1952) were considered similar to those described by Shortt *et al* in 1951. However, a few differences, which may be due to interpretation, were noted. For example, very little, if any, compression of host tissues surrounding the parasite was observed by these authors. Shortt *et al* described the tendency toward lobation in the parasite. Jeffery *et al* noted the same thing, but in addition, reported that it was not unusual to find parasites, including mature schizonts, with smooth outlines, although in many others, the lobose character was extremely pronounced. Jeffery *et al* felt it was not possible to designate a particular parasite as being of a specific age since inoculations were carried out over a period of 4 days which was some 3 to 6 days before biopsy was taken. Shortt *et al* (1951) also had inoculated their patient on 3 consecutive days and correlated their parasites with time, designating them as being 4, 5, and 6 days of age on the basis of size. On this basis, then, the smallest parasite found by Jeffery *et al*, which was 15 μ, could have been 3 days old, whereas the smallest parasites found by Shortt *et al* were about twice that size and were designated as being 4 days old.

Shortt *et al* (1951), in comparing the pre-erythrocytic stages described for cynomolgi and vivax malaria with those of falciparum malaria, indicated several points of difference; namely, 1) the larger size of the mature schizont, 2) the smaller size of the merozoites, 3) the greater number of merozoites, and 4) the rapidity of development of the tissue stages to full maturity, i.e., 6 days for *P. falciparum* compared with 8 or more for *P. vivax* and *P. cynomolgi*.

Bray (1958, 1960) and Bray and Gunders (1962, 1963) studied the tissue stages of *P. falciparum* in chimpanzees. The youngest forms were 2-day stages. These were described as lying within a vacuole in the liver parenchymal cell and measuring about 4 μ in diameter. The 2-day parasite was enclosed in a well-defined envelope and contained 2 nuclei which were triangular in shape. At 2 days and 15 hours, the tissue stages measured 7 μ and contained up to 20 nuclei. Three-day forms, still within a vacuole in the liver cell cytoplasm, averaged

9 μ and contained 25 nuclei. At 4 days, the parasite measured 18 μ and contained flocculated cytoplasm studded with about 145 large nuclei.

Bray (1958) considered the 5-day forms in the chimpanzee liver similar in all respects to the 4-day stages described by Shortt et al and the smaller schizont described by Jeffery et al. The average greatest dimension was 32 μ, with a range of 41 to 28 μ. The outline of the parasite was generally regular without lobations. The cytoplasm was rarely vacuolated. However, when vacuoles were present, they were small and rarely numbered more than 2. The contour of the parasite was indented by the host cell nucleus.

Three different types of nuclei could be seen in the chimpanzee material: 1) parasites with tiny dots of chromatin measuring 0.5 μ in diameter and usually associated with a smooth homogeneous appearance of the cytoplasm, 2) parasites with round pieces of chromatin approximately 1 μ in diameter, and 3) parasites with relatively large pieces of chromatin measuring 1.0 to 1.7 μ which were circular, oblong, or even square in shape, and these were associated with a cytoplasm which tended to display aggregates of basophilic material.

The exoerythrocytic cycle of falciparum malaria appears to be slightly longer in the chimpanzee than it is in man. Bray (1958) considered the 8-day parasites in his chimpanzee material to be nearly mature and resembled the 6-day schizonts of Shortt et al and the large schizonts of Jeffery et al.

The final stages of schizogony were described as very complex, and defined by Bray (1960) as aposchizogony. Garnham (1966) stated that the common appearance of the tissue schizont on the 6th day is that of an ovoid structure, about 40 μ in its greatest dimension, containing hundreds of cytomeres, each cytomere measuring 3 to 5 μ in diameter. The cytomeres are considered as hollow spheres, the surface studded with small nuclei. At first there are only a few of these cytoplasmic islands or cytomeres, but by the process of aposchizogony (Bray, 1960) a large number of cytomeres are eventually produced, each becoming smaller and with progressively fewer nuclei (i.e., 8, 4, 2 nuclei) with each division. At maturity, merozoites become differentiated from the 2 nucleate cytomeres.

There is direct and indirect evidence to suggest that the exoerythrocytic cycle of falciparum malaria is limited to a single generation—the first. In other words, no true relapse occurs because no tissue stages remain after the development of the primary falciparum malaria infection. Bray (1958) found no tissue schizonts in biopsies of liver taken 12 days after infection. This contrasts greatly with the ease with which he found P. vivax and P. ovale, under similar experimental conditions, in liver biopsies from chimpanzees; P. vivax and P. ovale are relapsing malarias.

Sodeman et al (1969) described 6- and 7-day stages of P. falciparum in the liver tissue of the owl monkey, Aotus trivirgatus. The parasites resembled the 2.5 to 5-day stages observed in the chimpanzee and in man. The owl monkey EE bodies were considered non-viable because the host failed to develop a patent infection.

Fairley et al (1947), by subinoculating a large volume of blood from volunteers exposed to falciparum infection by bites of 7 to 20 infected mosquitoes, concluded that the tissue cycle ended at 6½ days. When blood taken 160 hours, or later, after exposure to infection, was subinoculated into volunteers, the subinoculees developed patent falciparum infections. As stated earlier, Shortt et al found that blood taken from their one volunteer at 135 hours after exposure to infection with approximately 716 infected mosquitoes was infectious when inoculated into another volunteer. It appears obvious that the difference of 25 hours was probably due to the difference in the number of infective bites (maximum of 20 versus approximately 700). Ciuca et al (1937) showed that the tissue cycle of a Roumanian strain of falciparum malaria was completed during the 6th day after exposure to infection.

Garnham (1966) states that the prepatent period for falciparum malaria is 5½ days since the tissue schizont ruptures at that time releasing merozoites into the blood stream as indicated by experiments similar to those of Fairley, i.e., that a large volume of blood taken from the volunteer at 135 hours after exposure was injected into another volunteer and the subinoculee developed malaria.

Course of Infection

The course of infection is inaugurated with the entry of merozoites into red cells of the circulating blood, and according to Garnham (1966), Shute demonstrated a parasite in a thick blood film from a patient who had received 500,000 sporozoites of a Roumanian strain of *Plasmodium falciparum* intravenously 5 days earlier. Shortt *et al* (1951) showed that the prepatent period could be as early as 5½ days when exposure to infection was massive and blood was subinoculated into volunteers. We prefer to define prepatent period as the interval from the time of exposure to the demonstration of parasites in the blood of the host by more conventional methods; namely, the thick blood film. On this basis, the prepatent period observed by Shortt *et al*, in the volunteer from whom liver biopsy material was obtained, was 7 days. In addition, Shortt *et al* observed a prepatent and incubation period of 8 days in a patient who served as a control for mosquito infectivity and who was bitten by a total of 370 mosquitoes on 4 consecutive days.

Ciuca *et al* (1937a), in their description of 12 falciparum malaria infections, induced by the bites of infected mosquitoes and/or the intravenous inoculation of sporozoite suspensions, reported prepatent periods ranging from 11 to 20 days and incubation periods from 11 to 21 days, with medians of 12 days.

Burgess and Young (1946) experimentally transmitted the McLendon strain of falciparum malaria by bites of *Anopheles quadrimaculatus* and *A. freeborni* and obtained prepatent periods of 15 days and incubation periods of 12 and 18 days in non-immunes. Coatney *et al* (1947) reported that prepatent periods for 31 mosquito-induced infections of falciparum malaria (McLendon strain) ranged from 9 to 13 days with a mean of 11 days; the incubation periods, based on the first temperature of 101° F or higher, ranged from 10 to 15 days with a mean of 12.2 days.

Fairley *et al* (1947) reported prepatent periods ranging from 7 to 12 days (mean 9.5 days) with New Guinea strains of *P. falciparum*. Kitchen (1949) reported a mean prepatent period of 11 days for 220 naturally induced falciparum infections involving 6 different strains, which included the Costa and the Long strain. The mean incubation period for this same group was 13.1 days. The range for the prepatent periods was 6 to 25 days; for the incubation period, 7 to 27 days. Seventy-five percent of the prepatent periods ranged from 9 to 11 days. Among the 220 infections, only 2, 1, and 1 patients had prepatent periods of 6, 7, or 8 days, respectively.

Eyles and Jeffery (1949) transmitted Santee-Cooper strain falciparum and Panama strain falciparum by bites of *Anopheles albimanus*. With the former the prepatent period was 13 days, and with the latter, 10 to 13 days (median of 11.5 days). Later, Eyles and Young (1951), working with mosquito inoculated Santee-Cooper falciparum, reported prepatent periods from 7 to 13 days. Jeffery *et al* (1952), in their studies on the fixed tissue stages of falciparum malaria, observed prepatent periods ranging from 7 to 13 days after massive exposures to infection, either by mosquito bite or by inoculation of suspensions of sporozoites. The total number of mosquitoes biting ranged up to 8,516, with an 86.8 percent infection rate. The median was 9 days. Jeffery *et al* (1963) in studies with a Thailand strain of resistant falciparum malaria reported prepatent periods of 11 days in 2 control patients who received no medication; and, interestingly enough, prepatent periods as short as 10 days in patients receiving drug suppressively to which this strain was resistant. Of interest, also, was the fact that these infections were in patients all of whom had experienced previous malaria infections. The incubation periods ranged from 15 to 19 days.

Lunn *et al* (1964) and Contacos *et al* (1964), working with a Southern Rhodesian strain of *P. falciparum*, reported prepatent periods of 10 and 11 days and 9 to 19 days, respectively. Powell *et al* (1965) records prepatent periods of 9 days for Thailand and Malayan Camp strains of falciparum. In fact, they observed a single 8-day prepatent period in an individual who had received ineffective antimalarial suppression and/or prophylaxis. Chin *et al* (1967) reported prepatent periods with 3 chloroquine resistant, or multi-resistant, strains of falciparum malaria, which ranged from 9 to 11 days. Contacos and Collins (1968) and Collins *et al* (1968) reported prepatent periods of 11 and 12 days for Malayan IV strain infections.

The studies of Boyd and Kitchen (1937) seemed to indicate that increases in dosages of sporozoites (principally the number of infected mosquitoes biting) 1) did not materially change the proportion of takes, 2) did not appreciably shorten the prepatent period, and 3) did not shorten the incubation period (i.e., elevation of temperature to 100° F or more). In 60 cases with 5 strains, prepatent periods ranged from 6 to 25 days with a median of 11 days. The incubation periods ranged from 7 to 27 days with a median of 12 days. They did observe, however, that the duration of the incubation period tended to vary with the season of the year; being shortest in the 4th quarter (mean of 10.1 days) and longest in the 2nd quarter (mean of 13 days).

As was stated earlier, it has been the intent in this monograph to stress the biologic rather than clinical aspects of primate malaria and, especially, the human malarias. Therefore, for a description of the various clinical "pernicious forms" (cerebral, algid, gastrointestinal, etc.) and blackwater fever (hemoglobinuria), the reader is referred to Boyd's Malariology (1949) and James *et al* (1932) for excellent descriptions of these features of falciparum malaria.

In contrast to *P. vivax*, *P. falciparum* infections are considered to be more malignant than the benign vivax. Kitchen (1949) stated that most persons who have had experience with falciparum infections "will attest the capacity of *P. falciparum* both to assume a malignant role and to evoke protean clinical manifestations." Of all the human malarias, this one is potentially the most dangerous.

Boyd and Kitchen (1937) found that falciparum malaria infections exhibit the same general types of febrile reactions that are observed in vivax infections, although pronounced differences did occur. In 60 cases of falciparum malaria, the succession of the different febrile types was not observed as often as in vivax and a larger proportion of the intermittent fevers were tertian. The onset was described, usually, as a remittent fever with a tendency to higher fever peaks. Remittent fever, when present,

appears at the onset and may last for a week or even longer. Its presence suggests a high degree of susceptibility by the patient and/or a greater invasiveness on the part of the parasite. Patients showing a remittent course of fever throughout are more likely to be overwhelmed by the infection unless the fever pattern changes over to an intermittent pattern. Most commonly the infection begins and continues as an intermittent fever which is more often tertian than quotidian in type. The duration of the paroxysms tends to be longer than observed for vivax and the peak of the paroxysms is usually broken into several secondary peaks. In their experience, patients whose clinical onset preceded the appearance of parasites in the peripheral blood may have an abrupt onset, with cerebral symptoms.

Jeffery *et al* (1959) saw that the mean maximum fever varied very little between Panama, McLendon, and Santee-Cooper strain falciparum infections. The mean maximum temperature recorded for McLendon strain was 105.5, for the Panama strain 105.1, and the Santee-Cooper strain 105.0° F. The maximum fever, usually occurred some time between the 5th and 7th day of patent parasitemia. In their experience, the initial fever patterns for each of the 3 strains were quotidian, followed by a tertian, and then a remittent type of fever for the Santee-Cooper and McLendon strains, but a remittent and then tertian pattern for the Panama strain. In many cases of Panama strain falciparum, the fever might more accurately be described as continuous, rather than remittent. These authors stated "it is not surprising that there seems to be some confusion in the literature describing the *P. falciparum* febrile attack. It is almost impossible to describe a 'typical' fever curve for *P. falciparum*." Quotidian periodicity prevailed as the initial pattern in their series of infections. Some of them remained quotidian until the termination of the infection whereas others converted to tertian periodicity. Jeffery *et al* (1959) emphasized that the most prominent characteristic of the fever patterns, in the 3 strains of falciparum studied by them, was extreme variability; in other words, no typical periodicity or pattern could be determined.

Boyd and Kitchen (1937) reported that

there is no apparent limit to the parasite density which may obtain in *P. falciparum* infections; the potentialities of this species for multiplication being so great they regarded daily smears and counts to be essential in following the infections. In our studies, falciparum infections are followed even more closely; namely, blood smears are made, stained, and read every 8 hours to preclude infections getting out of hand.

Boyd and Kitchen (1945) reported that the mean interval from the first day of parasitemia to the day of maximum parasitemia ranged from 4.2 to 11 days for 8 different strains of falciparum malaria; the mean for the exotic strains was 6.7 and the indigenous strains, 8.9 days. The mean maximum parasite counts for these various strains ranged from 11,140 to 369,200 per mm^3. The mean for the exotic strains was 83,870 and the indigenous strains 103,950 per mm^3.

Coatney *et al* (1947) reported, in 7 patients, that parasite densities went above 100,000 per mm^3 of blood. The maximum parasite densities in the primary attacks ranged from 10 to 250,000 per mm^3, the latter corresponding to 5 to 10 percent of the red cells. They described 10-fold increases or decreases in the parasite count within a 12 hour period even in the absence of treatment. This calls attention to the fact that in developed infections, low parasite counts are no guarantee of a favorable prognosis. In a Thailand strain (Jeffery *et al*, 1963), maximum parasite counts ranged from 3,394 up to 35,022 per mm^3 of blood.

According to Kitchen (1949), a count of 500,000 parasites per mm^3 (12.5 percent) probably gives a patient about a 50–50 chance of surviving provided treatment is started immediately and pernicious symptoms do not appear. Field and Niven (1937) showed, by analysis of some 750 cases, that the mortality rate increased greatly as parasite counts increased above 100,000 per mm^3 (less than 0.5 percent mortality with counts less than 100,000; 7 to 20 percent mortality with counts ranging from 100,000 to 500,000; and 63 percent mortality with counts over 500,000). Chopra *et al* (1932) reported a patient with more than 50 percent of the erythrocytes parasitized who died within 12 hours of admission. We have observed a situation where 35 percent of the erythrocytes were parasitized in a Negro patient who became comatose and developed renal failure but survived this malignant experience.

The duration of the primary attack in falciparum malaria, according to Boyd and Kitchen (1937), is shorter than that of vivax malaria, the mean being 10.8 days and the range, 2 to 36 days. However, the data of other workers show that the time of such attacks is extremely variable. Ciuca *et al* (1955) reported parasitemia continuing for up to 27 months, and African strains persist for up to approximately 18 months according to Covell (1960). Some of the American strains have persisted for 503 days. Verdrager (1964) reported falciparum infections of 3 years duration.

Eyles and Young (1951), in summarizing their observations on the duration of *Plasmodium falciparum* infections induced by sporozoites or parasitized blood, reported that following and including one or more clinical attacks, parasites were present continuously in the blood stream for varying periods of time and that the height of parasitemia in these successive waves tended to become lower and lower as time went by. The length of this period of continuous remittent parasitemia had a mean of 121 days with extremes of 32 and 224 days after the beginning of patent parasitemia. They reported further, that the period of continuous parasitemia was followed by a period of intermittent parasitemia which averaged 100 days with a range of 0 to 283 days. The duration of infection appeared to be similar, whether infections were induced by mosquito bites (sporozoites) or by parasitized blood. Three of the infections persisted for more than one year, the longest being 480 days.

Eyles and Young (1951), in studying a group of 13 sporozoite-induced cases, Santee-Cooper strain, observed 9 of them throughout their infections and for 6 months after the last parasites were seen. All 13 infections were observed through the long primary attack with continuous parasitemia. Apparently, 4 had to be treated because of dangerously high parasitemias. They described the general pattern of the infections as characterized by a clinical attack which varied from practically asymptomatic to one of severe dimensions. The clinical period was followed by an asymptomatic period during which patients carried parasties in their blood continuously. This was then followed by a period of varying duration during which parasites were only intermittently observed in peripheral smears. The mean length of the initial clinical episode was 9 days and the mean number of clinical episodes was 1.4. The mean total hours of fever, over 101.0° F, orally, was 90.4. The median maximum parasitemia was 65,000 per mm^3 of blood. The fact that only one clinical episode was observed in most cases and the fact that two-thirds of their original 13 cases were able to terminate their clinical symptoms spontaneously indicated to them that they were working with a strain of low virulence.

Jeffery and Eyles (1954) carried out studies on the Panama strain of *P. falciparum*. Of the 24 sporozoite-induced infections, 12 had attacks which had to be partially suppressed. The mean length of the initial clinical episode was 13.1 days; the mean number of clinical episodes was 3.3. The mean total hours of fever, over 101.0° F, was 124.8. The median maximum parasite count was 49,121 per mm^3; the mean maximum parasite count was 73,741 per mm^3. The general pattern of this strain of malaria was very similar to that of the Santee-Cooper strain (Eyles and Young, 1951). Probably the most significant difference was the greater severity of the primary clinical period observed with the Panama strain; its clinical attack was described as being quite severe. The mean length of the period of continuous remittent parasitemia for the Panama strain was 115.7 days with a range of 36 to 220 days. The terminal period of intermittent parasitemia had a mean duration of 168.3 days. The mean total duration of infection was 279 days with a range of 114 to 503 days.

Boyd and Kitchen (1937) observed renewal of clinical activity after spontaneous cessation of the primary attack or subcurative therapy of the primary attack in, roughly, 58 percent of their cases. Renewal of clinical activity was observed as many as 4 times in some patients. Most of the recurrences were observed within a period of 8 weeks following the primary attack. Kitchen (1949) reported recrudescences

within 2 months (8 weeks) of the termination of clinical activity but did not observe any clinical reactivation after 24 weeks; whereas James *et al* (1932) reported secondary clinical attacks in 3.3 percent of their infections after 24 weeks. In our studies with drug resistant strains of falciparum malaria, we have found that recurrences (recrudescences) could occur up to 80 days after subcurative or ineffective antimalarial therapy. For this reason, we require a 90-day period of follow-up before recording a cure.

Since 1960, a large number of strains of falciparum malaria have been found resistant to antimalarial drugs. They are resistant not only to chloroquine and other quinolines, but also to one, or more, or all, of the synthetic antimalarials, including chlorguanide, pyrimethamine, and mepacrine. In addition, some strains from Southeast Asia have shown varying degrees of resistance to quinine.

The susceptibility of the chimpanzee to falciparum malaria has been studied by several workers. Mesnil and Roubaud (1920) failed to infect these animals when exposure was by the bites of infected mosquitoes. Lefrou and Martignoles (1954) demonstrated the persistence of *P. falciparum* parasites for as long as 3 weeks in 3 of 4 chimpanzees inoculated with blood containing the parasite. However, Bray (1958, 1960) studied the susceptibility of the chimpanzee to falciparum malaria in detail and showed that the sporozoite was able to develop in the parenchymal cells of the liver. Although patent parasitemia obtained in the intact chimpanzee, it did not persist for more than one or, at the most, 2 cycles. However, if a splenectomized chimpanzee was exposed to infection by the bites of infected mosquitoes, the blood stages appeared, developed, and multiplied rapidly; the gametocytes failed to reach maturity (Bray, loc. cit.; Rodhain and Jadin, 1964).

In the *Aotus trivirgatus* monkey, *P. falciparum* often produces very high parasitemias. Geiman and Meagher (1967) reported a peak parasitemia, in a splenectomized monkey, on the first passage from man, of 180,000 per mm^3. Subsequent passage into splenectomized *A. trivirgatus* monkeys produced even higher peak parasitemias, some reaching levels as high as

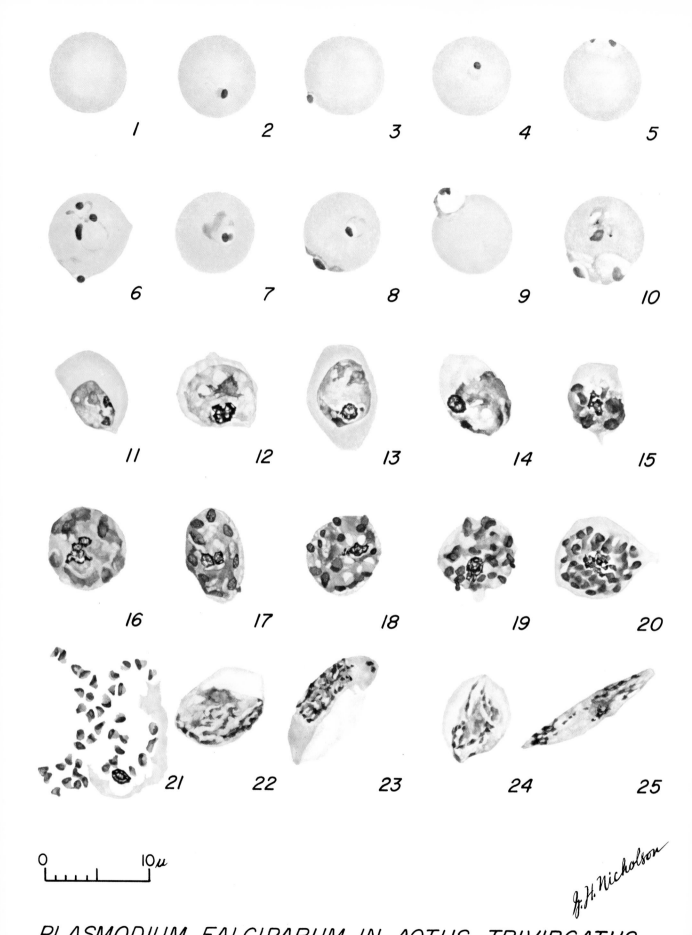

PLASMODIUM FALCIPARUM IN AOTUS TRIVIRGATUS

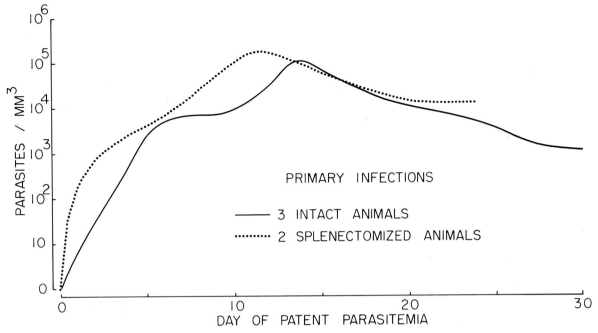

FIGURE 58.—Median parasitemia curves of *Plasmodium falciparum* infections in *Aotus trivirgatus* monkeys infected by the intravenous inoculation of parasitized blood from man.

87 percent of the red cells being infected (Geiman *et al*, 1969).

In our studies, *P. falciparum* has been passed from man to the *A. trivirgatus* monkey on 5 occasions, in intact animals 3 times, and in splenectomized animals, twice (see Plate XLIV). We have elected to term sub-passages in monkeys as secondary infections. The primary infections had similar courses of parasitemia in both the splenectomized and the intact monkeys (Fig. 58). On subsequent passage (Fig. 59), peak parasitemias of approximately 300,000 per mm³ obtained in the splenectomized monkeys by day 8 and in intact animals, by day 14. The number of parasites in the inoculum greatly affected subsequent parasitemia in intact *A. trivirgatus*

monkeys (Fig. 60). During the first, or primary, passage from man to intact monkeys, peak parasitemias of approximately 70,000 per mm³ were obtained after 14 days of patent parasitemia. Secondary infections, initiated by a small number of parasites given to intact monkeys, resulted in peak parasitemias of approximately 300,000 per mm³ on patent parasitemia day 14 and subsequently declined. However, if a large number of parasites were given, the parasitemia reached a peak of approximately 1,000,000 per mm³ by day 10 after which the animal, in most cases, died; some were saved from death by administering antimalarial drugs.

The gametocytes in *A. trivirgatus* monkeys were readily infectious to mosquitoes (Con-

PLATE XLIV.—*Plasmodium falciparum* in the owl monkey, *Aotus trivirgatus.*

Fig. 1. Normal red cell.
Figs. 2–5. Young trophozoites.
Figs. 6–10. Growing trophozoites.
Figs. 11, 12. Mature trophozoites.

Figs. 13–18. Developing schizonts.
Figs. 19–21. Nearly mature and mature schizonts.
Figs. 22, 23. Mature macrogametocytes.
Figs. 24, 25. Mature microgametocytes.

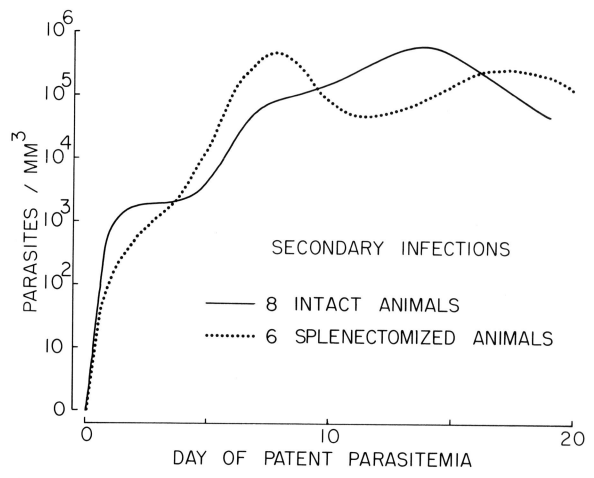

FIGURE 59.—Median parasitemia curves of *Plasmodium falciparum* infections in *Aotus trivirgatus* monkeys infected by the intravenous inoculation of parasitized blood from other *A. trivirgatus* monkeys.

tacos and Collins, 1968; Collins *et al*, 1968). This is illustrated in Figure 61 where *Anopheles freeborni* mosquitoes were allowed to feed on a monkey infected with a Malaysian strain of *P. falciparum*. This animal (AO–23) had been infected by blood-passage from man. After a low, transient course of parasitemia, the animal was able to eliminate the infection. Following splenectomy, the monkey was re-inoculated with the same strain of parasite. Eight days after inoculation, the first mosquito infections were obtained and these continued for the next 40 days. On 16 of the days, the infection rate was 100 percent and, in many instances, the number of oocysts per gut exceeded 500.

Young and Baerg (1969) observed infections

of *P. falciparum* in the white faced monkey, *Cebus capucinus*. The animals were infected by the inoculation of parasitized blood from infected *A. trivirgatus* and *C. capucinus* monkeys. The prepatent periods ranged up to 30 days; the periods of patent parasitemia up to 72 days. Infections reached high parasitemia levels in 3 of 8 monkeys; the highest was 662,700 per mm³. In all cases but one, the infection was self-limiting.

In the squirrel monkey (*Saimiri sciureus*), *P. falciparum* infections are remarkably transient. Young and Rossan (1969) reported an infection in an intact monkey which persisted at a detectable level for 21 days with a maximum parasitemia of 2,210 per mm³. After 49 days, parasites were again demonstrable for 3 con-

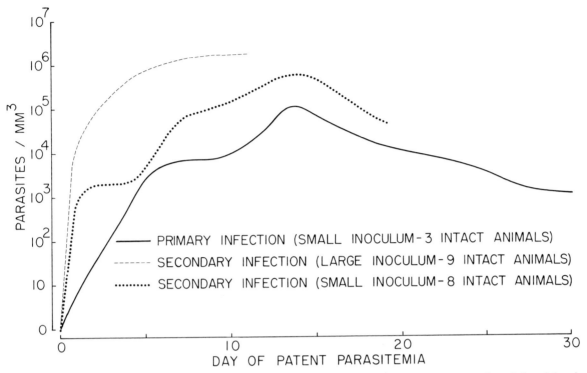

FIGURE 60.—Median parasitemia curves of *Plasmodium falciparum* infections in *Aotus trivirgatus* monkeys infected by the inoculation of parasitized blood.

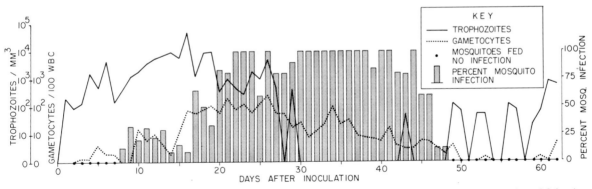

FIGURE 61.—Parasitemia and infectivity of *Anopheles freeborni* mosquitoes to a strain of *Plasmodium falciparum* from Malaysia (Malayan–IV in an *Aotus trivigatus* monkey.

secutive days, but were not seen again. On one occasion we gave a heavy inoculum to a splenectomized *S. sciureus* monkey; 3 days later, the parasite count was approximately 120,000 per mm³. This high level was maintained for approximately 2 weeks; 20 days after infection, the parasite count had dropped to 15,400 per mm³. Thereafter, the parasitemia

declined rapidly; parasites were last seen 29 days after inoculation. Upon reinoculation, the animal experienced a low, transient parasitemia. When mosquitoes were allowed to feed, they became infected but the infection was low.

Porter and Young (1967) recorded infections of *P. falciparum* in the marmoset, *Saguinus*

was epidemic or absent. Allison suggests that the sickle cell trait may confer a certain degree of resistance against malaria and, for that reason, the trait survives more successfully where the malaria infection rates are more severe.

It is thought, in some quarters, that the parasite cannot effectively utilize the abnormal hemoglobin in the sickled cell. Mackay and Vivarelli (1954) reported that sickle cells were seldom parasitized in a blood film from an individual with sickle-cell trait even when the sickle cells predominated. Miller *et al* (1956), on the other hand, reported results contrary to those of Mackay and Vivarelli; namely, that falciparum malaria parasites can and do, enter and develop readily in cells which undergo sickling. In 2 of their 3 cases, parasites were found as frequently in sickled cells as in non-sickled cells.

Miller *et al* (1956) suggested that it was not necessarily the sickle cell hemoglobin alone which was detrimental to the development of the falciparum parasites, but other factors were functioning, too. When the parasitized red cells, containing sickle cell hemoglobin, adhere to the walls of blood vessels, as falciparum infected red cells have a tendency to do, the oxygen supply to these parasitized cells would be very much decreased; and, under such circumstances, the loss of oxygen would bring about a relative anoxia which could conceivably induce sickling of the parasitized erythrocyte, thereby interfering with the multiplication of the parasite.

Another genetic trait which acts adversely is the deficiency of the enzyme glucose- 6-phosphate dehydrogenase (G6PD). High frequencies of this deficiency are found in malarious areas, and especially, in those endemic for falciparum malaria. It has been suggested that such a deficiency may limit parasite multiplication. Allison and Clyde (1961) found a significant lowering of the parasite rate in males deficient in G6PD and the proportion of falciparum infections with parasite counts above 1,000 per mm^3 was significantly lower in G6PD deficient children than in normal children.

Acquired immunity to falciparum malaria, as with the other human malarias, is strain specific. Garnham (1966) stated that *P. falciparum* parasites induce "a highly effective degree of premunition in the indigenous host in the sense that the children look thoroughly healthy, although 80 percent or more have a heavy load of parasites in the blood, while the adults appear strong, well grown, and energetic, with a relatively low parasitemia." However, if residents of the endemic areas move to other endemic areas, and are exposed to new strains, they develop very heavy infections.

Most studies have indicated that immunity to malaria is a residual immunity acquired through infection and that this immunity is not life-long. Rather, it is usually of short duration unless the individual is infected repeatedly. Boyd *et al* (1936) concluded that homologous but not heterologous immunity is acquired through infections of *P. falciparum*. This is contrary to what they observed with vivax malaria. In falciparum malaria, they found that reinoculation with a different strain resulted in an infection oftentimes as severe as the first. The homologous immunity lasted approximately 4 months. The latter is generally characterized as a clinical immunity; namely, no clinical attack with or without low patent parasitemia—if you will—an asymptomatic attack. The degree of immunity, acquired through infection, is probably dependent on the parasite densities and the duration of the parasitemia. Ciuca *et al* (1934) observed that repeated inoculations with falciparum malaria progressively increased the degree and/or the duration of immunity.

Boyd *et al* (1939) recorded absence of cross-immunity between vivax and falciparum malarias whether the reinoculations were effected during the incubation period, the acute primary attack, or shortly after termination of that attack.

However, Boyd and Kitchen (1945) reexamined and modified their opinions concerning heterologous immunity between falciparum malarias. They stressed the fact that the primary attacks of falciparum malaria were more severe in Caucasian than in Negro patients. In Caucasians, the primary infections usually consisted of 2 or 3 successive waves of patent parasitemia whereas in Negro patients only one wave of patent parasitemia was commonly observed. Generally, the heterologous immunity was characterized by a shortened period of clinical activity. In addition, reinoculation of Caucasian patients with heterologous strains resulted in infections similar to the primary infections in Negro patients; namely, one wave of patent parasitemia with parasite densities lower in the Negro patients. Their final conclusion was that immunity acquired from a falciparum malaria infection has "appreciable heterologous value."

That humoral immunity exists in falciparum malaria was shown by Cohen *et al* (1961) and Cohen and McGregor (1963). They demonstrated that malarial immunity can be transferred passively in the 7S fraction of gamma globulin of hyperimmune serum from adults in hyperendemic areas of the Gambia. When they administered such gamma globulin preparations in large doses to acutely ill Gambian children with heavy infections, a consistent pattern of response was observed; namely, rapid clinical recovery and a highly significant reduction in parasitemia. This was confirmed by Edozien *et al* (1962) in Nigeria. McGregor (1964) was of the opinion that immune 7S gamma globulin acted against the late asexual forms (schizonts) or the liberated (extracellular) merozoites.

That humoral malarial immunity could be passively transferred from mother to offspring had been postulated for years. This was confirmed by Edozien *et al* (1962) when they demonstrated that antimalarial antibodies (gamma globulins) can cross the placental barrier when they treated falciparum infections with gamma globulin prepared from cord blood.

If one turns to serology for insight into relationships between various primate malarias, some interesting facts emerge. In this regard, Kuvin and Voller (1963) studied the differences in response of sera from 26 individuals from West Africa, previous malarial histories unknown, against *P. falciparum* and B strain *P. cynomolgi* antigens. The mean titers of the former were 1:24 versus 1:18 for *P. cynomolgi* indicating a high level of cross-reactivity. Diggs and Sadun (1965), using sera from known infections of *P. falciparum* and *P. vivax*, quantitated the levels of cross-reactivity. Their *P. falciparum* antisera gave a homologous response, as measured by the geometrical mean of the reciprocal titers, of 1:28.2 and a heterologous response of 1:6.3. Using the *P. vivax* antisera, the homologous geometrical mean of the reciprocal titers was 1:17.2 and the heterologous mean titer was 1:9.3. Collins *et al* (1966) were able to show that antiserum to *P. falciparum* would react with a number of simian malaria antigens but that the highest heterologous response was to *P. fieldi*. Meuwissen (1968) demonstrated that although the antisera to *P. falciparum* would react at a high level to both the B strain *P. cynomolgi* and *P. fieldi* antigens, the highest heterologous response was to the latter.

REFERENCES

ALLISON, A. C., 1954. The distribution of the sickle-cell trait in East Africa and elsewhere, and its apparent relationship to the incidence of subtertian malaria. Trans. Roy. Soc. Trop. Med. & Hyg. *48* : 312–318.

ALLISON, A. C., 1954a. Protection afforded by sickle-cell trait against subtertian malarial infection. Brit. Med. Jour. *1* : 290–294.

ALLISON, A. C., 1961. Genetic factors in resistance to malaria. Ann. N.Y. Acad. Sci. *91* : 710–729.

ALLISON, A. C., 1963. Inherited factors in blood conferring resistance to protozoa. In Immunity to Protozoa. A symposium of the Brit. Soc. for Immunology. Edited by P. C. C. Garnham, A. E. Pierce, and I. Roitt. Blackwell Scientific Publications, Oxford.

ALLISON, A. C. and CLYDE, D. F., 1961. Malaria in African children with deficient erythrocyte glucose-6-phosphate dehydrogenase. Brit. Med. Jour. *1* : 1346–1349.

ANTOLISEI, E. and ANGELINI, A., 1890. Osservazioni sopre alcuni casi d'infezione malarica con forme semilunari. Riv. Clin. Arch. Ital. Clin. Med. *29* : 1–23. (NS).

BASTIANELLI, G., BIGNAMI, A., and GRASSI, B., 1898. Coltivazione delle semilune malariche dell'uomo nell-'*Anopheles claviger* Fabr. (sinonimo *Anopheles maculipennis* Meig.) b. Nota preliminare. Atti R. Accad. Lincei, Rendic. *7* : 313. Annali d'Igiene *9* : 258. (NS).

BASTIANELLI, G. and BIGNAMI, A., 1899. (I.) Sulla struttura dei parassiti malarici e in specie dei gameti dei parassiti estivo-autumnali. (II.) Sullo sviluppo dei parassiti terzana nell'*Anopheles claviger*. Annali d'Igiene *9* : 245–272. (NS).

BLACKLOCK, B. and ADLER, S., 1922. A parasite resembling *Plasmodium falciparum* in a chimpanzee. Ann. Trop. Med. & Parasit. *16* : 99–106.

BOYD, M. F., 1949. Malariology, 2 Vols. W. B. Saunders Co., Phila. pp. 1643.

REFERENCES—Continued

BOYD, M. F. and KITCHEN, S. F., 1937. Observations on induced falciparum malaria. Am. J. Trop. Med. *17* : 213–235.

BOYD, M. F. and KITCHEN, S. F., 1945. On the heterologous value of acquired immunity to *Plasmodium falciparum*. J. Nat. Mal. Soc. *4* : 301–306.

BOYD, M. F., STRATMAN-THOMAS, W. K., and KITCHEN, S. F., 1936. On acquired immunity to *Plasmodium falciparum*. Am. J. Trop. Med. *16* : 139–145.

BOYD, M. F., KITCHEN, S. F., and MATTHEWS, C. B., 1939. Consecutive inoculations with *Plasmodium vivax* and *Plasmodium falciparum*. Am. J. Trop. Med. *19* : 141–150.

BRAY, R. S., 1958. Studies on malaria in chimpanzees. VI. Laverania Falciparum. Am. J. Trop. Med. & Hyg. *7* : 20–24.

BRAY, R. S., 1960. Observations on the cytology and morphology of the mammalian malaria parasites. I. A process of apparent plasmotomy in the preerythrocytic phase of *Laverania falciparum*. Riv. di Parassit. *21* : 267–276.

BRAY R. S., 1963. The malaria parasites of anthropoid apes. J. Parasit. *49* : 888–891.

BRAY, R. S. and GUNDERS, A. E., 1962. Studies on malaria in chimpanzees. IX. The distribution of the pre-erythrocytic forms of *Laverania falcipara*. Am. J. Trop. Med. & Hyg. *11* : 437–439.

BRAY, R. S. and GUNDERS, A. E., 1963. Studies on malaria in chimpanzees XI. The early forms of the pre-erythrocytic phase of *Laverania falcipara*. Am. J. Trop. Med. & Hyg. *12* : 13–18.

BURGESS, R. W. and YOUNG, M. D., 1946. Experimental transmission of *P. falciparum* by *Anopheles maculipennis freeborni*. J. Nat. Mal. Soc. *5* : 151–152.

CADIGAN, F. C., JR., SPERTZEL, R. O., CHAICUMPAN, V., and PUHOMCHAREON, S., 1966. *Plasmodium falciparum* in non-human primates (macaque monkeys). Mil. Med. *131* : 959–960.

CADIGAN, F. C., JR., WARD, R. A., and CHAICUMPA, V., 1969. Further studies on the biology of human malarial parasites in gibbons from Thailand. Mil. Med. *134* : 757–766.

CHIN, W., CONTACOS, P. G., COATNEY, G. R., JETER, M. H., and ALPERT, E., 1967. Evaluation of CI-564, a 1:1 mixture of cycloguanil pamoate (CI-501) and 4,4'-diacetylaminodiphenylsulfone (CI-556), against multiresistant falciparum malarias. Am. J. Trop. Med. & Hyg. *16* : 580–584.

CHOPRA, R. N., DAS GUPTA, B. M., and SEN, B., 1932. A fatal case of severe malignant tertian malaria. Ind. Med. Gaz. *67* : 680–681.

CHRISTOPHERS, R. and SINTON, J. A., 1938. The correct name of the malignant tertian malaria parasite. Brit. Med. Jour. *2* : 1130–1134.

CIUCA, M., BALLIF, L., and CHELARESCU-VIERU, M., 1934. Immunity in malaria. Trans. Roy. Soc. Trop. Med. & Hyg. *27* : 619–622.

CIUCA, M., BALLIF, L., CHELARESCU, M., ISANOS, M., and GLASER, L., 1937. Contributions à l'étude de la tierce maligne expérimentale. Pouvoir infectant du sang au cours de l'incubation. Riv. di Malariol. *16* : 85–90.

CIUCA, M., BALLIF, L., CHELARESCU, M., and LAVRINENKO, N., 1937a. IV. Contribution à l'étude del'infection expérimentale au *Pl. falciparum*. Sonderabdruck aus der Festschrift Nocht, 81–101.

CIUCA, M., CHELARESCU, M., SOFLETEA, A., CONSTANTINESCU, P., TERITEANU, E., CORTEZ, P., BALANOVSCHI, G., and ILIES, M., 1955. Contribution expérimentale à l'étude de l'immunité dans le paludisme. Acad. de la République Populaire Roumaine, 61–108.

COATNEY, G. R. and YOUNG, M. D., 1941. The taxonomy of the human malaria parasites with notes on the principal American strains. Am. Assoc. Adv. Sci. (No. 15), 19–24.

COATNEY, G. R., COOPER, W. C., YOUNG, M. D., and McLENDON, S. B., 1947. Studies in human malaria. I. The protective action of sulfadiazine and sulfapyrazine against sporozoite-induced falciparum malaria. Am. J. Hyg. *46* : 84–104.

COHEN, S. and McGREGOR, I. A., 1963. Gamma globulin and acquired immunity to malaria. In Symposium on Immunity to Protozoa. Blackwell Scientific Publications, Oxford.

COHEN, S., McGREGOR, I. A., and CARRINGTON, S., 1961. Gamma-globulin and acquired immunity to human malaria. Nature *192* : 733–737.

COLLINS, W. E., 1962. Comparative infectivity of *Plasmodium falciparum* (Colombia strain) to *Anopheles quadrimaculatus* Say and *Anopheles albimanus* (Wied.). Mosq. News *22* : 257–259.

COLLINS, W. E., JEFFERY, G. M., and BURGESS, R. W., 1963. Comparative infectivity of two strains of *Plasmodium falciparum* to *Anopheles quadrimaculatus* Say, *Anopheles freeborni* Aitken, and *Anopheles albimanus* (Wied.). Mosq. News *23* : 102–104.

COLLINS, W. E., JEFFERY, G. M., SKINNER, J. C., and HARRISON, A. J., 1964. Comparative infectivity of a strain of *Plasmodium falciparum* from Panama to three species of *Anopheles* as studied by membrane feeding. Mosq. News *24* : 28–31.

COLLINS, W. E., JEFFERY, G. M., GUINN, E., and SKINNER, J. C., 1966. Fluorescent antibody studies in human malaria. IV. Cross-reactions between human and simian malaria. Am. J. Trop. Med. & Hyg. *15* : 11–15.

COLLINS, W. E., CONTACOS, P. G., GUINN, E. G., JETER, M. H., and SODEMAN, T. M., 1968. Monkey to man transmission of *Plasmodium falciparum* by *Anopheles freeborni* mosquitoes. J. Parasit. *54* : 1166–1170.

CONTACOS, P. G., COATNEY, G. R., LUNN, J. S., and KILPATRICK, J. W., 1964. The antimalarial activity of CI-501 (Camolar) against falciparum malaria. Am. J. Trop. Med. & Hyg. *13* : 386–390.

CONTACOS, P. G. and COLLINS, W. E., 1968. Falciparum malaria transmissible from monkey to man by mosquito bite. Science *161* : 56.

COVELL, G., 1960. Relationship between malarial parasitaemia and symptoms of the disease. A review of the literature. Bull. Wld. Hlth. Org. *22* : 605–619.

DIGGS, C. L. and SADUN, E. H., 1965. Serological cross reactivity between *Plasmodium vivax* and *Plasmodium*

REFERENCES—Continued

falciparum as determined by a modified fluorescent antibody test. Exp. Parasit. *16* : 217–223.

EDOZIEN, J. C., GILLES, H. M., and UDEOZO, I. O. K., 1962. Adult and cord-blood gamma-globulin and immunity to malaria. Lancet *2* : 951–955.

EYLES, D. E. and JEFFERY, G. M., 1949. The experimental transmission of *Plasmodijm falciparum* by *Anopheles albimanus.* J. Nat. Mal. Soc. *8* : 344–345.

EYLES, D. E. and YOUNG, M. D., 1951. The duration of untreated or inadequately treated *Plasmodium falciparum* infections in the human host. J. Nat. Mal. Soc. *10* : 327–336.

FAIRLEY, N. H. *,et al,* 1947. Sidelights on malaria in man obtained by subinoculation experiments. Trans. Roy. Soc. Trop. Med. & Hyg. *40* : 621–676.

FELETTI, R. and GRASSI, B., 1890. Sui parassiti della malaria. Arch. Ital. Biol. *13* : 287–296.

FIELD, J. W. and NIVEN, J. C., 1937. A note on prognosis in relation to parasite counts in acute subtertian malaria. Trans. Roy. Soc. Trop. Med. & Hyg. *30* : 569–574.

FIELD, J. W. and SHUTE, P. G., 1956. The microscopic diagnosis of human malaria. II. A morphological study of the erythrocytic parasites. Inst. Med. Res., Fed. Malaya, No. 24. pp. 251.

GARNHAM, P. C. C., 1948. The incidence of malaria at high altitudes. J. Nat. Mal. Soc. *7* : 275–284.

GARNHAM, P. C. C., 1966. Malaria parasites and other haemosporidia. Blackwell Scientific Publications, Oxford. pp. 1114.

GEIMAN, Q. M. and MEAGHER, M. J., 1967. Susceptibility of a new world monkey to *Plasmodium falciparum* from man. Nature *215* : 437–439.

GEIMAN, Q. M., SIDDIQUI, W. A., and SCHNELL, J. V., 1969. Biological basis for susceptibility of *Aotus trivirgatus* to species of plasmodia from man. Mil. Med. *134* : 780–786.

GIOVANNOLA, A., 1935. *Plasmodium immaculatum* (Grassi and Feletti 1892) Schaudinn 1902. The correct name for the parasite causing malignant tertian malaria. Proc. Helm. Soc. Wash. *2* : 90–91.

GOULD, D. J., CADIGAN, F. C., JR. and WARD, R. A., 1966. Falciparum malaria: transmission to the gibbon by *Anopheles balabacensis.* Science *153* : 1384.

GRASSI, B., 1891. Weiteres zur Malariafrage. II. Verschiedene Untersuchungen. Zentralbl. Bakt. 1 Abt. Orig. *10* : 517.

GRASSI, B. and FELETTI, R., 1890. Parasites malariques chez les oiseaux. Arch. Ital. de Biologie *13* : 297–300.

GRASSI, B. and FELETTI, R., 1892. Contribuzione allo studio die parassiti malarici. Atti Accad. Gioenia. Series 4,5 : 1–81.

GRASSI, B., BIGNAMI, A., and BASTIANELLI, G., 1898. Ulteriori ricerche sul ciclo dei parassiti malarici umani nel corpo del zanzarone. (Nota preliminare.) Atti. R. Accad. Lincei, Rendic, 5 ser., *8* : 21–28. (NS).

HACKETT, L. W., 1945. The malaria of the Andean region of South America. Rev. Inst. Salub. enferm. trop., Mex. *6* : 239–252.

HEMMING, F., (Ed.), 1954. Opinions and declarations rendered by the International Commission on Zoological Nomenclature. Opinion 283, Vol. 7, London. pp. 225.

International Commission on Zoological Nomenclature, 1928. Opinion No. 104, Smithsonian Misc. Collect. Publication No. 2979, *73* : 25–28.

JAMES, S. P., NICOL, W. D., and SHUTE, P. G., 1932. A study of induced malignant tertian malaria. Proc. Roy. Soc. Med. *25* : 1153–1186. (Sec. Trop. Dis. & Parasit. 37–70).

JEFFERY, G. M. and EYLES, D. E., 1954. The duration in the human host of infections with a Panama strain of *Plasmodium falciparum.* Am. J. Trop. Med. & Hyg. *2* : 219–224.

JEFFERY, G. M., EYLES, D. E., and YOUNG, M. D., 1950. The comparative susceptibility of *Anopheles quadrimaculatus* and two strains of *Anopheles albimanus* to a Panama strain of *Plasmodium falciparum.* J. Nat. Mal. Soc. *9* : 349–355.

JEFFERY, G. M., WOLCOTT, G. B., YOUNG, M. D., and WILLIAMS, D., JR., 1952. Exo-erythrocytic stages of *Plasmodium falciparum.* Am. J. Trop. Med. & Hyg. *1* : 917–926.

JEFFERY, G. M., YOUNG, M. D., BURGESS, R. W., and EYLES, D. E., 1959. Early activity in sporozoite-induced *Plasmodium falciparum* infections. Ann. Trop. Med. & Parasit. *53* : 51–58.

JEFFERY, G. M., COLLINS, W. E., and SKINNER, J. C., 1963. Antimalarial drug trials on a multiresistant strain of *Plasmodium falciparum.* Am. J. Trop. Med. & Hyg. *12* : 844–850.

KITCHEN, S. F., 1949. Falciparum malaria. Malariology, Vol. II, edited by Mark F. Boyd. W. B. Saunders Co., Phila.

KUVIN, S. F. and VOLLER, A., 1963. Malarial antibody titres of West Africans in Britain. Brit. Med. Jour. *2* : 477–479.

LABBÉ, A., 1894. Récherches zoologiques et biologiques sur les parasites endoglobulaires du sang des vertebrates. Arch. Zool. exp. *2* : 55–258.

LAVERAN, A., 1880. Note sur un nouveau parasite trouvé dans le sang de plusieurs malades atteints de fièvre palustre. Bull. Acad. Med. *9* : 1235–1236.

LAVERAN, A., 1881. Nature parasitaire des accidents de l'impaludisme. Description d'un nouveau parasite trouvé dans le sang des malades atteints de fièvre palustre. Paris, Baillière et Fills. pp. 104.

LEFROU, G. and MARTIGNOLES, J., 1954. Contribution a l'étude des *Plasmodium* chimpanzés. Inoculation de *Pl. falciparum* humain au chimpanzé. Bull. Soc. Path. Exot. *47* : 895–903.

LEWKOWICZ, X., 1897. Ueber den Entwickelungsgang und die Einteilung der Malariaparasiten. Zentralbl. Bakt. 1 Abt. Orig. *21* : 130–133.

LUNN, J. S., CHIN, W., CONTACOS, P. G., and COATNEY, G. R., 1964. Cycloguanil pamoate (CI-501) as a causal prophylactic against a Southern Rhodesian strain of falciparum malaria. Am. J. Trop. Med. & Hyg. *13* : 783–785.

MACKEY, J. P. and VIVARELLI, F., 1954. Sickle-cell anemia (correspondence). Brit. Med. Jour. *1* : 276.

MANNABERG, J., 1893. Die Malaria-Parasiten. Wien.

REFERENCES—Continued

pp. 195.

MARCHIAFAVA, E. and CELLI, A., 1885. Weitere Untersuchungen über die Malariainfection. Fortschr. Med. *3* : 791.

MARCHIAFAVA, E. and BIGNAMI, A., 1892. Sulle febbri malariche estivoautumnali. E. Loescher & Co., Rome. (NS).

McGREGOR, I. A., 1964. The passive transfer of human malarial immunity. Am. J. Trop. Med. Hyg. *13* : 237–239.

MESNIL, F. and ROUBAUD, E., 1920. Essais d'inoculation du paludisme au chimpanzé. Ann. Inst. Pasteur *34* : 466–480.

MEUWISSEN, J. H. E. TH., 1968. Antibody responses of patients with natural malaria to human and simian Plasmodium antigens measured by the fluorescent antibody test. Trop. geogr. Med. *20* : 137–140.

MILLER, M. J., NEEL, J. V., and LIVINGSTONE, F. B., 1956. Distribution of parasites in the red cells of sickle-cell trait carriers infected with *Plasmodium falciparum*. Trans. Roy. Soc. Trop. Med. & Hyg. *50* : 294–296.

POLUMORDVINOV, A. D., 1945. Highland malaria in southern Tadjikistan. Med. Parasit. and Parasitic Dis., Moscow *14* : 18–20.

PORTER, J. A., JR. and YOUNG, M. D., 1967. The transfer of *Plasmodium falciparum* from man to the marmoset, *Saguinus geoffroyi*. J. Parasit. *53* : 845–846.

POWELL, R. D., DEGOWIN, R. L., and EPPES, R. B., 1965. Studies on the antimalarial effects of cycloguanil pamoate (CI-501) in man. Am. J. Trop. Med. & Hyg. *14* : 913–921.

RAFFAELE, G. and COLUZZI, A., 1949. Relazione sulla malaria nella provincia di Frosinone negli anni 1945–48. L'epidemia malaria di Cassino. Riv. di Malariol. *28* : 61–106.

RODHAIN, J., 1939. Les plasmodiums des anthropoides de l'Afrique centrale et leurs relations avec les plasmodiums humains. Ann. Soc. Belge de Méd. Trop. *19* : 563–572.

RODHAIN, J. and JADIN, J., 1964. La transmission du *Plasmodium falciparum* au chimpanzé splénectomisé. Ann. Soc. Belge Méd. Trop. *44* : 531–536.

ROSS, R., 1897. On some peculiar pigmented cells found in two mosquitoes fed on malarial blood. Brit. Med. Jour. *2* : 1786–1788.

SERGENT, ED., SERGENT, ET., and CATANEI, A., 1929. Une question de nomenclature le nom de *Plasmodium praecox* doit-il designer un parasite du paludisme humain ou un parasite du paludisme aviare? Arch. Inst. Pasteur Algér. *7* : 223–238.

SERGENT, ED., SERGENT, ET., PARROT, L., and CATANEI, A., 1939. Nomenclature of the malaria parasites. Brit. Med. Jour. *1* : 747–748 and Arch. Inst. Pasteur Algér. *17* : 242–243.

SHORTT, H. E., FAIRLEY, N. H., COVELL, G., SHUTE, P. G., and GARNHAM, P. C. C., 1949. The pre-erythrocytic stage of *Plasmodium falciparum*. A preliminary note. Brit. Med. Jour. *2* : 1006–1008.

SHORTT, H. E., FAIRLEY, N. H., COVELL, G., SHUTE, P. G., and GARNHAM, P. C. C., 1951. The pre-erythrocytic stage of *Plasmodium falciparum*. Trans. Roy. Soc. Trop. Med. & Hyg. *44* : 405–419.

SHUTE, P. G. and MARYON, M., 1952. A study of human malaria oocysts as an aid to species diagnosis. Trans. Roy. Soc. Trop. Med. & Hyg. *46* : 275–292.

SODEMAN, T. M., CONTACOS, P. G., SMITH, C. S., JUMPER, J. R., and COLLINS, W. E., 1969. The exoerythrocytic stages of *Plasmodium falciparum* in *Aotus trivirgatus*. J. Parasit. *55* : 682–683.

SOPER, F. L. and WILSON, D. B., 1943. *Anopheles gambiae* in Brazil 1930 to 1940. The Rockefeller Foundation, New York.

TALIAFERRO, W. H. and TALIAFERRO, L. G., 1934. The transmission of *Plasmodium falciparum* to the howler monkey, *Alouatta* sp. I. General nature of infections and morphology of the parasites. Am. J. Hyg. *19* : 318–334.

TALIAFERRO, W. H. and CANNON, P. R., 1934. Transmission of *Plasmodium falciparum* to the howler monkey, *Alouatta* sp. II. Cellular reactions. Am. J. Hyg. *19* : 335–342.

THAYER, W. S. and HEWESTON, J., 1895. The malarial fevers of Baltimore. Johns Hopkins Hosp. Reports *5* : 1–218.

VERDRAGER, J., 1964. Observations on the longevity of *Plasmodium falciparum*: with special reference to findings in Mauritius. Bull. Wld. Hlth. Org. *31* : 747–751.

VOLLER, A., RICHARDS, W. H. G., HAWKEY, C. M., and RIDLEY, D. S., 1969. Human malaria (*Plasmodium falciparum*) in owl monkeys (*Aotus trivirgatus*). J. Trop. Med. & Hyg. *72* : 153–160.

WARD, R. A. and CADIGAN, F. C., JR., 1966. The development of erythrocytic stages of *Plasmodium falciparum* in the gibbon, *Hylobates lar*. Mil. Med. *131* : 944–951.

WARD, R. A., MORRIS, J. H., GOULD, D. J., BOURKE, A. T. C., and CADIGAN, F. C., JR., 1965. Susceptibility of the gibbon *Hylobates lar* to *Plasmodium falciparum*. Science *150* : 1604–1605.

WELCH, W. H., 1897. Malaria: definition, synonyms, history, and parasitology. Loomis and Thompson, Syst. Practice Med. *1* : 17–76. Lea Bros. & Co., New York.

YOUNG, M. D. and BAERG, D. C., 1969. Experimental infections of *Plasmodium falciparum* in *Cebus capucinus* (white faced capuchin) monkeys. Mil. Med. *134* : 767–771.

YOUNG, M. D. and ROSSAN, R. N., 1969. *Plasmodium falciparum* induced in the squirrel monkey, *Saimiri sciureus*. Trans. Roy. Soc. Trop. Med. & Hyg. *63* : 686–687.

(NS) = Not seen.

23

Plasmodium coatneyi Eyles, Fong, Warren, Guinn, Sandosham, and Wharton, 1962

IN the course of studies on simian malaria begun by the late Dr. Don Eyles in Malaya, he and his co-workers isolated a new species of malaria from a wild caught anopheline mosquito, *Anopheles hackeri*. This unique experience is the first instance of finding a new species of malaria in the vector before it was known from the primate host. The mosquito was taken in the nipah palm area of Kampong Rantau Panjang near the town of Klang in the State of Selangor in November, 1961. Upon dissection, the mosquito was found to be positive with sporozoites which were injected into an uninfected rhesus monkey, *Macaca mulatta*, without delay. The monkey exhibited infection after a prepatent period of 14 days. The parasite was first taken to be *Plasmodium knowlesi* on morphological grounds but when the periodicity was found to be tertian, rather than quotidian, it was obvious that the investigators were dealing with an undescribed species which they named *Plasmodium coatneyi* in honor of the American malariologist Dr. G. Robert Coatney. Later, Eyles *et al* (1962) isolated *P. coatneyi* from a kra monkey, *M. irus* (= *fascicularis*) taken in the same area as the original infected mosquito and then again in 1963 (Eyles *et al*, 1963) from the blood of an *M. irus* (= *fascicularis*) from the Philippines.

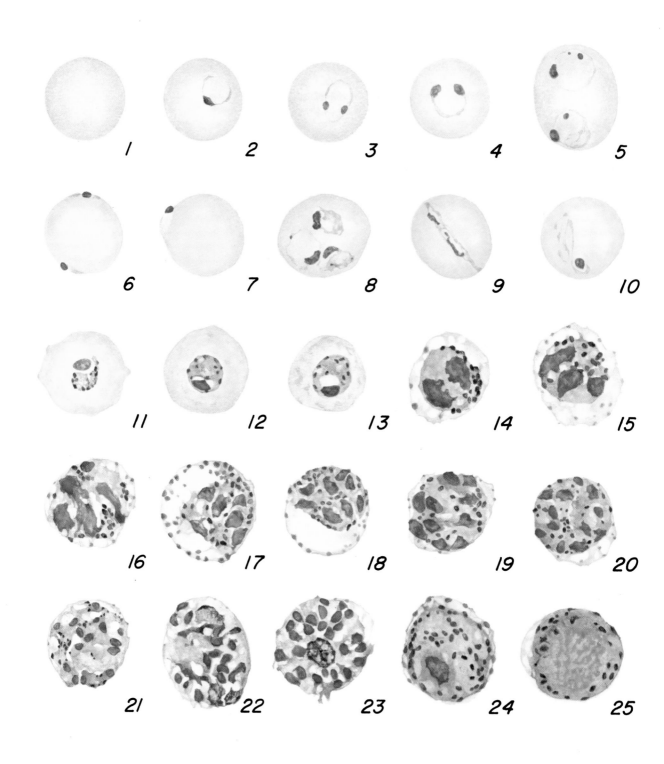

PLASMODIUM COATNEYI

G. H. Nicholson

0   10 μ

Cycle in the Blood

PLATE XLV

The young ring forms of *P. coatneyi* closely resemble those of the human parasite, *P. falciparum*. The youngest ring forms are smaller than the rings of other simian parasites (not shown on plate) except, possibly, *P. knowlesi*. The typical young trophozoite has a single or double chromatin body (Figs. 2–5) but they may number up to four. The position in the host cell is varied as is true with the same age growth forms of *P. falciparum*. Marginal, appliqué or accolé forms are common (Fig. 6), often considered diagnostic of *P. falciparum* along with displaced vesicular forms (Fig. 7) with one or two nuclei. In heavy infections, host cells may harbor two or more young parasites (Fig. 8); band and tenue forms are not uncommon (Figs. 9, 10). In some instances the host cell carrying the young parasites is smaller than the normal cell.

As the trophozoites mature, their number in the peripheral blood becomes less. The usual form is circular or oval, usually with a vacuole and with intense blue cytoplasm (Figs. 11–13). The youngest of these forms rarely show pigment, but as the parasite grows the granules become prominent; they do not coalesce. Maurer's spots or clefts are prominent and characteristic of this species. These were originally described by Eyles *et al* (loc. cit.) and their fine structure more recently by Rudzinska and Trager (1968). The bluish cast to the cytoplasm in Figures 11–13 probably illustrates these spots with Giemsa stain.

The early schizonts stain a deep blue, are compact, round, and occupy at least half the host cell. The pigment remains granular with a tendency to coalesce (Figs. 14–16). The older and the mature schizonts fill the host cell and produce about 20 merozoites (Figs. 22, 23).

The macrogametocytes take a medium blue stain with a red nucleus, generally eccentric, enclosing a deeper staining irregular area. The pigment, scattered in the cytoplasm, is prominent and rice-grain shaped (Fig. 24). The microgametocyte stains reddish-purple and has a large circular mottled nucleus which may show a deeper staining bar. The pigment is dark to yellowish-brown and sometimes found entirely within a vacuole (Fig. 25).

The parasite, as pointed out by Eyles (1963) has a penchant for invading reticulocytes. Warren *et al* (1966) possessed a greater amount of material, and employed statistical methods to show that the parasite selectively invades mature erythrocytes.

In 1968, Rudzinska and Trager, after studying the fine structure of the parasite and its host cell, were able to show that the trophozoites do not have typical protozoan mitochondria, but they do have a double-membraned organelle which, it is assumed, carries out the functions of the mitochondria. The young parasite feeds on the host cell by pinocytosis, taking in portions of the erythrocytes through invaginations of the plasma membrane or through the cytostome. Digestion of the hemoglobin takes place in small vesicles derived from the food vacuole. The macrogametocytes have two plasma membranes; the inner one thickened in places. The cytoplasm displays Palade's particles, has toxonemes and vesicles of endoplasmic reticulum. The microgametocytes have the whole inner membrane thickened, the cytoplasm displays few Palade's particles and there are no toxonemes.

The host cells with trophozoites are irregularly shaped and show elevated points with knob-like projections and a double membrane. The host erythrocyte has numerous Mauer's clefts which, because they are sometimes continuous with the membranes of the parasite,

PLATE XLV.—*Plasmodium coatneyi.*

Fig. 1.   Normal red cell.
Figs. 2, 3, 6, 7.   Young trophozoites.
Figs. 4, 5, 8–11.   Growing trophozoites.
Figs. 12, 13.   Mature trophozoites.
Figs. 14–17.   Early schizonts.

Figs. 18–21.   Developing schizonts.
Figs. 22, 23.   Nearly mature and mature schizonts.
Fig. 24.   Mature macrogametocyte.
Fig. 25.   Mature microgametocyte.

suggests that they may take their origin from them.

The asexual cycle in the blood occupies 48 hours.

Sporogonic Cycle

PLATE XLVI

Warren and Wharton (1963) were able to infect *A. kochi*, *A. letifer*, *A. maculatus*, *A. sundaicus*, and *A. vagus* but they made no comments on the development of the oocysts. Eyles (1963) in commenting on the sporogonic cycle of *P. coatneyi* reported that no distinguishing characteristics were seen. Subsequently Collins *et al* (1967) reported the infection of *Anopheles b. balabacensis* and *A. freeborni* but only the latter consistently produced sporozoites in the salivary glands. More recently, studies were made to determine the growth rate of the oocysts of *P. coatneyi* in *A. b. balabacensis*, *A. maculatus*, and *A. freeborni*. The results of these observations were presented in Table 36.

In *A. b. balabacensis*, the oocysts at day 6 had a mean diameter of 19 μ with a range of 12 to 26 μ. The oocysts continued to grow so that by day 11, the mean size was 61 μ with a range of 24 to 90 μ and sporozoites were present in the salivary glands.

In *A. maculatus*, the oocysts appeared to slow down in their rate of growth after day 7. However, oocyst differentiation was seen as early as day 9 and sporozoites, though scarce, were present in the salivary glands on day 12. The mean diameters of the oocysts in *A. maculatus* were considerably smaller on days 8 through 11 than were those of *A. b. balabacensis*.

In *A. freeborni*, the development was apparently normal through day 10. After day 10, there was no evidence of further development; by day 12, many of the oocysts were in various stages of degeneration. No sporozoites were found in the salivary glands although as indicated earlier (Collins *et al*, 1967) low level infections of the salivary glands of *A. freeborni* have been found. An interesting sidelight was that fully developed infections in intact animals, carrying abundant gametocytes, were rarely infectious to mosquitoes. However, once the animals were splenectomized, mosquito

infections followed almost immediately with the intensity of the infection in the mosquitoes usually correlated with the 48-hour asexual periodicity (Fig. 62).

A comparison of the mean oocyst diameters of *P. coatneyi* with *P. cynomolgi* (Fig. 63) indicates that *P. coatneyi* is a smaller parasite and it requires one day longer for the sporozoites to appear in the salivary glands.

The sporozoites in *A. b. balabacensis* were shown to be infective; infections were transmitted to 6 *M. mulatta* monkeys by mosquito bites with prepatent periods from 10 to 15 days with a mean of 13.2 days. Dissected salivary glands and triturated bodies of *A. freeborni* mosquitoes infected with *P. coatneyi* were inoculated into 5 *M. mulatta* monkeys. Three of the animals developed an infection with prepatent periods of 14, 15, and 15 days, respectively. We do not know if *A. maculatus* will transmit this parasite although we have seen seemingly viable sporozoites in their glands. Three attempts to transmit the infection by bites of *A. freeborni* mosquitoes to rhesus monkeys have failed.

Cycle in the Tissue

PLATE XLVII

Following the Held *et al* (1967) technique of intrahepatic inoculation of sporozoites, Held and Contacos (1967) carried out a detailed study of the growth stages of *P. coatneyi* in the rhesus monkey. Liver biopsies were done on days 6, 7, 8, 9, 10, and 11 following the introduction of sporozoites; and growth forms for each of the days, except day 11, were described and illustrated in a series of 69 figures. The 6-day forms measured 19 to 22 μ and the oldest forms, i.e., 10-day measured 40 to 48 μ. Different parasites studied on the same day demonstrated the wide extent of heteromorphism in the species which served to confirm their opinion that the tissue stages do not exhibit morphological characteristics which will allow for the separation of species.

Course of Infection

The natural host of *P. coatneyi* is *Macaca irus* (= *fascicularis*), the kra monkey, and in that

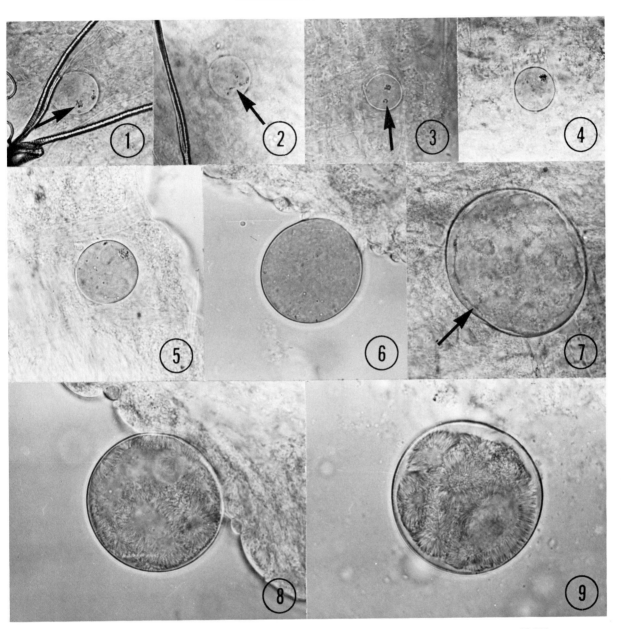

PLATE XLVI.—Developing oocysts of *Plasmodium coatneyi* in *Anopheles b. balabacensis* mosquitoes. X 580.

Fig. 1.   6-day oocyst showing clumped pigment.
Fig. 2.   6-day oocyst showing linear arrangement of pigment.
Fig. 3.   7-day oocyst showing two clumps of pigment.
Fig. 4.   7-day oocyst showing large clump of pigment.
Fig. 5.   8-day oocyst.

Fig. 6.   9-day oocyst.
Fig. 7.   10-day oocyst showing early stages of differentiation.
Fig. 8.   11-day differentiated oocyst.
Fig. 9.   Fully differentiated 11-day oocyst showing withdrawal of sporozoite mass from oocyst wall.

animal, the parasite produces a mild low-grade infection that persists for a long time. When the infection is transferred to clean, laboratory-reared *M. fascicularis* by blood inoculation, the peak parasitemias range from 15,000 to 57,000 per mm³ with the older parasites retreating from the peripheral circulation (Fig. 64).

Other monkeys, *Presbytis cristatus*, *M. nemestrina*, and *M. speciosa* (= arctoides) were more resistant to infection than *M. fascicularis* (Fig. 64); gibbons, *Hylobates lar*, either refused the infection or allowed it to run a very low course. In each of the hosts, the morphology of the parasite remained unchanged and continued to express the tertian cycle.

In the rhesus monkey, *M. mulatta* (Fig. 65), blood-induced infections may be explosive with peak counts greater than 500,000 per mm³, resulting in death of a large proportion of the animals (40 percent of our test animals) unless the infection is treated with schizontocidal drugs well ahead of the crisis. Sporozoite-induced infections in intact *M. mulatta* monkeys had a 33 percent mortality rate. The mortality rate in splenectomized *M. mulatta* monkeys was 100 percent.

TABLE 36.—Oocyst diameters of *Plasmodium coatneyi* in *Anopheles b. balabacensis*, *A. maculatus*, and *A. freeborni*.

Days after infection	A. b. balabacensis			A. maculatus			A. freeborni		
	No.	Range	Mean*	No.	Range	Mean	No.	Range	Mean
5							114	8–19	14
6	114	12–26	19	111	12–26	21	188	12–30	19
7	125	14–40	25	107	14–40	25	104	14–45	26
8	134	19–60	37	111	20–51	31	101	18–51	34
9	119	17–67	44	134	21–65	39†	140	12–66	41†
10	107	14–74	54†	122	20–54	38†	124	19–80	53†
11	103	24–90	61†**	124	18–70	43†	111	18–78	54†
12				131	26–63	44†**	74	21–90	49†‡
Totals	702	12–90		840	12–70		956	8–90	

* Measurements expressed in microns; incubation temperature 25° C.
† Oocyst differentiation.
‡ Oocyst degeneration.
** Sporozoites present in the salivary glands.

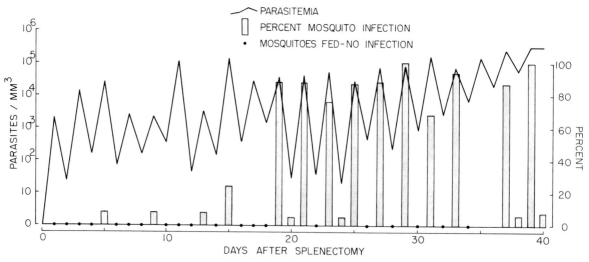

FIGURE 62.—Infectivity of *Plasmodium coatneyi* to *Anopheles freeborni* mosquitoes when fed on a splenectomized *Macaca mulatta* monkey.

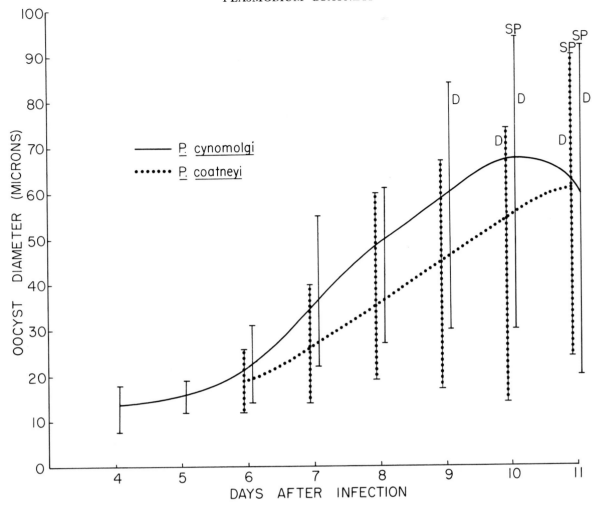

FIGURE 63.—Range in oocyst diameters and the mean oocyst diameter curve of *Plasmodium coatneyi* and *P. cynomolgi* in *Anopheles b. balabacensis* mosquitoes. (D = oocyst differentiation; SP = sporozoites present in the salivary glands).

Infections induced through the bites of *A. b. balabacensis* in intact rhesus monkeys appear to follow the general pattern of blood-induced infections. Three such animals (Fig. 66) exhibited prepatent periods of 10, 11, and 14 days after which the initial parasitemia climbed rapidly to peak counts of 160,000 to 800,000 per mm³ between the 7th and 9th days of patent parasitemia only to decline, and then, exhibit a second rise some three weeks later. After the second rise, the parasitemia continued to decline but evidenced the alternate high and low parasite counts during an observation period of 60 days.

Host Specificity

In nature, *P. coatneyi* appears to be limited to the natural host, *Macaca fascicularis*, of peninsular Malaysia and the Philippines (Eyles *et al*, 1962; 1963). The best experimental host is the rhesus monkey, *Macaca mulatta*, which is highly susceptible to infection either by the inoculation of parasitized blood or by sporozoites. Attempts to infect other simian hosts, the silvered leaf coloboid *P. cristatus*, *M. arctoides*, and *M. nemestrina* have been successful but the infections were all of a low order. Following the discovery of this parasite with its

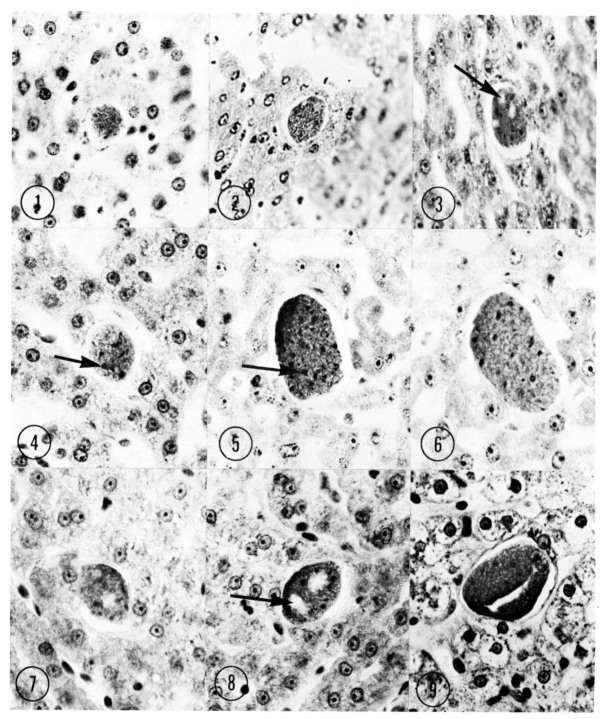

PLATE XLVII.—Exoerythrocytic bodies of *Plasmodium coatneyi* in liver tissue of *Macaca mulatta* monkeys. X 580 (Except Fig. 6).

Fig. 1.   6-day body.
Fig. 2.   7-day body.
Fig. 3.   7-day body showing three prominent vacuoles.
Fig. 4.   8-day body showing abundant large flocculi.
Fig. 5.   9-day body showing abundant, irregular-shaped flocculi.

Fig. 6.   9-day body. X 740.
Fig. 7.   10-day body.
Fig. 8.   10-day body showing two prominent vacuoles.
Fig. 9.   10-day body.

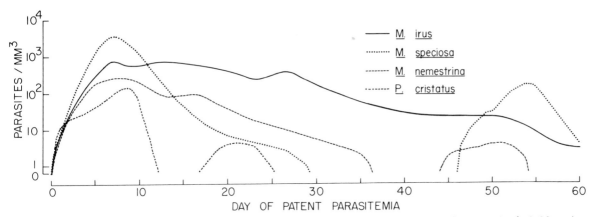

FIGURE 64.—Median parasitemia curves of infections of *Plasmodium coatneyi* in 8 *Macaca irus* (= *fascicularis*), 3 *M. speciosa*, (= *arctoides*), 3 *M. nemestrina* and 3 *Presbytis cristatus* monkeys.

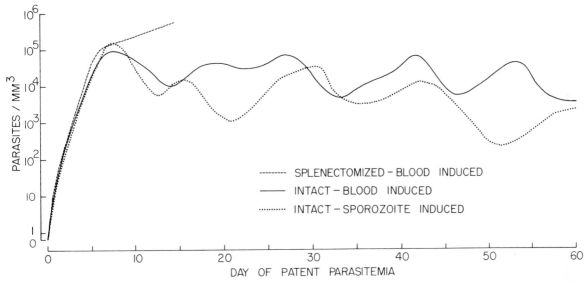

FIGURE 65. Median parasitemia curves of infections of *Plasmodium coatneyi* in 77 intact (66 blood-induced and 11 sporozoite-induced infections) and 6 splenectomized *Macaca mulatta* monkeys.

falciparum-like characteristics, investigators were anxious to learn if the parasite would express the same characteristics if it became established in man. However, to date all attempts in that direction have failed. Garnham (1965) reported the transfer of parasitized blood from a rhesus monkey to a paretic patient and we (1963 and 1967) made three unsuccessful attempts, over a four-year period, to infect nine volunteers with observation periods extending from 90 to 180 days after biting episodes utilizing *A. freeborni* and *A. b.*

balabacensis mosquitoes. It is of interest in this connection that among 6 rhesus monkeys, *M. mulatta*, exposed at the same time as the volunteers, and, to bites of the same mosquitoes, five developed normal patent infections.

Warren and Wharton (1963) were of the opinion, based on finding *P. coatneyi* in *A. hackeri*, that the vector was zoophilic. They were able to obtain infection, through the development of oocysts, in: *A. maculatus*, *A. kochi*, *A. sundaicus*, *A. vagus*, *A. philippinensis*, and *A. letifer*. More recently we have infected

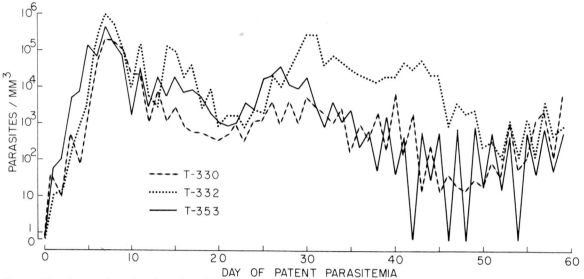

FIGURE 66.—Course of parasitemia in three *Macaca mulatta* monkeys infected with *Plasmodium coatneyi* by sporozoite inoculation.

A. b. balabacensis, A. freeborni, A. stephensi, A. albimanus, A. atroparvus, A. quadrimaculatus, and *A. maculatus.* Among the 13 species of mosquitoes known to be susceptible, only four: *A. b. balabacensis, A. hackeri, A. maculatus,* and *A. freeborni* have carried the infections to the production of sporozoites in the salivary glands. The susceptibility to infection with *P. coatneyi* varies (Table 37); *A. b. balabacensis* was the most susceptible followed by *A. freeborni, A. maculatus, A. stephensi, A. albimanus, A. atroparvus,* and *A. quadrimaculatus.* The feedings with the other species were too limited to permit proper evaluation.

Immunity and Antigenic Relationships

In order to elucidate some aspects of immunity, Eyles (1963), challenged rhesus monkeys harboring chronic *P. coatneyi* infections with superinfections. These animals were in-oculated with parasitized blood of *P. knowlesi, P. inui,* and *P. cynomolgi.* The *P. knowlesi* infections were severe but not fatal indicating some degree of protection; the *P. inui* and *P. cynomolgi* infections were normal indicating no dampening of the infection due to infection with *P. coatneyi.* Voller *et al* (1966) concluded there was considerable cross immunity between *P. knowlesi, P. coatneyi,* and *P. fragile.* However, Voller and Rossan (1969) demonstrated that rhesus monkeys with chronic *P. knowlesi* infections were susceptible to infection with *P. coatneyi.*

Antisera to *P. coatneyi* gave a fluorescent antibody cross-reaction at a very high level to *P. fieldi* (mean reciprocal titer ratio of 100 : 107) but reacted at a much lower level to other primate malaria antigens (Collins *et al,* 1966). In the reverse procedure, *P. coatneyi* antigen cross-reacted highest to *P. inui* (mean reciprocal titer ratio of 100 : 57) and at a much lower level to the *P. cynomolgi* and *P. knowlesi* antigens (mean reciprocal titer ratios of 100 : 27).

TABLE 37.—Comparative infectivity of *Plasmodium coatneyi* to *Anopheles b. balabacensis*, *A. freeborni*, *A. maculatus*, *A. stephensi*, *A. albimanus*, *A. atroparvus*, and *A. quadrimaculatus*.

Mosq. species comparison*	Number tests	Number of mosquitoes		Percent infection		GII** ratios
		Standard	Other	Standard	Other	
Bal						100
Bal : F–1	20	288	389	22.6	47.6	45.7
Bal : Mac	10	93	511	67.7	46.4	15.3
Bal : St–1	8	70	133	35.7	6.0	2.9
Bal : Alb	10	163	144	53.4	1.4	0.4
Bal : Atro	5	60	166	80.0	1.2	0.15
Bal : Q–1	6	62	144	80.6	1.4	0.08

* Bal = *Anopheles b. balabacensis*, F–1 = *A. freeborni*, Mac = *A. maculatus*, St–1 = *A. stephensi*, Alb = *A. albimanus*, Atro = *A. atroparvus*, Q–1 = *A. quadrimaculatus*.

** GII = Gut Infection Index = average number of oocysts per 100 guts; the GII ratio is the relationship of the GII of *A. b. balabacensis* to another species where the GII of *A. b. balabacensis* = 100.

REFERENCES

COLLINS, W. E., CONTACOS, P. G., GUINN, E. G., and HELD, J. R., 1967. Studies on the transmission of simian malaria. III. Infection and transmission of *Plasmodium coatneyi* with *Anopheles freeborni* and *A. balabacensis balabacensis* mosquitoes. J. Parasit. *53* : 1130–1134.

COLLINS, W. E., SKINNER, J. C., and GUINN, E. G., 1966. Antigenic variations in the plasmodia of certain primates as detected by immuno-fluorescence. Am. J. Trop. Med. & Hyg. *15* : 483–485.

EYLES, D. E., FONG, Y. L., WARREN, McW., GUINN, E., SANDOSHAM, A. A., and WHARTON, R. H., 1962. *Plasmodium coatneyi*, a new species of primate malaria from Malaya. Am. J. Trop. Med. & Hyg. *11* : 597–604.

EYLES, D. E., 1963. The species of simian malaria: taxonomy, morphology, life cycle, and geographical distribution of the monkey species. J. Parasit. *49* : 866–887.

EYLES, D. E., DUNN, F., WARREN, McW., and GUINN, E., 1963. *Plasmodium coatneyi* from the Philippines. J. Parasit. *49* : 1038.

GARNHAM, P. C. C., 1965. The pathology of *Plasmodium coatneyi* malaria. Omagiu Lui. Prof. Dr. M. Ciuca, Edit. Acad. Rep. Pop. Romane. pp. 199–203.

HELD, J. R., CONTACOS, P. G., JUMPER, J. R., and SMITH, C. S., 1967. Direct hepatic inoculation of sporozoites for the study of the exo-erythrocytic stages of simian malarias. J. Parasit. *53* : 656–657.

HELD, J. R. and CONTACOS, P. G., 1967. Studies of the exoerythrocytic stages of simian malaria. II. *Plasmodium coatneyi*. J. Parasit. *53* : 910–918.

RUDZINSKA, M. A. and TRAGER, W., 1968. The fine structure of trophozoites and gametocytes in *Plasmodium coatneyi*. J. Protozool. *15* : 73–88.

VOLLER, A., GARNHAM, P. C. C., and TARGETT, G. A. T., 1966. Cross immunity in monkey malaria. J. Trop. Med. & Hyg. *69* : 121–123.

VOLLER, A. and ROSSAN, R. N., 1969. Immunological studies on simian malaria parasites. IV. Heterologous superinfection of monkeys with chronic *Plasmodium knowlesi* infections. Trans. Roy. Soc. Trop. Med. & Hyg. *63* : 837–845.

WARREN, McW. and WHARTON, R. H., 1963. The vectors of simian malaria: identity, biology, and geographical distribution. J. Parasit. *49* : 892–904.

WARREN, McW., SKINNER, J. C., and GUINN, E., 1966. Biology of the simian malarias of Southeast Asia. I. Host cell preferences of young trophozoites of four species of Plasmodium. J. Parasit. *52* : 14–16.

24

Plasmodium fragile Dissanaike, Nelson, and Garnham, 1965

DURING the months of May and June, 1919, Donovan (1920) examined the blood of 76 macaques, *Macaca sinicus* (= *radiata*) and 10 langurs (*Presbytis priamus*) taken in the valleys of the Nilgiri hills in southern India, but failed to find examples of the genus *Plasmodium*. However, in an addendum to the paper, he mentioned that a slide of the blood of a *M. sinicus* monkey had been sent to him and on it he had found a plasmodium. According to Ramakrishnan and Mohan (1961), Sinton and Mulligan (1933) had given a tentative identification of *P. inui* var. *cynomolgi* to this parasite. The monkey which had supplied the blood for the smear had been taken at an altitude of 4,000 feet. This was the first instance of malaria not only from that area but also from that species of monkey, and Donovan suggested further study of the blood of monkeys from that area.

In 1960, stimulated by the Eyles *et al* (1960) account of *P. cynomolgi* in man, Ramakrishnan and Mohan (loc. cit.) examined the blood of 13 brown monkeys (*M. radiata*) caught in the area of Kallar, Nilgiri hills. Nine were found infected with a parasite tentatively identified as *P. inui* and, following splenectomy, a parasite resembling *P. cynomolgi* appeared also.

Samples of blood, from two different naturally infected animals, were sent from the Nilgiris to the Malaria Institute of India at Delhi where Prakash and Chakrabarti (1962) studied infections in a total of 241 *M. mulatta* monkeys; 124 were infected with the cynomolgi parasite and 117 with the inui-like parasite.

Following these studies, the latter parasite was sent to Dr. Eyles in Kuala Lumpur, Malaysia, through the kindness of Dr. Ramakrishnan.

Eyles (1963) determined that the parasite actually had an asexual cycle of 48 hours and, therefore, a tertian rather than quartan periodicity; and, that it was a new species. At the Washington, D. C. Symposium on Recent Advances in Simian Malaria, in 1963, as part of the XVI International Congress of Zoology, he outlined the salient features of the parasite: its penchant for deep circulation schizogony, small rings resembling *P. coatneyi*, *P. knowlesi*, and *P. falciparum*, trophozoites with heavy pigment and no enlargement of the host cell. He did not name the parasite, preferring to discuss it as the "New Nilgiri Parasite." He did mention, however, that a full description with a color plate was in preparation. His sudden untimely death left the text and plate unfinished.

About this same period in time, Dissanaike had begun the study of parasites in the blood of monkeys in Ceylon, and among the malarias which came to light was the "New Nilgiri Parasite" (Dissanaike *et al*, 1965). Because of Dr. Eyles' connection with the parasite, the Dissanaike group considered naming it for him but by the time they made their decision, we had already reserved his name for a new malaria parasite of gibbons (see chapter 7). When advised of this, Dissanaike *et al* (1965) proposed the name *Plasmodium fragile* to emphasize its effect on the host cell.

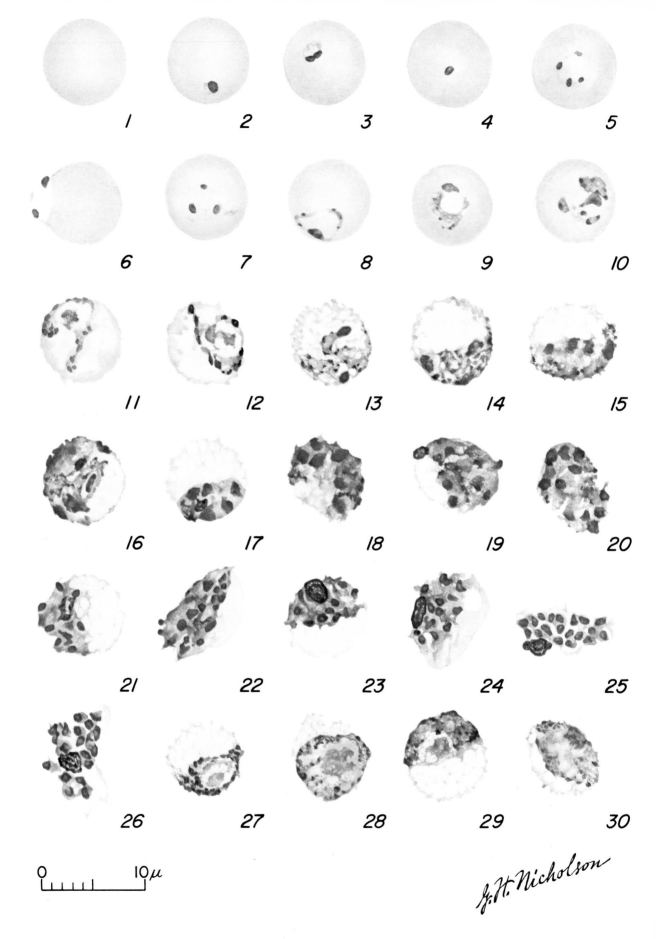

1 2 3 4 5 6 7 8 9 10 11 12 13 14 15 16 17 18 19 20 21 22 23 24 25 26 27 28 29 30

0 ⊢⊢⊢⊢⊢⊢⊢ 10μ

G. H. Nicholson

PLASMODIUM FRAGILE

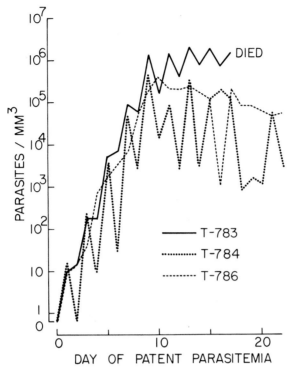

FIGURE 69.—Parasitemias of *Plasmodium fragile* in three *Macaca mulatta* monkeys infected via the bites of *Anopheles b. balabacensis* mosquitoes.

during an observation period of 6 months. The sporozoites were proven infective when the infection in the control monkey became patent after 17 days.

The normal invertebrate host of *P. fragile* is not known. It is not unlikely that *Anopheles elegans* is the culprit in the Nilgiris because Choudhury *et al* (1963) incriminated it in the transmission of *P. cynomolgi* and *P. inui*, and probably the Nilgiri Parasite (= *P. fragile*). It will be recalled that the Nilgiri Parasite was first taken to be *P. inui*. However, until the natural vector is determined for the Nilgiris and for Ceylon, information on its vector potential and sporogonic cycle will have to be based on information derived from experimental vectors. We have infected *A. freeborni*, *A. b. balabacensis*, *A. maculatus*, and *A. quadrimaculatus* mosquitoes. Sporozoites were demonstrated in the salivary glands of only the first two. A comparison of the intensity of the infections (Table 39) shows that the most susceptible mosquito was *A. freeborni* followed by *A. b. balabacensis*, *A. maculatus*, and, finally, *A. quadrimaculatus*.

Immunity and Antigenic Relationships

There is not much one can say about antigenic relationships and immunity because of the paucity of information. About all that can be said at present is that *P. fragile* can exist as a mixed infection with *P. cynomolgi* in nature. Voller *et al* (1966) infected monkeys having a previous history of *P. cynomolgi*, *P. knowlesi*, and *P. coatneyi* infections with *P. fragile*. In the former, a normal infection developed, but in the monkey previously infected with *P. knowlesi*, there was a low parasitemia; in the monkey infected with *P. coatneyi*, there was complete immunity.

Serum samples from animals infected with *P. fragile* gave fluorescent antibody cross-reactions to *P. fieldi* at relatively high levels (mean reciprocal titer ratio of 100 : 93) and lower reactions to *P. gonderi* and *P. cynomolgi*. When the procedure was reversed, *P. fragile* antigen failed to cross-react at high levels with any of the 9 other simian antigens (Collins *et al*, 1966).

TABLE 39.—Comparative infectivity of *Plasmodium fragile* in *Anopheles freeborni*, *A. b. balabacensis*, *A. maculatus*, and *A. quadrimaculatus*.

Mosq. species comparison*	Number tests	Number of mosquitoes		Percent infection		GII** ratios
		Standard	Other	Standard	Other	
F–1						100
F–1 : Bal	8	143	152	23.1	16.4	35.8
F–1 : Mac	6	79	123	53.2	4.1	2.2
F–1 : Q–1	5	54	36	74.1	2.8	0.06

* F–1 = *Anopheles freeborni*, Bal = *A. b. balabacensis*, Mac = *A. maculatus*, Q–1 = *A. quadrimaculatus*.

** GII = Gut Infection Index = average number of oocysts per 100 guts; the GII ratio is the relationship of the GII of *A. freeborni* to another species where the GII of *A. freeborni* = 100.

REFERENCES

CHOUDHURY, D. S., WATTAL, B. L. and RAMAKRISHNAN, S. P., 1963. Incrimination of *Anopheles elegans* James (1903) as a natural vector of simian malaria in the Nilgiris, Madras State, India. Ind. J. Malariol. *17* : 243–247.

COLLINS, W. E., SKINNER, J. C., and GUINN, E. G., 1966. Antigenic variations in the plasmodia of certain primates as detected by immuno-fluorescence. Am. J. Trop. Med. & Hyg. *15* : 483–485.

DISSANAIKE, A. S., NELSON, P. and GARNHAM, P. C. C., 1965. Two new malaria parasites, *Plasmodium cynomolgi ceylonensis* subsp. nov. and *Plasmodium fragile* sp. nov., from monkeys in Ceylon. Ceylon J. Med. Sci. *14* : 1–9.

DONOVAN, C., 1920. Malaria of monkeys. Ind. J. Med. Res. *7* : 717–721.

EYLES, D. E., COATNEY, G. R., and GETZ, M. E., 1960. Vivax-type malaria parasite of macaques transmissible to man. Science *131* : 1812–1813.

EYLES, D. E., 1963. The species of simian malaria: taxonomy, morphology, life cycle, and geographical dis-

tribution of the monkey species. J. Parasit. *49* : 866–887.

PRAKASH, S., and CHAKRABARTI, S. C., 1962. The isolation and description of *Plasmodium cynomolgi* (Mayer, 1907) and *Plasmodium inui* (Halberstadter and Prowazek, 1907) from naturally occurring mixed infections in *Macaca radiata radiata* monkeys of the Nilgiris, Madras State, India. Ind. J. Malariol. *16* : 303–311.

RAMAKRISHNAN, S. P. and MOHAN, B. N., 1961. Simian malaria in the Nilgiris, Madras State, India. Bull. Nat. Soc. Ind. Mal. Mosq. Dis. *9* : 139.

SINTON, J. A. and MULLIGAN, H. W., 1933. A critical review of the literature relating to the identification of the malarial parasites recorded from monkeys of the families Cercopithecidae and Colobidae. Rec. Malar. Surv. Ind. *III* : 381–443.

VOLLER, A., GARNHAM, P. C. C., and TARGETT, G. A. T., 1966. Cross immunity in monkey malaria. J. Trop. Med. Hyg. *69* : 121–123.

25

Plasmodium reichenowi Sluiter, Swellengrebel, and Ihle, 1922

REICHENOW (1917, 1917a), working in the Cameroons, saw parasites of malaria in anthropoid apes. In 1920 he published a more detailed study of the blood parasites of the chimpanzee and the gorilla with figures of falciparum-like parasites. His contention was that since these animals live in the vicinity of human habitations and are therefore exposed to bites by the same vectors, their parasites are probably one and the same with those of man. Blacklock and Adler (1922) and Adler (1923) saw parasites resembling *P. falciparum* of man in chimpanzees from Sierra Leone. These investigators were aware that Mesnil and Roubaud (1920) had had partial success in their attempt to infect the chimpanzee with *P. falciparum* via blood inoculation but failed via sporozoites. Inasmuch as Blacklock and Adler doubted Reichenow's conclusion that the infection in the chimpanzee was actually *P. falciparum*, they attempted (1922) to infect man by direct inoculation with the falciparum-like parasite from a heavily infected chimpanzee. The attempt failed. In 1922, according to Adler (1923) they repeated the same experiment with *P. falciparum* which they injected into a three-month-old chimpanzee. The animal did not become infected. They concluded, on the basis of their studies, that the two parasites were different and proposed the name *Plasmodium reichenowi* for the parasite in the chimpanzee. However, Sluiter, Swellengrebel and Ihle had applied the name *Laverania reichenowi* to the chimpanzee parasite in 1922, which Blacklock acknowledged in a short note in 1926, and therefore the credit for the name goes to them. Later investigators have dealt with these parasites as distinct species.

Schwetz (1933, 1933a, 1934) found *P. reichenowi* in the blood of chimpanzees from the Stanleyville area and the upper Congo, and Rodhain (1938) demonstrated the parasite from the same host near Leopoldville. Ducke in 1921, according to Brumpt (1939), found "crescents in the blood of animals taken in Uganda," and Bray (1956) reported the parasite from chimpanzees in Liberia. In 1964, van den Berghe *et al* examined the blood of some fifty chimpanzees and thirty gorillas in the eastern Congo at elevations up to 2,000 meters and failed to find *P. reichenowi* or any other parasite of malaria. More recently (1968), through the kindness of Dr. Betty June Meyers, of the Southwest Foundation for Research and Education, we were able to isolate the parasite from a chimpanzee taken in the eastern part of the Democratic Republic of the Congo near Lake Edward. From these reports it would appear that the parasite occurs in the area bounded by 10°W—30°E and 10°N—5°S.

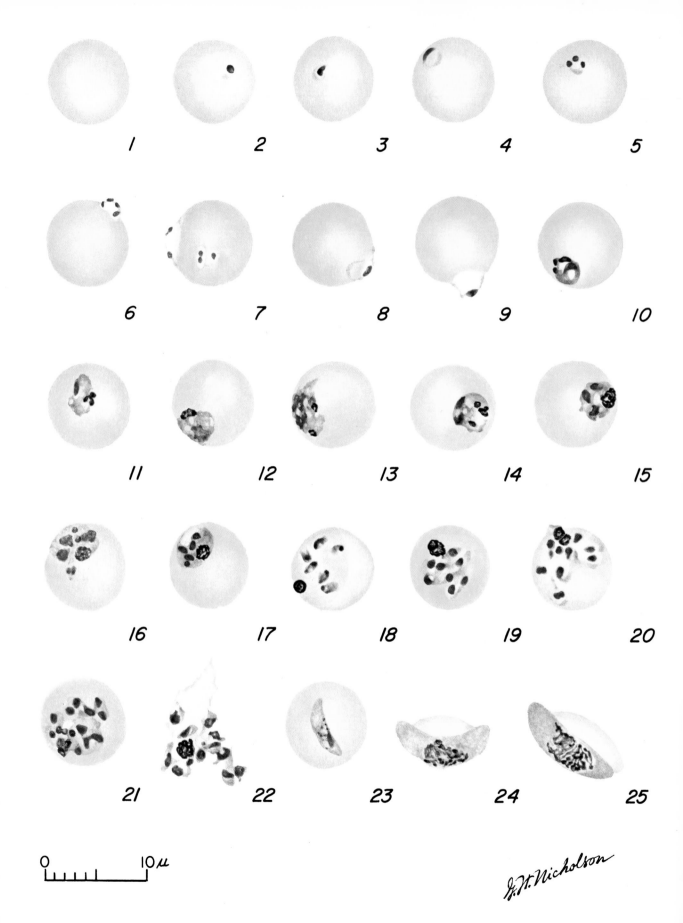

PLASMODIUM REICHENOWI

Cycle in the Blood

PLATE L

All investigators agree that *Plasmodium reichenowi*, as seen in the peripheral blood, closely resembles *P. falciparum* in the peripheral blood of man. Usually, the parasitemia is marked by the presence of rings and crescents. Other stages appear under stressful conditions or as a result of splenectomy.

The youngest parasites are small rings with a prominent nucleus (Figs. 2–4) or they may contain up to four small chromatin dots (Figs. 5, 6); multiple invasion is not uncommon (Fig. 7).

A prominent feature is the presence of marginal forms which appear as clear blebs with single or double nuclei (Figs. 6, 7, 9). In Bray's experience, accolé forms accounted for 13 percent of the rings. Schwetz (1934) mentioned the abundance of tenue-type forms but these were not a prominent feature of our material. At about 24 hours, the rings generally retreat into the deeper circulation where development continues. Under conditions where growth continues in the peripheral blood, i.e., especially following splenectomy, the pigment appears in discrete clumps, the cytoplasm increases in amount and takes a pronounced blue stain; the nucleus stains bluish-purple to wine color (Figs. 11, 12). With the advent of schizogony, which begins at about 42 hours and moves rapidly, the pigment comes together as a yellowish-black mass, vacuoles appear in the cytoplasm, and the host cell tends to lose color (Figs. 18, 20), but at no time is it fully occupied by the parasite. The mature schizonts contain 10 to 12 merozoites (Fig. 22). The asexual cycle takes approximately 48 hours. Most authors mention the prominence of Mauer's clefts and beading along the periphery of the host cell but they are not shown on our plate because we did not employ special stains. The plate depicts what is seen ordinarily with regular Giemsa stain.

Very young gametocytes rarely appear in the peripheral blood of the intact animal; but, with splenectomy, they make their appearance. According to Bray (1957) and others, these latter forms have difficulty in maturing properly. The development of the gametocytes is well described by Garnham *et al* (1956) and by Bray (1957). The young oval forms, with discrete granules or short rods of pigment, appear first. The oval body is rigid on one side and the other side bends around it in an arc. Cytoplasm collects along the border opposite the nucleus and the pigment (Fig. 23). As the gametocyte grows, it swells and assumes the usual sausage or crescent-shape first described and figured by Reichenow (1920).

The mature macrogametocyte is crescent-shaped and somewhat slender. The cytoplasm stains a pale blue and encloses a compact pale red-staining nucleus with greyish-black pigment granules collected around it (Fig. 24). The microgametocyte is more robust than the distaff parasite. The cytoplasm stains bluish-red and surrounds the centrally located diffuse pale red-staining nucleus and the dispersed brownish pigment (Fig. 25).

Although there is little difference between the parasites of *P. reichenowi* and *P. falciparum*, one difference which appears constant is that the mature gametocytes of reichenowi malaria are more slender and shorter than falciparum parasites. This is easily seen if one compares these forms in Plate XLII with the same forms in Plate L.

The asexual cycle in the blood occupies 48 hours.

Sporogonic Cycle

There are no data on the sporogonic cycle of *Plasmodium reichenowi*.

PLATE L.—*Plasmodium reichenowi.*

Fig. 1.   Normal red cell.
Figs. 2–9.   Young trophozoites.
Figs. 10–13.   Growing and mature trophozoites.
Figs. 14–17.   Developing schizonts.

Figs. 18–22.   Mature schizonts.
Figs. 23–24.   Young adult and mature macrogametocytes.
Fig. 25.   Mature microgametocytes.

Cycle in the Tissue

There are no data on this phase of the life-cycle of reichenowi malaria. This is due to the fact that no suitable vector has been found and until that hurdle has been cleared, no progress can be made toward elucidating the tissue phase of the parasite.

Course of Infection

Nothing is known about the course of the early natural infection. All our data are based on observations on naturally infected and blood inoculated captive animals; this information is meager indeed.

Except for the cursory examination of the blood stages by Reichenow (1917, 1917a), Blacklock and Adler (1922), Peel and Rodhain (1946) and others, plus the more detailed studies of these stages by Bray (1956) and by Garnham *et al* (1956) in splenectomized animals, very little is known about the overall infection. The latter authors write of a single animal harboring a natural infection of *P. schwetzi* and *P. reichenowi* which was treated successfully. Two years later the animal was splenectomized only to have *P. reichenowi* parasites appear in the circulating blood. The total length of the observed infection was in the neighborhood of three years; the total length of the infection was undoubtedly a great deal longer.

There is no evidence that the parasite will grow in the rhesus monkey. Rodhain (1938) gave the parasite to *M. mulatta* without success and that has been our experience too. In other simians, the transfer has failed also. For example, Rodhain (1939) transferred parasitized *P. reichenowi* blood to *Cercopithecus schmidti* without success and Bray (1963) failed to gain infection after two attempts using *Cercocebus atys*.

The situation in man generally follows the same line. Blacklock and Adler (1922) gave *P. reichenowi* to two Europeans using both the intravenous and subcutaneous routes without obtaining infection. Later, Rodhain (1939, 1939a) gave *P. reichenowi* blood to two patients and neither one became infected which led

Rodhain to say that *P. falciparum* and *P. reichenowi* were not only distinct but also non-transferrable outside the original host species.

Host Specificity

The earliest attempt to find a vector for *P. reichenowi* was that of Blacklock and Adler (1922) who found no evidence of infection after dissecting 40 *Anopheles costalis* (= *gambiae*) mosquitoes which had fed on an infected chimpanzee on two different nights. Rodhain (1941) dissected 76 *A. maculipennis atroparvus*, out of a lot of 165 allowed to feed on a chimpanzee with low gametocyte levels, and found no evidence of infection. The results led Rodhain to suggest that a "special vector" was required. In 1957, Bray tried to infect *A. gambiae* with *P. reichenowi* and found only 4 out of 112 dissected showed oocysts and in 3 of them the oocysts were degenerate. No sporozoites were encountered. He concluded that *A. gambiae* "will not act as a host for *P. reichenowi* . . ." There appears to have been no further attempts until we made our trials in 1968. At that time we had an infected chimpanzee whose reichenowi infection showed many apparently mature gametocytes and consequently three species of mosquitoes were allowed to feed: *A. b. balabacensis*, *A. freeborni*, and *A. stephensi*. When dissected some 6 to 8 days later none showed any evidence of infection. In a way, this was somewhat surprising because *P. schwetzi*, which was being studied at about the same time, had infected two of these species readily. The parasite of malaria is a capricious animal and failure in this instance does not necessarily signify rejection by the mosquitoes but rather it may mean that our feedings were carried out at the wrong time in the course of infections, or, that the physiological conditions of the vertebrate host were other than ideal for the parasite. We believe that further trials, if they present themselves, will lead to success, for it is hard to imagine that under the right conditions this or any other primate malaria would fail to develop in the virtually universal vector, *A. b. balabacensis* or in one of the other experimental vectors available to us.

Immunity and Antigenic Relationships

There is not much to be said on this subject because of the paucity of information. We know that one, two, or all three of the chimpanzee malarias may occur in a single animal at the same time (Schwetz, 1933) or in tandem; but, there is little information on the phenomenon of dominance. In the human malarias, the dominance of *P. falciparum* over *P. vivax* is well recognized and it would be expected that the situation would prevail with *P. reichenowi* and *P. schwetzi* in the chimpanzee. This point was tested recently when we (Coatney, 1968 and Contacos *et al*, 1970) transferred each of these parasites to a splenectomized and to an intact chimpanzee by the inoculation of parasitized blood. Each of the animals developed good infections but what was surprising was that 99 percent of the parasites were *P. schwetzi*. Further study is needed before we can say more about the phenomenon of dominance among the malarias of chimpanzees.

REFERENCES

ADLER, S., 1923. Malaria in chimpanzees in Sierra Leone. Ann. Trop. Med. Parasit. *17* : 13–19.

BLACKLOCK, B., 1926. *Plasmodium reichenowi* Blacklock and Adler, 1924. Ann. Trop. Med. Parasit. *20* : 145.

BLACKLOCK, B., and ADLER, S., 1922. A parasite resembling *Plasmodium falciparum* in a chimpanzee. Ann. Trop. Med. & Parasit. *16* : 99–106.

BRAY, R. S., 1956. Studies on malaria in chimpanzees. I. The erythrocytic forms of *Plasmodium reichenowi*. J. Parasit. *42* : 588–592.

BRAY, R. S., 1957. Studies on malaria in chimpanzees. III. Gametogony of *Plasmodium reichenowi*. Ann. Soc. Belge Med. Trop. *37* : 169–174.

BRAY, R. S., 1963. Malaria infections in primates and their importance to man. Ergeb. Microb. Immunit. Experim. Therap. *36* : 168–213.

BRUMPT, E., 1939. Les parasites du paludisme des chimpanzeés. C. R. Soc. Biol. *130* : 837–840.

COATNEY, G. R., 1968. Simian malarias in man: facts, implications, and predictions. Am. J. Trop. Med. & Hyg. *17* : 147–155.

CONTACOS, P. G., COATNEY, G. R., ORIHEL, T. C., COLLINS, W. E., CHIN, W., and JETER, M. H., 1970. Transmission of *Plasmodium schwetzi* from the chimpanzee to man by mosquito bite. Am. J. Trop. Med. & Hyg. *19* : 190–196.

GARNHAM, P. C. C., LAINSON, R., and GUNDERS, A. E., 1956. Some observations on malaria parasites in a chimpanzee, with particular reference to the persistence of *Plasmodium reichenowi* and *Plasmodium vivax*. Ann. Soc. Belge Med. Trop. *36* : 811–821.

MESNIL, F., and ROUBAUD, E., 1920. Essais d'inoculation du paludisme au chimpanzé. Ann. Inst. Pasteur, Paris. *34* : 466–480.

PEEL, E., and RODHAIN, J., 1946. Contribution a l'étude des Plasmodiums des anthropoides africains. La schizogonie du *Plasmodium reichenowi* dans le sang périphérique. Ann. Soc. Belge Med. Trop. *26* : 341–348.

REICHENOW, E., 1917. Sobre el problema de la immunidad de los negros contra el paludismo. Bol. Inst. Nac. Hig. Alfonso XIII *13* : 29–42.

REICHENOW, E., 1917a. Parásitos de la sangre y del intestino de los monos antropomorfos africanos. Bol. R. Soc. Espan. Hist. Nat. *17* : 312–332.

REICHENOW, E., 1920. Ueber das vorkommen der malariaparasiten des menschen bei den afrikanischen menschenaffen. Centralbl. f. Bakt. I. Abt. Orig. *85* : 207–216.

RODHAIN, J., 1938. Les plasmodium des anthropoides de l'Afrique centrale et leur relation avec les plasmodium humains. Acta. Convent. Tertii de Trop. Atque Malar. Morbis. *2* : 539–544.

RODHAIN, J., 1939. La réceptivité du chimpanzé *Pan satyrus* au *Plasmodium vivax* humain. C. R. Soc. Biol. *132* : 69–70.

RODHAIN, J., 1939a. Les plasmodiums des anthropoides de l'Afrique centrale et leurs relations avec les plasmodiums humains. Ann. Soc. Belge Med. Trop. *19* : 563–572.

RODHAIN, J., 1941. Les plasmodiums des anthropoides de l'Afrique centrale et leurs relations avec les plasmodiums humains. Bull. Acad. Roy. Med. Belge *6* : 21–60.

SCHWETZ, J., 1933. Sur une infection malarienne triple d'un chimpanzé. Centralb. f. Bakt. I. Abt. Orig. *130* : 105–110.

SCHWETZ, J., 1933a. Sur les parasites malariens (*Plasmodium*) des singes superiéurs (Anthropoides) africains. C. R. Soc. Biol. *112* : 710–711.

SCHWETZ, J., 1934. Contribution á l'étude des parasites malariens des singes supérieurs africains. Riv. Malariol. *13* : 143–147.

SLUITER, C., SWELLENGREBEL, N., and IHLE, J., 1922. De Dierlijke Parasieten van den mensch en van onze huisdieren. Scheltema and Holkema's Boekhandel, Amsterdam, p. 121.

VAN DEN BERGHE, L., CHARDOME, M., and PEEL, E., 1964. The filarial parasites of the eastern gorilla in the Congo. J. Helminth. *38* : 349–368.

SECTION 6
Other Type Parasites

26

Plasmodium knowlesi Sinton and Mulligan, 1932

IT is not unlikely that Franchini (1927) was the first person to see *Plasmodium knowlesi* and to recognize that the parasite he saw in the blood of *Silenus cynomolgus* (= *Macaca fascicularis*) was different from *P. inui* and *P. cynomolgi*. Later (1931) it was seen by Dr. H. G. M. Campbell who was working in kala-azar and had no particular interest, at the time, in the plasmodium he encountered in *M. fascicularis*. Dr. Napier, on the other hand, with whom Dr. Campbell was working, drew blood and inoculated it into 3 other monkeys, one of which was a rhesus; it developed a fulminating infection. The original monkey was given to Dr. Das Gupta who maintained the strain for some time by subpassage (see Knowles, 1935). Napier and Campbell (1932) investigated the tendency for the parasite to produce hemoglobinuria in *Cercopithecus pygerythrus* (actually, *M. fascicularis*) and *M. rhesus* (= *M. mulatta*). In the same year (1932) Knowles and Das Gupta described the blood forms of the parasite and showed that it could be transmitted to man. From this vantage point, one wonders why neither group elected to name the parasite. It must be remembered, however, that not all investigators are taxonomic addicts and, too, maybe they recognized that the literature on these parasites was already in a state of disorganized chaos and elected to leave the naming to "the brave." Sinton and Mulligan (1932), after studying the Knowles and Das Gupta material and their own isolate from a *M. fascicularis*, obtained in Singapore, noted the distinctive stippling in the red cells, the presence of an accessory dot, and the 24-hour schizogonic cycle which convinced them that the parasite represented a new species. They

gave it the name *Plasmodium knowlesi* in honor of Dr. R. Knowles. In 1935, Mulligan wrote a more detailed description of the parasite accompanied by a well executed plate which gave increased stature to the parasite's distinctive nature.

Malariologists have puzzled over a paper by Ionesco-Mihaiesti *et al* (1934) in which they claimed to have found *P. inui* in the blood of a baboon. The parasite was said not only to infect rhesus but, also, that it would infect man. Baboons are not infected naturally with malaria and until recently, *P. inui* failed to grow in man. The puzzle was cleared up in 1964 when Professor Garnham visited Roumania and, through the kindness of Dr. G. Lupascu, who had kept the original slides, was able to examine the original material; the parasite in question was actually *P. knowlesi*. The monkey-to-man passage was thus cleared up because *P. knowlesi* will infect man as first shown by Knowles and Das Gupta (loc. cit.). The baboon had been given inoculations of emulsified spleen and other organs from a *M. fascicularis*, the natural host of *P. knowlesi*, which would account for its infection. The infection in the baboon was recognized as mild which might be expected of an abnormal host except, as was shown in this laboratory, *P. knowlesi* will kill baboons when infection is induced through the inoculation of parasitized blood.

The true home of *P. knowlesi* is peninsular Malaysia where monkeys, especially *M. fascicularis*, are commonly infected. Their infections may include species other than *P. knowlesi* and their separation may require the employment of several techniques and more than a dash of patience. Its range extends east to the Philippines (Lambrecht *et al*, 1961) and north to Taiwan (Yokagawa *et al*, 1941). If careful surveys were made, it probably would be found in Java, southern Thailand, and possibly in similar climatic areas in Cambodia and South Vietnam.

From time to time, variants and/or strains, or subspecies, of *P. knowlesi* have been isolated and described. Sinton and Mulligan (1933) isolated 5 different strains, but found no significant points of difference between them and their original strain. In 1953, Edeson and Davey isolated a strain from a *M. fascicularis* trapped in Negri Sembilan, Malaya; which, following studies there, in India, and in England, turned up no features that would distinguish it. The strain isolated directly from *Anopheles hackeri* (Wharton and Eyles, 1961) is now known as the 'hackeri' strain and it, too, behaves like the earlier isolates.

Among the variants, the first to be described was by Brug (1934) who described variety *sintoni* from a *M. fascicularis* (actual source is unknown but credited by some authors to Java) which he considered different from the typical *P. knowlesi*. The distinguishing characteristics were absence of cellular distortion, rod-shaped pigment, and red-staining rims around the schizonts which sometimes extended as septa between the merozoites. No other like material has come to hand and so, for the present, judgment is withheld as to whether *sintoni* is a valid form.

Yokagawa (1941) gave the variety name *arimai* to the parasite seen by Arima (1933) in blood from a *M. cyclopis*, the only species of monkey found on Taiwan. In the same paper, Yokagawa offered the name *Plasmodium taiwanensis* for a new species which he said had an asexual cycle of 11 to 24 days. As one reviews the literature, difficult at best, but cleared up somewhat by Hsieh (1960), it would appear that var. *arimai* was described again by Yokagawa *et al* (1941, 1942) and Yokagawa (1942, 1942a). In 1951 according to Hsieh (loc. cit.), Yokagawa mentioned that *P. knowlesi* var. *arimai* was close to *P. knowlesi* but that it would not infect man. Because the data on the length of its asexual cycle is in doubt, its low pathogenicity to monkeys, and its failure to grow in man, the parasite is most

likely *P. inui*. The species *taiwanensis* is surely a *Hepatocystis* to which, according to Hsieh (loc. cit.), Garnham agrees. Another species variety *Plasmodium cynomolgi cyclopis* Inoki *et al*, 1942 with *knowlesi* affinities has also been described from Taiwan; it is discussed in Chapter 6. Because so little is known about the malarias on Taiwan, including a complete blank on the vectors, it is hoped that investigators will find time to pursue the problem there.

This leaves us with *P. knowlesi edesoni* Garnham, 1963. The parasite exhibits a quotidian cycle with near absence of schizogony in the peripheral blood, reminiscent of *P. coatneyi* and *P. falciparum* up to the appearance of gametocytes which are spherical as against crescentic in *P. falciparum*. It is infectious to rhesus monkeys, many of which recover unless splenectomized.

The rings appear in the circulation about midnight and many of them carry an accessory chromatin dot; multiple infections may appear. As growth proceeds, the parasites become drawn out, stretching across the host cell with the nucleus on one side of the band. In late evening, the more compact parasites begin to leave the peripheral circulation only to disappear completely about 3 hours before sporulation pours young forms into the cirulation again. The mature schizonts, with condensed pigment, carry in the neighborhood of 12 merozoites.

The mature macrogametocytes occupy the entire red cell with a nucleus larger than ordinary; dark pigment is scattered in the cytoplasm. The adult microgametocytes take up most of the host cell and support a large red-staining nucleus which may be surrounded by a thick rim of pigment.

It is unfortunate that this strain is no longer available to allow for comparison of the sporogonic and other cycles with classical *P. knowlesi* and with *P. coatneyi*. Because the original infection in *M. fascicularis* came from an area near Kuantan, Pahang, Malaysia, it is hoped that it can be re-isolated. Until overall comparisons can be made, the subspecies is considered valid.

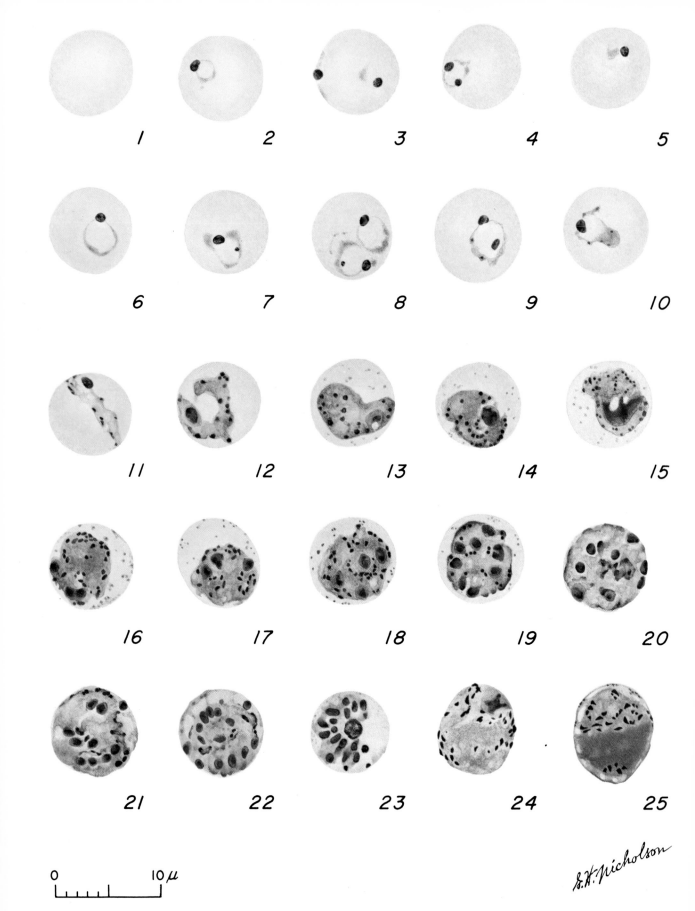

1 *2* *3* *4* *5*

6 *7* *8* *9* *10*

11 *12* *13* *14* *15*

16 *17* *18* *19* *20*

21 *22* *23* *24* *25*

0 10 μ

S.A.Nicholson

PLASMODIUM KNOWLESI

Cycle in the Blood
PLATE LI

The young ring forms in the rhesus monkey and in man may appear in large numbers in the circulating blood. They resemble *P. falciparum* rings but their nucleus is spherical and prominent, many times lying inside the ring. Appliqué forms appear (Fig. 3) along with regular rings harboring one or more accessory chromatin dots (Figs. 4, 7–9). Sinton and Mulligan (1933) regarded the latter as diagnostic of *P. knowlesi* but we know now that these structures occur in other simian forms, too. When full grown, the non-amoeboid rings may occupy half or more of the host erythrocyte. At this stage of growth, band forms appear, reminiscent of *P. malariae* (Fig. 11). With the loss of its vacuole, the parasite shrinks, becomes compact, and pigment appears in the form of dark grains; the nucleus increases in size, and takes a deep red stain. The cytoplasm stains a deep blue. The host erythrocyte shows stippling which some authors have called 'Sinton and Mulligan's' stippling, since it is not of the Schüffner type (Figs. 13–18). With the advent of schizogony, the nucleus divides and the process continues until as many as 16 merozoites, average 10, are produced. The process of schizogony results in some contraction of the parasite (Fig. 19) but with further development, it eventually fills the host cell (Fig. 20). At first, the pigment is scattered but now collects into one or more yellowish-black masses, and eventually into a single mass in the mature schizont (Fig. 23).

The early sexual forms may be recognized as small solid bodies which appear to grow more slowly than the asexual forms consuming probably 48 hours to complete their development. This parasite like some other species, notably *P. eylesi* and *P. jefferyi*, displays a striking color difference in the sexual forms (Figs. 24, 25). The mature macrogametocyte is generally spherical and fills the host cell which may be enlarged to a diameter of 8.5 μ. The cytoplasm stains a distinctive blue and the nucleus, placed eccentrically, takes a deep pink stain enclosing a heavier stained irregular area. The black pigment granules are prominent and scattered irregularly in the cytoplasm (Fig. 24). The microgametocyte is sometimes smaller than the distaff parasite but this is not always true. The cytoplasm stains a medium pink with the nucleus a darker shade. The nucleus makes up about one-half the body of the parasite and which is without pigment granules. The latter are jet black and scattered in the cytoplasm (Fig. 25).

The asexual cycle in the blood occupies 24 hours, the only example of a quotidian cycle among the primate malarias.

Sporogonic Cycle
PLATE LII

The development of *Plasmodium knowlesi* to the point of sporozoite-positive salivary glands has been reported in *Anopheles annularis* (Sinton and Mulligan, 1933; Singh *et al*, 1949), in *A. aztecus* (Garnham *et al*, 1957), in *A. stephensi* (Singh *et al*, 1949; Hawking and Mellanby, 1953; Hawking *et al*, 1957; and Garnham *et al*, 1957), in *A. atroparvus* (Weyer, 1937; Hawking *et al*, 1957), and in *A. b. balabacensis* and *A. freeborni* (Collins *et al*, 1967). In *A. stephensi* and *A. atroparvus*, the oocysts developed on the guts but sporozoites were rarely found in the salivary glands. In our studies, we have followed the sporogonic development in *A. b. balabacensis*, *A. freeborni*, *A. maculatus*, *A. quadrimaculatus*, and *A. atroparvus* (Table 40).

In *A. b. balabacensis*, at day 4, the mean

PLATE LI.—*Plasmodium knowlesi.*

Fig. 1.   Normal red cell.
Figs. 2–9.   Young trophozoites.
Figs. 10–12.   Growing trophozoites.
Figs. 13–15.   Mature trophozoites.

Figs. 16–23.   Developing schizonts, nearly mature, and mature schizonts.
Fig. 24.   Mature macrogametocyte.
Fig. 25.   Mature microgametocyte.

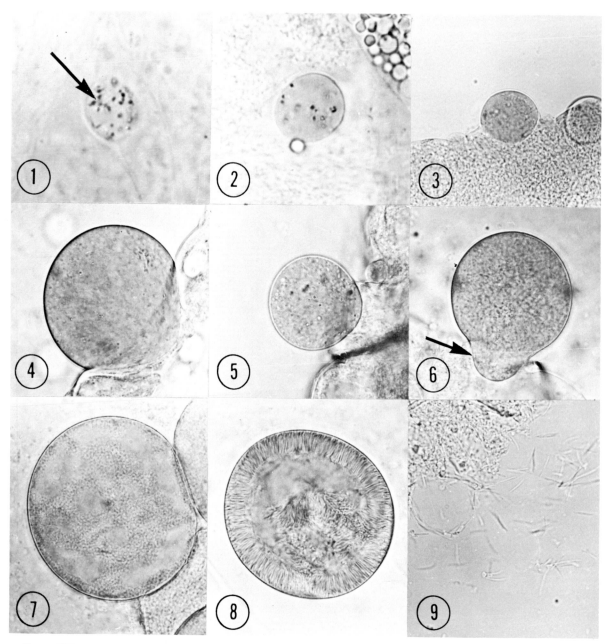

PLATE LII.—Developing oocysts and sporozoites of *Plasmodium knowlesi* in *Anopheles b. balabacensis* mosquitoes. X 580. (Except Figs. 1 & 2).

Fig. 1.   4-day oocyst showing scattered pigment. X 1300.
Fig. 2.   5-day oocyst. X 1300.
Fig. 3.   7-day oocyst.
Fig. 4.   8-day oocyst.
Fig. 5.   9-day oocyst.

Fig. 6.   10-day oocyst showing peduncle.
Fig. 7.   11-day oocyst showing early differentiation.
Fig. 8.   11-day fully differentiated oocyst.
Fig. 9.   Sporozoites near salivary gland tissue.

oocyst diameter was 8 μ with a range of 5 to 12 μ. The oocysts continued to grow and by day 10, the mean size was 62 μ with a range of 18 to 103 μ. Sporozoites were present at this time in the salivary glands.

In *A. freeborni* and *A. maculatus*, the oocysts developed, but the mean diameters were smaller than in *A. b. balabacensis*. In addition, the sporozoites, although present in the salivary glands of both species at day 12, were very scarce. The oocysts in *A. quadrimaculatus* were actually larger on comparable days than were those in the *A. b. balabacensis*. Sporozoites were present in the salivary glands on day 11. Sporozoites were not found in *A. atroparvus* although dissections were carried out through day 11. The extrinsic incubation periods in the mosquitoes ranged from 12 to 15 days (mean of 13.0 days). The sporozoites were shown to be infective in that transmission was obtained, by bites of *A. b. balabacensis* mosquitoes, in rhesus monkeys on 30 occasions. The prepatent periods ranged from 6 to 9 days (mean 7.1 days). On 9 other occasions, dissected guts and glands of *A. b. balabacensis* (2 times), *A. freeborni* (6 times), and *A. maculatus* (once) were inoculated into rhesus monkeys. The prepatent periods under these conditions ranged from 5 to 12 days with a mean of 7.2 days.

A comparison of the growth curves of *P. knowlesi* and *P. cynomolgi* in *A. b. balabacensis*

mosquitoes (Fig. 70) indicates a close similarity between the two. It is surprising that the tertian parasite (*P. cynomolgi*) and the quotidian parasite (*P. knowlesi*) should have similar growth patterns when the growth phases in the blood and in the fixed tissue are so dissimilar.

Cycle in the Tissue
PLATE LIII

The tissue forms of *P. knowlesi*, like the other primate forms, develop in the parenchyma cells of the liver and display structures which appear to be highly distinctive. Certain stages in the exoerythrocytic cycle were demonstrated by Garnham *et al*, 1957.

The earliest forms were seen at 92 hours after infection. At that stage, they occupied most of the enlarged host cell with the parasite oval in shape and with a smooth outline. The most arresting feature of the interior was the decided separation of chromatin and cytoplasm with the latter condensed into flocculi. Vacuoles were present. The nuclei were large, numerous, and appeared as an aggregate of chromatin dots. In the main, there was no continuity between nucleus and cytoplasm. The smallest EE bodies measured 11 x 21 μ and the largest 29 x 29 μ. Only one 117-hour (4¾ days) form was seen. It was an oval parasite which measured 33 x 50 μ. In appearance,

TABLE 40.—Oocyst diameters of *Plasmodium knowlesi* in *Anopheles b. balabacensis*, *A. freeborni*, *A. maculatus*, *A. quadrimaculatus*, and *A. atroparvus*.

Days after infection	A. b. balabacensis			A. freeborni			A. maculatus			A. quadrimaculatus			A. atroparvus		
	No.	Range*	Mean	No.	Range	Mean	No.	Range	Mean	No.	Range	Mean	No.	Range	Mean
4	72	5–12	8										52	12–18	14
5	246	8–24	15	145	8–22	14	36	8–18	14				166	12–32	19
6	266	11–35	20	306	11–38	19	56	12–28	19	6	26–41	31	72	20–53	33
7	244	12–53	34	155	9–60	33	177	9–50	23	28	24–47	40	113	19–64	42
8	226	14–77	45	215	14–63	39	129	18–63	37	19	35–74	55	75	24–74	42
9	309	13–92	57†	190	13–87	51†	155	18–74	43†	134	22–78	51†	144	20–87	54
10	195	18–103	62†**	242	18–101	58†	279	14–81	47†	122	25–100	72†	10	52–89	78†
11	199	24–100	67†**	83	26–106	64†	136	27–89	53†	88	27–99	71†**			
12	50	27–79	58†**	5	44–67	54†**	104	20–83	53†**						
Totals	1907	5–103		1341	8–106		1072	8–89		397	22–100		632	12–89	

* Measurements expressed in microns.
† Oocyst differentiation.
** Sporozoites present in the salivary glands.

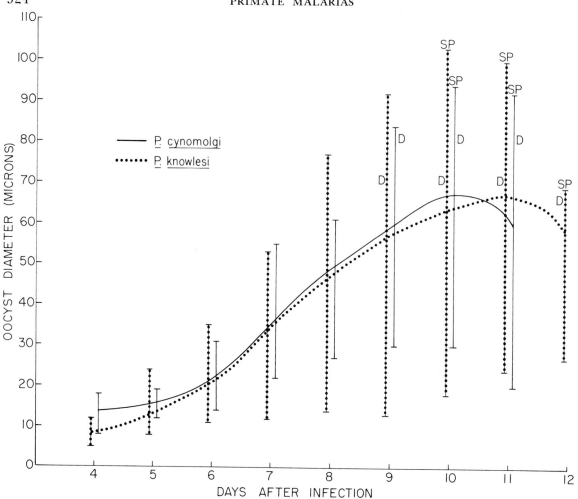

FIGURE 70.—Range in oocyst diameters and the mean oocyst diameter curve of *Plasmodium knowlesi* and *P. cynomolgi* in *Anopheles b. balabacensis* mosquitoes. (D = oocyst differentiation; SP = sporozoites present in the salivary glands).

this form was much like the earlier ones except that vacuoles were absent.

The biopsy material at 124 hours (5¼ days) caught the parasites just prior to the final division to form merozoites because 14 hours later, ring forms were in the circulating blood; they appeared to be about 8 hours old.

The EE bodies were easily recognized because of their large size. They were oval bodies with an even border and prominent clefts or spaces in the cytoplasm. Sometimes these parasites were pear- or hourglass-shaped. Cytoplasmic flocculi were present, and the striking feature was the early differentiation of the cytoplasm which is not seeded with nuclear material until later. The nuclei of these 5-day forms appeared to be of 3 types: clusters of

dots, very small dots of chromatin scattered in the cytoplasmic masses, and bars. The size of the EE bodies ranged from 38.2 x 25.5 μ to 52 x 52 μ.

These authors also found a 141-hour (5¾ days) ruptured form surrounded by phagocytes. The infection had become patent some hours before. The EE body area was approximately 75 x 110 μ; only a few merozoites were seen in the center of the area.

In our own studies, we have infected monkeys with the *A. hackeri* strain of *P. knowlesi* following the technique of Held *et al* (1966) in which infected salivary glands from *A. b. balabacensis* mosquitoes are injected directly into the liver. Beginning at 48 hours after injection, biopsies were taken at 8 hour intervals

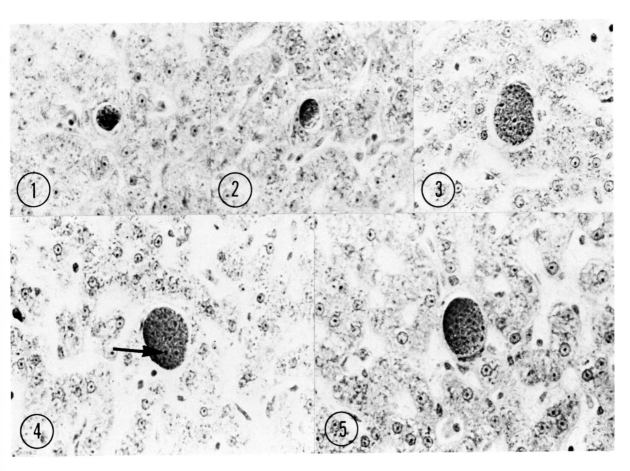

PLATE LIII.—Exoerythrocytic bodies of *Plasmodium knowlesi* in liver tissue of *Macaca mulatta* monkeys. X 580.

Fig. 1. 3-day body.

Fig. 2. 3-day body.

Fig. 3. 4-day body showing numerous flocculi.

Fig. 4. 4-day body.

Fig. 5. 4-day body.

through 120 hours. Studies of the sections revealed numerous EE bodies at each of the time periods. At 120 hours young ring forms were present in the circulating blood and, at the same time, fully mature EE bodies were demonstrable in the liver sections. The greatest rate of growth appeared to take place between 72 and 96 hours (Plate LIII). Numerous flocculi were present in the sections, but vacuoles were not demonstrable.

It is quite apparent that the EE cycle of *Plasmodium knowlesi*, at least in this strain, is less than 120 hours.

Course of Infection

In the rhesus monkey (*M. mulatta*), *Plasmodium knowlesi* is a fulminating infection resulting, almost always, in the death of the animal. Studies on sporozoite-induced infections (Fig. 71) show that parasites are first apparent in the peripheral blood by day 6. The median parasitemia curve exhibits a dramatic rise beginning on day 10, which reaches a median infection level of approximately 3.5 parasites per 100 RBC on day 11. At this time, the first animals died. The level of parasitemia continued to rise until day 13, after which it leveled off to approximately 12 parasites per 100 RBC. The mean time of death was 13.6 days with a range of 11 to 16 days.

One of our *M. mulatta* monkeys (T-722) was inoculated with parasitized blood which had been frozen for approximately one year. The infection was slow to develop, not reaching its

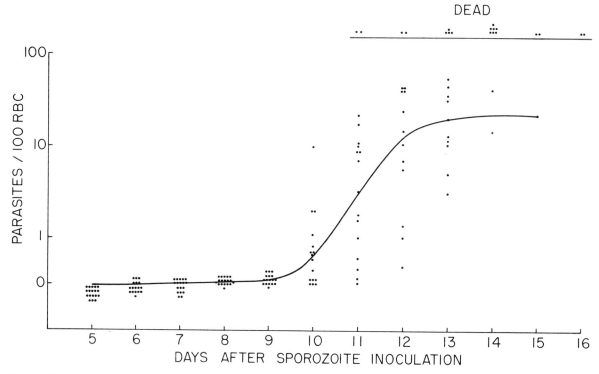

FIGURE 71.—Parasitemias and times of death of 19 *Macaca mulatta* monkeys infected with sporozoites of *Plasmodium knowlesi*.

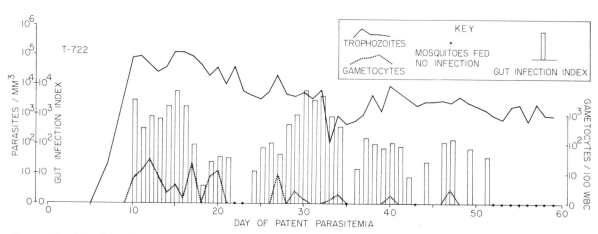

FIGURE 72.—Infectivity of *Plasmodium knowlesi* gametocytes, in a *Macaca mulatta* monkey, to *Anopheles b. balabacensis* mosquitoes.

peak parasitemia until day 15 (Fig. 72) and thereafter slowly declined for the remainder of the 60-day observation period. No treatment was employed. When the nature of the infection became apparent (day 10), daily feeding of *A. b. balabacensis* mosquitoes was initiated and continued, with few interruptions, for the next 50 days. During this period, mosquitoes were infected on 35 of 47 feeding days. There appeared to be 4 distinct waves of mosquito infections which were correlated, partially at least, with gametocytemia.

Plasmodium knowlesi was first shown to infect man by Knowles and Das Gupta (1932) followed by the report of Ionesco-Mihaiesti *et al* (1934). Van Rooyen and Pile (1935) employed

P. knowlesi therapeutically for the treatment of general paresis and reported that non-immunes accepted the infection readily but those with previous experience with *P. vivax* were resistant. An editorial following the von Rooyen-Pile paper called attention to the loss of virulence following continued passage in man. The next week, Nicol (1935) in commenting on *P. knowlesi* infection in man mentioned the loss of virulence following man to man passage, also. Chopra and Das Gupta (1936) used *P. knowlesi* transferred directly from a *Silenus rhesus* (= *M. fascicularis*) monkey, for the treatment of neurosyphilis in 2 patients. They were satisfied with the results and pointed out the advantages of the procedure over one employing *P. vivax*. In 1937, Ciuca *et al* published two papers (1937, 1937a) which dealt with a total of 321 patients exposed to infection with *P. knowlesi*. In the first group, probably non-immunes, 79.8 percent developed fever and parasites in their blood. In the second group, most of whom were thought to have had experience with malaria previously, only 46 percent became infected. Following these reports, Ciuca and his colleagues continued to employ *P. knowlesi* for the treatment of general paresis until in 1955 they reported that after 170 transfers, the infection became so virulent it had to be terminated with drugs. Shortly, thereafter, they abandoned the use of the strain. If they were satisfied with the efficacy of the treatment, which is obvious since they continued to use it for so many years, one wonders why they failed to obtain a new isolate, and use it. In contrast to the increased virulence aspect in man encountered by Ciuca *et al*, Jolly *et al* (1937) reported that although *P. knowlesi* produced fulminating infections in their experimental lower animal hosts, it produced only mild infections in *C. papio* after being passed through man. They characterized the disease in man as mild with a tendency toward spontaneous recovery.

Milam and Coggeshall (1938) carried out duration of infection studies in Caucasians and Negroes in this country and produced corroborative evidence as to the mildness and short duration of the initial infection. In general, the infections in Negro patients were milder than those occurring in Caucasians. In the same year, Milam and Kusch (1938) offered *P. knowlesi* infections to a series of 35 patients, of whom 20 had not experienced malaria before, while the remainder had had mild attacks, or had failed to accept infection with *P. vivax*. Included in the series were 6 Negroes. Each of the 29 Caucasian patients developed infections while among the 6 Negroes, 4 experienced only mild infections and 2, none. However, the latter 2 did have low-grade infections because subinoculation of their blood to normal monkeys revealed parasites for up to 3 weeks following their inoculation. Clinically, the course of the disease followed closely that of *P. vivax* except the duration was shorter. Initial fevers were about 102.2° F but later ones had peaks of 104 to 105.8° F which appeared daily for about 10 days and then 'tailed' off to normal. Paroxysms varied from 2 to 15 with an average of 10; definite chills were experienced by only about half of the patients. The highest parasite counts seldom exceeded 100 parasites per 10,000 RBC. However, one patient showed 1,200 parasites per 10,000 RBC. Relapses (recrudescences) occurred which were both clinical and parasitological; they terminated within 3 days.

Through all the work enumerated above, the infection was passed solely by the inoculation of parasitized blood although attempts were made to pass the infection via mosquito bite on occasion (Coggeshall, 1941). Later (1957) Dr. Lainson, according to Garnham (1966) received 90 bites from a lot of *A. labranchiae* mosquitoes, showing 84 percent infected with *P. knowlesi*. Although he was observed for months, no infection developed. The question of transferring *P. knowlesi* to man via mosquito bite, either experimentally or in nature, remained in limbo until a fortunate circumstance occurred in 1965.

Following the accidental sporozoite-induced infection of man in this country with *P. cynomolgi* in May of 1960 (see Chapter 6), investigations were begun in Malaysia where the infecting parasite had originated. That study had several objectives; the one which concerns us here was the possible zoonotic potential of the simian malarias. We were confident this phenomenon could be demonstrated in the field, and the senior author had gone so far as to cast *P. cynomolgi* in the starring role. This was not to be, as shown in the following account of an episode which under reasonable circumstances could *not* happen— but did!

In the spring of 1965, a 37 year old American male was detailed by the Army to peninsular Malaysia for a short while and, as part of his assignment, he spent 5 days alone in the bush on Bukit Kertau, working by night and sleeping by day. He returned directly to Kuala Lumpur, the Capitol, and after about a week he left for home. Enroute, he stopped off in Bangkok, Thailand, and on the third morning he felt ill (anorexia, fatigue, and some nausea). He decided home was the best place for him and so he departed. He arrived at the Travis Air Force Base in California on Friday night where he was seen by a base physician. He complained of sore throat, chills, fever, and profuse sweating. He was treated for an upper respiratory infection and departed immediately for his home in Silver Spring, Maryland. He was still sick the next morning (Saturday) whereupon he consulted the family physician. When seen by the doctor, he was having a chill. When questioned, he offered the information that he might have malaria since he had been in Malaysia recently. When his blood smear was examined, the doctor saw only rings and jumped to the conclusion that the patient had falciparum malaria. He told the senior author later, that he did not want to treat the patient because he was unfamiliar with the disease, not having seen a case since his intern days, but remembered that falciparum was deadly.

The doctor decided to refer the patient to the Army's Walter Reed Hospital in Washington, D. C., because the physicians there were familiar with the treatment of the disease and the man was their dependent. Saturday was not an admitting day, and the doctor was told to hold the patient until Monday; this he was afraid to do. He next turned to the NIH Clinical Center in Bethesda, Maryland, where, luckily, the physician on duty was interested in malaria and was well aware of our interest, too. His comment was "send him over." When a blood smear was examined at NIH, some 6 hours later, numerous band forms were in evidence. The diagnosis was *P. malariae*. Because it was known that our group was looking for a strain of *P. malariae*, blood was drawn and (refrigerated) where it remained until sent to our installation at the U.S. Penitentiary in Atlanta, Georgia, on Monday. There it was put into a volunteer who subsequently developed malaria. One can imagine our surprise when the parasite turned out to be *P. knowlesi*. The ring was joined—simian malaria is a zoonosis (see Chin *et al*, 1965). Needless to say, the original patient was cured of his infection and later visited our laboratory on several occasions to fill us in on the many details. One other facet might be mentioned as frosting on the cake. Before the patient left for Malaysia he obtained some chloroquine tablets and later, even though he suspected he had malaria, he refrained from taking them because of an admonition that "drugs should be taken only on advice of a physician." If he had taken one tablet this tale would have died with the parasite.

Subsequent to the original blood-induced infection at the U.S. Penitentiary (Atlanta, Ga.), the disease has been passed, by the same route, 11 times (Chin *et al*, loc. cit. and later) and on 8 occasions by the bites of infected mosquitoes (Chin *et al*, 1968). The daily parasite counts in the volunteers infected by the inoculation of parasitized blood and those infected through the bites of infected mosquitoes showed no appreciable difference, so the data were combined, and are shown in Figure 73 along with the median parasitemia curve. The latter shows that the peak parasite count was reached on day 8 following which the parasitemia fell rapidly to a low level by day 13. Although parasite counts as high as 1200 per mm^3 were encountered as late as the 28th day of parasitemia, most of the patients exhibited no parasitemia after day 16.

The salient features of the blood-induced infections were: the quodidian asexual cycle in the blood, temperatures as high as 104.8° F, and parasite counts as high as 20,850 per mm^3. The clinical manifestations were moderate to severe with attacks terminating spontaneously after two weeks. In the series of sporozoite-induced cases, the course of infection was not

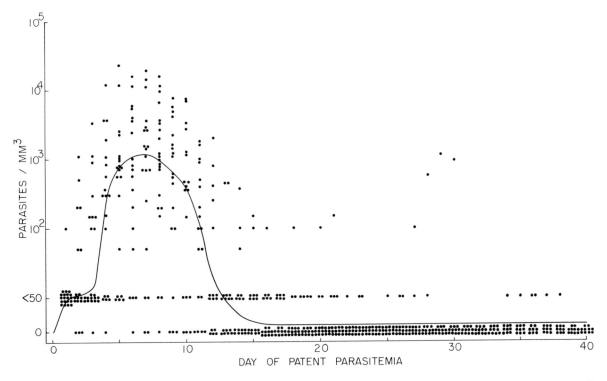

FIGURE 73.—Median parasitemia curve and individual parasite counts in 20 *Plasmodium knowlesi* infections in man (8 sporozoite-induced and 12 blood-induced).

much different from that of the blood-induced cases.

In the main, the data supplied by the investigators who observed the parasite in man agree. At the same time, there are certain points of difference which probably should be mentioned: 1) Van Rooyen and Pile (1935) and Nicol (1935) commented on the loss of virulence when *P. knowlesi* was passaged to man, but the more extensive work of Ciuca *et al* (1955) showed quite the opposite. The work of Chin *et al* lends support to that thesis. 2) Milam and Kusch (1938) remarked about the difficulty of infecting Negroes with *P. knowlesi* but Chin *et al*, in their work, were able to infect Negroes easily and saw no difference between infections in Caucasians and non-whites. What should be stressed is that here, for the first time (Chin and colleagues), *P. knowlesi* was transferred to man by sporozoites, at each attempt, (in one case, following the bite of a single mosquito) with prepatent periods of 9 to 12 days. It is of interest, too, that not only was the infection transferred from

man to man via mosquito bites, but also, back, to the rhesus monkey.

Host Specificity

The natural host of *P. knowlesi* is *Macaca irus* (= *fascicularis*) from Malaysia (Sinton & Mulligan, 1932, 1933) and the Philippines (Lambrecht *et al*, 1961). It has also been found in *M. nemestrina* (Eyles *et al*, 1962) and *Presbytis melalophos* (Eyles *et al*, 1962a) in Malaysia.

Experimentally, the parasite readily infects *M. mulatta* as demonstrated by many authors. Experimental infections in other simians are given below:

SPECIES	REFERENCES
Callithrix jacchus	Cruz and de Mello, 1947
Cebus spp.	Garnham, 1966
Cercocebus fuliginosus	Rodhain, 1936
Cercopithecus cephus	Rodhain, 1936
Cercopithecus grisio viridis	Rodhain, 1936
Cynocephalus papio	Jolly, Lavergne and Tanguy, 1937
Hylobates hoolock	Garnham, 1966

SPECIES	REFERENCES
Hylobates lar	Eyles, 1963
Macaca cynomolgus	Jolly, Lavergne and
(= *fascicularis*)	Tanguy, 1937
Macaca nemstrina	Eyles, 1962
Macaca radiata	unpublished data
Macaca speciosa	Eyles, 1963
(= *arctoides*)	
Papio doguera	unpublished data
Papio jubilaeus	Rodhain, 1936
Papio papio	Garnham, 1966
Presbytis cristatus	Eyles, 1963
Saimiri sciureus	Chin *et al*, 1965
Semnopithecus entellus	Garnham, 1966

A natural vector of *P. knowlesi* in Malaysia is *Anopheles hackeri* as shown by Wharton and Eyles (1961). In addition, we have found *A. vagus*, *A. sinensis*, *A. b. introlatus*, *A. maculatus*, *A. kochi*, *A. b. balabacensis*, and *A. quadrimaculatus* mosquitoes, all but the latter indigenous to peninsular Malaysia, susceptible to infection. Other species which have supported growth of the parasite, at least the presence of oocysts on the gut, are:

SPECIES	REFERENCES
Anopheles annularis	Singh *et al*, 1949
Anopheles atroparvus	Weyer, 1937; Hawking *et al*, 1957
Anopheles aztecus	Garnham *et al*, 1957
Anopheles freeborni	Collins *et al*, 1967
Anopheles labranchiae	Garnham, 1966
Anopheles stephensi	Mulligan, 1935; Singh *et al*, 1949; Hawking and Mellanby, 1953; Garnham *et al*, 1957; Hawking *et al*, 1957

Relative susceptibility studies, using eight species of *Anopheles*, (Table 41) indicated that *A. b. balabacensis* was the most susceptible and that *A. albimanus* was refractory to infection. Other species reported to be refractory are *A. fluviatilis* (Singh *et al*, 1950), *A. punctipennis* (Coggeshall, 1941), and *A. subpictus* (Singh *et al*, 1949).

Immunity and Antigenic Relationships

Mulligan and Sinton (1933, 1933a) found that a chronic or latent infection with one strain of *P. knowlesi* conferred an effective immunity against the clinical effects of superinfection with the same strain of parasite. However, such infections did not confer effective immunity against an acute attack following superinfection with a different strain of the same parasite. Multiple heterologous superinfections with certain strains of *P. knowlesi* appeared to produce a marked degree of tolerance to other heterologous strains which had common immunologic factors, but in the absence of such common factors, multiple heterologous superinfections produced no effective tolerance. Shortt *et al* (1938) found that *P. knowlesi* infections which had been cured by administration of drug, gave no residual immunity to infection with the homologous strain of the parasite. Voller and Rossan (1969) were able to show there was no relationship between prior total parasite experience and immunity. A chronic infection, even at a low level, elicited a more effective immunity than frequent cure and challenge. The actual duration of previous parasitemia seemed to be more important than the density of parasitemia in determining the ability of an animal to control infections or to resist challenge.

Brown *et al* (1968) reported that a number of antigenic stabilates are produced during the course of an infection with *P. knowlesi*. It was shown, however, by Voller and Rossan (1969) that although populations of parasites isolated from different recrudescences, of chronic *P. knowlesi* infections, were antigenically distinct, the immunity produced by repeated exposure to one antigenic variant was effective against challenge with heterologous variants.

No cross-immunity between infections due to *P. knowlesi* and those due to *P. cynomolgi* was found by Mulligan and Sinton (1933). Voller *et al* (1966) however, showed that monkeys previously infected with *P. knowlesi* were protected against subsequent challenge with *P. cynomolgi* or *P. coatneyi*. Later work (Voller and Rossan, 1969a) indicated that monkeys with chronic infections of *P. knowlesi*, although refractory to homologous challenge, were susceptible to infection by *P. cynomolgi* and by *P. coatneyi*. Infections of *P. inui* developed somewhat more slowly in monkeys with chronic *P. knowlesi* infections than in control animals.

In man, Ciuca *et al* (1937) demonstrated

27

Plasmodium girardi Bück, Coudurier, and Quesnel, 1952

WORKERS in Madagascar have long suspected that the lemurs were infected with malaria but the parasite was not seen until 1951 when it was discovered in the blood of a *Lemur fulvus rufus*. The parasites were scanty, so the animal was splenectomized. A heavy infection developed 12 days later. The infection was studied daily; after about a week, a second species appeared. Each organism was recognized as a new species. The first one was given the name *Plasmodium girardi* in honor of Dr. G. Girard, the former director of the Pasteur Institute of Tananarive. The other parasite was given the name *Plasmodium foleyi* in honor of Dr. H. Foley of the Pasteur Institute of Algeria. The latter parasite is now considered to be a hepatocystis and therefore it will not be discussed in its entirety here. The description of the parasites is accompanied by a beautifully colored plate painted by Dr. Foley.

The lemurs of Madagascar are protected animals and consequently there are few opportunities for studying their parasites. However, a few animals were examined by members of the University of California expedition to Madagascar in 1948, and another malaria parasite (*P. lemuris*) was discovered; it is discussed in Chapter 28.

According to Garnham (1966) the original material on *P. girardi* is no longer available. In 1962, at his request, Drs. Raymond and Brygoo splenectomized two animals; one of them exhibited a low-grade infection with *P. girardi* and that material was used for a more extended study of the parasite. Only the blood stages of the parasite have been seen.

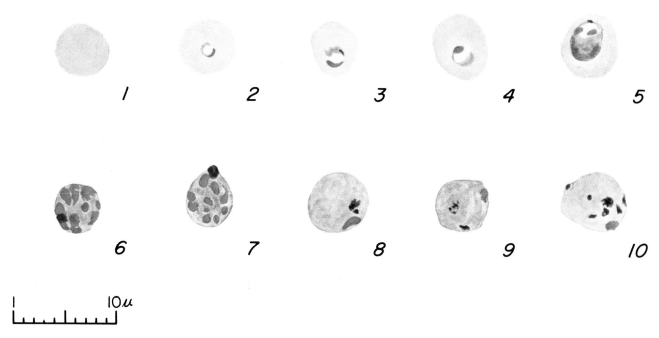

1 *2* *3* *4* *5*

6 *7* *8* *9* *10*

10μ

PLASMODIUM GIRARDI

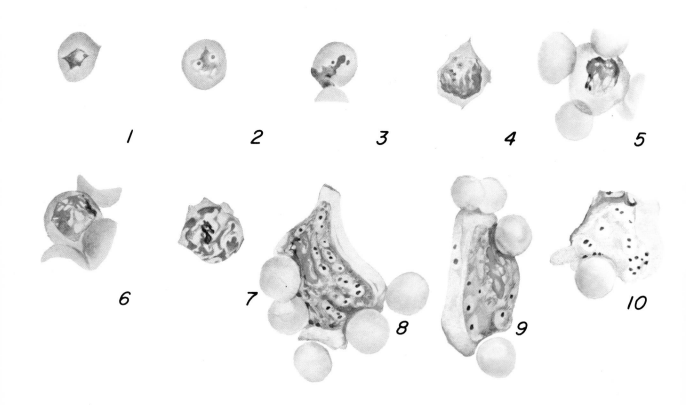

1 *2* *3* *4* *5*

6 *7* *8* *9* *10*

PLASMODIUM LEMURIS

Cycle in the Blood
PLATE LIV

The youngest forms are small solid bodies, approximately 1.8 μ in diameter, with a large nucleus and a small rim of cytoplasm which stains a deep blue. The youngest stages exhibit a granule of dark pigment which the original authors stated did not appear until the parasite occupied about a fourth of the host cell. The pigment body lies on the edge of the cytoplasm. Projections of cytoplasm may occur but for the most part, the parasite is compact and dense even though a vacuole occurs later.

As the trophozoite grows, it may occupy one-half the cell whereupon it loses its vacuole and the parasite as a whole shrinks; the amount of pigment increases and takes up a position on or near the periphery of the parasite. The nucleus becomes enlarged, sometimes diffuse, but always with lighter and darker areas. Very small vacuoles may be seen in the cytoplasm.

With continued growth, the nucleus divides in to two rather large portions, each with a dense core area. Pigment continues to form and now comprises 4 or 5 dark grains arranged on the periphery of the parasite. As division continues beyond the 4-nucleate stage, the host cell becomes pallid, distorted, and develops fimbriated projections. The mature schizont fills the host cell without enlargement, and displays 10 to 12 merozoites; the pigment is still placed eccentrically. Host cell stippling appears to be absent.

The macrogametocyte is spherical and stains a deep blue with granular cytoplasm and heavy dark pigment in an aggregation of distinct grains. The nucleus is deep red and found near the periphery of the cell. The host cell is not enlarged. The cytoplasm of the microgametocyte takes a lilac stain. The pigment is granular to bacilliform and is located in 4 or 5 aggregates of unequal size. The nucleus takes a deep red stain and is located peripherally. The parasite fills the host cell without host cell enlargement.

It is interesting that cirrhosis of the liver of the host animal was known long before malaria parasites were found in them. Whether this cirrhotic change is due to, or is connected with, their malarias is not known. The spleen appears normal when the infection is latent which makes it appear that these animals handle the infection easily. If the spleen is removed, the infection comes to the fore and then again subsides.

Plasmodium girardi may have a distinct place in the evolution of the malarias of primates, but the extent is in limbo until more is known about its life cycle. The blood phase of the infection leads one to suspect that it probably belongs with the quartan type parasites and, if so, it is their most primitive example. One thing appears certain, and that is, that the distribution of the pigment in these parasites is not like what is found in the malarias of simians. We shall have to wait for an explanation as to why this difference occurs.

REFERENCES

BÜCK, G., COUDURIER, J., and QUESNEL, J. J., 1952. Sur deux nouveaux plasmodium observés chez un lémurien de Madagascar splénectomisé. Arch. Institut. Pasteur d'Algérie *30* : 240–243.

GARNHAM, P. C. C., 1966. Malaria parasites and other haemosporidia. Blackwell Scientific Publications, Oxford, pp. 1114.

PLATE LIV.—*Plasmodium girardi and P. lemuris.*

P. girardi: Figures after Bück *et al*, 1952.
Fig. 1.   Normal erythrocyte.
Figs. 2–4.   Uninucleate trophozoites.
Figs. 5–7.   Schizonts.
Figs. 8, 9.   Macrogametocytes.
Fig. 10.   Microgametocyte.

P. lemuris (1000 X): Figures after Huff and Hoogstraal, 1963.
Figs. 1–5.   Uninucleate trophozoites.
Fig. 6.   Binucleate schizont.
Fig. 7.   Multinucleate schizont.
Figs. 8, 9.   Macrogametocytes.
Fig. 10.   Microgametocyte.

28

Plasmodium lemuris Huff and Hoogstraal, 1963

HOOGSTRAAL and Lawless, in the course of studies of the fauna and its parasites of Madagascar, made a blood film from a black lemur, *Lemur collaris*, housed in the Tananarive Zoo. Some years later the slide was examined at the Naval Medical Research Institute in Bethesda, Maryland, where thirty malaria parasites were found. The morphology of the parasite was different from any of the described species and, therefore, the authors created a new species, *Plasmodium lemuris*. Only the blood stages are known for this species.

Cycle in the Blood

PLATE LIV

The young trophozoites are small and occupy three-tenths to four-tenths of the erythrocytes. The nucleus stains rose-red. Larger trophozoites are more irregular tending toward amoeboidity. The pigment is in granules; there is no stippling of the host cell. The schizonts are in enlarged and distorted erythrocytes and display irregularly shaped nuclei. The pigment is brown and clumped into a diffused mass. Mature schizonts have not been seen.

The gametocytes are of large size and irregular in shape. The nuclei are band-like or lobed irregularly. The host erythrocyte is greatly enlarged and in many instances is almost completely filled by the parasite. In some of these forms, the rim of host cell cytoplasm, around the parasite, stains pink. It is assumed that the cells infected with this parasite are more pliable than normal cells because of the way they appear to flow around other cells in the smear.

The macrogametocytes have lavender to purple cytoplasm. The pigment is made up of small dark brown granules within vacuoles. The microgametocytes have red-staining nuclei and slate-gray cytoplasm. The pigment is like that in the macrogametocytes.

An interesting sidelight to the discovery of this parasite is that, when Dr. Huff first saw the macrogametocytes, he thought he was seeing a leucocytozoon in a mammal; strange, indeed, if it were true. He discovered later, however, that the bizarre form was in reality a distorted gametocyte inside the reddish stained sac of the host cell.

It should be relatively simple to distinguish between the malarias of lemurs. *Plasmodium foleyi* is probably a hepatocystis (see Chapter 27) since only gametocytes made their appearance in the peripheral blood. *Plasmodium girardi* is smaller than *P. lemuris* but shares other characteristics with it. Both cause distortion of the host erythrocyte and appear in bizarre shapes. *Plasmodium lemuris* has the larger gametocytes of the two but is without the pigment located at the edge of the parasite as is true with gametocytes of *P. girardi*.

So little is known about the malarias of lemurs, especially since the description of *P. lemuris* is based on only thirty specimens, that one hesitates to comment on them. It may be that there is only one species. Should that be true, *P. lemuris* would become a synonym of *P. girardi*.

REFERENCES

HUFF, C. G., and HOOGSTRAAL, H., 1963. *Plasmodium lemuris* n. sp. from *Lemur collaris*. J. Inf. Dis. *112* : 233–236.

SECTION 7

Indexes

Author Index

343

_____ (with Lupascu *et al*, 1968) 218

Contacos, P. G. (1962) 88, 92
_____ (1963) 53, 89, 241
_____ (1964) 273
_____ (1968) 274, 280, 282
_____ (1969) 218, 221, 223
_____ (1970) 15, 148, 151, 172, 313
_____ (with Chin, 1965) 8
_____ (with Chin, 1966) 36, 181
_____ (with Chin *et al*, 1965) 16, 23, 328, 330
_____ (with Chin *et al*, 1966) 172, 178, 179, 182
_____ (with Chin *et al*, 1967) 273
_____ (with Chin *et al*, 1968) 328, 329
_____ (with Coatney *et al*, 1961) 69, 88, 92
_____ (with Coatney *et al*, 1963) 52
_____ (with Coatney *et al*, 1966) 251, 254
_____ (with Collins, 1969) 214, 220, 221
_____ (with Collins *et al*, 1966) 25, 251, 256
_____ (with Collins *et al*, 1967) 25, 292, 321, 330
_____ (with Collins *et al*, 1968) 25, 189, 251, 256, 274, 280, 282, 328
_____ (with Collins *et al*, 1969) 146, 151, 155, 177, 236
_____ (with Held, 1967) 292
_____ (with Held *et al*, 1966) 324
_____ (with Held *et al*, 1967) 122, 133, 134, 190, 203, 292
_____ (with Held *et al*, 1968) 251
_____ (with Lunn *et al*, 1964) 273
_____ (with Sodeman *et al*, 1969) 124, 135, 237, 272, 282
_____ (with Sodeman *et al*, 1970) 81
_____ (with Sodeman *et al*, 1971) 121
_____ (with Tobie *et al*, 1962) 64, 95

Coombs, G. L. (1968) 189, 190
_____ (with Cheong, 1970) 90

Cooper, W. C. (1947) 35, 36
_____ (1949) 35, 79
_____ (with Coatney, 1948) 33, 34, 44, 53
_____ (with Coatney *et al*, 1947) 273, 275
_____ (with Coatney *et al*, 1950) 36, 44, 53

Cooper, W. (with Garnham *et al*, 1955) 149, 179, 180, 181, 182
_____ (with Garnham *et al*, 1957) 321, 323, 330
_____ (with Garnham *et al*, 1958)

107, 112, 113
_____ (with Shortt *et al*, 1954) 79

Corradetti, A. (1950) 34, 35
_____ (1965) 34
_____ (1966) 34, 35, 36

Cortez, P. (with Ciuca *et al*, 1955) 52, 226, 275, 327 ,329

Covell, G. (1960) 275
_____ (with Shortt *et al*, 1948) 33
_____ (with Shortt *et al*, 1949) 33, 269
_____ (with Shortt *et al*, 1951) 269, 271, 272, 273

Coudurier, J. (with Bück *et al*, 1952) 335

Coulston, F. (1949) 93
_____ (with Huff, 1944) 33, 79, 91
_____ (with Huff, 1948) 33, 34, 93
_____ (with Huff *et al*, 1943) 33
_____ (with Huff *et al*, 1947) 33
_____ (with Whorton *et al*, 1947) 58, 64

Craig, C. F. (1900) 171
_____ (1914) 171
_____ (1933) 171

Craige, B., Jr. (with Whorton *et al*, 1947) 54, 55, 57, 58, 64

Craik, R. (1920) 47

Crandall, L. S. (1964) 157

Cruz, W. O. (1947) 329

Darlington, P. J., Jr. (1957) 137

Das Gupta, B. M. (1938) 254, 255
_____ (with Chopra, 1936) 327
_____ (with Chopra *et al*, 1932) 275
_____ (with Knowles, 1932) 15, 317, 326
_____ (with Knowles *et al*, 1930) 210

Davey, D. G. (with Edeson, 1953) 318
Davey, T. H. (with Gordon, 1932) 223
Davis, J. (with Shiroishi *et al*, 1968) 163
Deane, L. M. (1964) 157
_____ (1965) 8, 157, 159
_____ (1966) 62, 155, 159, 160
_____ (1968) 157
_____ (1969) 4, 26, 153, 157, 160, 231, 242

Deane, M. P. (with Deane *et al*, 1965) 8, 159
_____ (with Deane *et al*, 1966) 155, 159

de Buck, A. (1935) 217, 223
Degowin, R. L. (with Powell *et al*, 1965) 273
Dellaert, R. (with Rodhain, 1943) 259, 260
_____ (with Rodhain, 1955) 148, 149, 151

De Meillon, B. (with Gillies, 1968) 25
de Mello, R. P. (with Cruz, 1947) 329
Depaoli, J. R. (with Malinow *et al*, 1968) 157

de Sousa, L. (with Porter *et al*, 1966) 231, 242
de Souza, W. T. (with Deane *et al*, 1966) 159, 160
de Zulueta, J. (with Renjifo *et al*, 1952) 242
Diamond, M. P. (1966) 221
Diggs, C. L. (1965) 64, 285
Dissanaike, A. S. (1963) 90
_____ (1965) 69, 76, 90, 91, 93, 197, 199, 202, 203, 204, 301, 303, 306
Dobrovolny, C. G. (with Collins *et al*, 1965) 25, 91, 93
_____ (with Eyles *et al*, 1962) 90, 193, 329
Dodd, S. (1913) 137, 139
Donovan, C. (1920) 301
_____ (1921) 137
Donovan, W. N. (with Hankey *et al*, 1953) 44, 53
Dranga, A. (1969) 226
Dunn, F. L. (1963) 231, 242
_____ (1965) 6
_____ (1966) 3
_____ (with Eyles *et al*, 1963) 289, 295
_____ (with Eyles *et al*, 1964) 22, 163, 165, 166
_____ (with Lambrecht *et al*, 1961) 251, 317, 329
Dunn, L. H. (with Clark, 1931) 16, 233, 240, 242
Durkee, T. (with Sodeman *et al*, 1970) 81
Earle, D. P. (with Shannon, 1945) 33
_____ (with Shannon *et al*, 1948) 53
Edeson, J. F. B. (1953) 318
Edozien, J. C. (1962) 285
Ehrman, F. C. (1945) 44
Eichelberger, L. (with Whorton *et al*, 1947) 54, 55, 57, 58, 64
Elder, H. A. (with Beye *et al*, 1961) 88, 92, 93
_____ (with Coatney *et al*, 1961) 69, 88, 92
_____ (with Coatney *et al*, 1963) 52
_____ (with Contacos *et al*, 1962) 88, 92
Ellis, J. M. (with Ehrman *et al*, 1945) 44
_____ (with Young *et al*, 1946) 58
Ellison, R. (with Schmidt *et al*, 1970) 92
El-Nahal, H. M. S. (1967) 95, 256
Emin, A. (1914) 171
Eppes, R. B. (with Powell *et al*, 1965) 273
Ercole, Q. N. (with Mackerras, 1948) 218, 220, 223
Evans, C. B. (with Tobie *et al*, 1962) 64, 95
Eyles, D. E. (1949) 273
_____ (1951) 273, 275, 276
_____ (1960) 16, 69, 80, 87, 88, 91,

Subject Index

362

☆ U. S. GOVERNMENT PRINTING OFFICE : 1971 O - 421- 460